science & ideas

science & Ideas

SELECTED READINGS

EDITED AND WITH AN INTRODUCTION BY

ARNOLD B. ARONS

PHYSICS DEPARTMENT, AMHERST COLLEGE

ALFRED M. BORK

PHYSICS DEPARTMENT, REED COLLEGE

PRENTICE-HALL, INC., ENGLEWOOD CLIFFS, N.J.

PRENTICE-HALL INTERNATIONAL, INC., *London*
PRENTICE-HALL OF AUSTRALIA, PTY., LTD., *Sydney*
PRENTICE-HALL OF CANADA, LTD., *Toronto*
PRENTICE-HALL FRANCE, S.A.R.L., *Paris*
PRENTICE-HALL OF INDIA (PRIVATE) LTD., *New Delhi*
PRENTICE-HALL OF JAPAN, INC., *Tokyo*
PRENTICE-HALL DE MEXICO, S.A., *Mexico City*

Englewood Cliffs, New Jersey

Library of Congress Catalog Card Number: 64–13251

PRINTED IN THE UNITED STATES OF AMERICA 79501–C

Introduction

During the years since World War II, many educational leaders have emphasized and reiterated the importance of conveying to all educated people—scientists and non-scientists alike—some knowledge of the history, nature, and limitations of scientific thought. It is our belief that this highly desirable goal will not be achieved for either group of individuals by *confining* their classroom experience to narrowly oriented presentations of scientific facts and theories and to drilling laboratory manipulations and problem solving.

We contend that students should indeed devote significant time to probing and mastering important scientific concepts in reasonable depth. But we also feel that this experience should be supplemented by an exposure to ideas; to views of the intellectual, philosophical, and humanistic content of scientific thought.

Students should be led to understand what is meant by "rigor" and by "axiomatic structure" in mathematics. They should be conscious of the separate roles of inductive and deductive reasoning in natural science. They should understand that scientific concepts are *created* by acts of human intelligence. They should understand something of the meaning of the words "law" and "theory." They should know from study of important examples that theories are not immutable and are not usually immediately accepted when proposed. They should see that theories pass through sometimes prolonged stages of testing, validation, acceptance, and subsequent modification.

Educated individuals should understand something

of the way in which science has lessened man's insecurity before nature and thus changed his outlook toward himself, toward other men, and toward the physical universe. They should be sensitive to the manner in which the unparalleled growth of scientific knowledge stems from free and uninhibited test and criticism in the market place of ideas. They should feel the force of the usually unspoken code of science, that "unpalatable truth is preferable to cherished error." In addition to this, they should know something at firsthand, not only of the strengths, but of the profound limitations of scientific concepts and analyses. They should become explicitly aware of the vast ranges of human experience about which science has been unable to ask fruitful questions or provide convincing answers.

In this small anthology we have tried to assemble material that would allow students in introductory science courses, or individuals with relatively little formal training in physical science, access to some of the ideas and perspectives just defined. Rather than attempt to assess the impact of the vast range of conceptual development from Galileo to quantum mechanics; rather than fragment the reading with cursory glances at numerous items in a huge list of heterogenous topics, we have tried to provide coherence and depth by focusing on several specific ideas and items of subject matter.

In the section on philosophy we have chosen to concentrate on epistemology: the nature of scientific knowledge, the role of careful operational definition in elucidating scientific concepts, the interplay of empirical and logical elements in science.

In the section on history we have focused attention on the evolution of Newton's great synthesis and its impact upon Western thought.

The more heterogeneous section on science and society is concerned with such themes as the various images of science within our society, the relevance of scientific attitudes to analyses and decisions regarding human conduct, the influence of a scientific instrument on a literary creation, and a sociological analysis of a direct technical question concerning the impact of society on science.

Readers who become more deeply interested in the interaction between science and other aspects of our culture will find a rich field for further exploration. Much interesting material remains in the original sources of these selections. Particularly rewarding would be the exploration of such additional areas as: the philosophical impact of twentieth century conceptual developments in atomic physics, relativity, and quantum mechanics; the corresponding impact of

Darwinism and of modern discoveries in biology; the role of science in government; the profound limitations of both science and the scientist in confronting problems different from those that science has learned to answer, particularly problems involving political and value judgments; and the social organization and channels of professional discipline within the community of science itself. These and many other important domains have been excluded from the present volume not because they lack importance, but because of our desire to strive for depth within the limitations of space.

We have tried to use a fairly wide spectrum of writings. Some are scholarly and relatively technical, some are intensely personal, one is whimsical and tongue-in-cheek. While trying to exhibit certain facets of science, we hoped that we might also help illuminate the personalities of a few representative scientists, showing their differences and similarities and avoiding the impression of stereotypes.

In no sense does the presence of a selection indicate that we agree with all its tenets or consider it definitive. Some of the selections are factual presentations, but others are meant to be provocative or even controversial. The reader is advised to approach them as a scientist should approach a scientific problem—with an open mind, prepared to question and to doubt. A variety of reactions, interpretations, and emphases is perfectly possible and appropriate, depending on the reader's frame of reference and the wider context in which his reading is placed.

We envisage this anthology as being useful both to the general reader and in the college classroom. In the latter case three principal applications might be:

(a) Supplementary reading in general education courses in the physical sciences. To assist in this objective we have arranged the selections so that most of the scientific back ground required for intelligent reading is attained relatively early in the usual course structure. Thus the reading can be distributed throughout most of the course instead of being packed in hurriedly at the end of the year after enough modern physics has been studied. The anthology should provide ample material for class discussions and, with further references to the original sources, would provide students with ideas and subject matter for more detailed term papers.

(b) Supplementary reading in introductory courses for science majors and engineers. In recent years increasing numbers of teachers of technical courses have shown an interest in exposing their students to intellectual and cultural aspects of the scientific enterprise. Being convinced that it is at least as important for our future professional scientists to know something of these overtones as it is for our liberal arts students, we hope that this collection might assist teachers striving for such objectives.

(c) Supplementary reading in philosophy, history, and social science courses. Teachers in these areas who wish their students to encounter some discussion of the interaction between science and the ideas and attitudes of Western civilization, may find these selections useful in conjunction with regular text and reading assignments that are not rooted in scientific ideas.

The readings have been deliberately chosen to embrace a wide range of levels, from the narrative and descriptive to the fairly technical and mathematical. It is not at all necessary that every selection be read in a given program. Depending upon the verbal and mathematical backgrounds of the students, the orientation of the course and its choice of subject matter, teachers will very properly wish to emphasize certain readings at the expense of others.

The selections discuss adult ideas in an adult vocabulary. All of them have been used in classroom situations. Our experience is that a majority of college students are very receptive to such discussions, but their capacities and interests in this respect are frequently underestimated. Furthermore, pertinent readings not requiring extensive and formidable scientific background are scattered and relatively inaccessible. Our purpose here has been to make a body of significant ideas more readily accessible both to students and to the general readers.

Contents

PHILOSOPHY OF SCIENCE

HISTORY OF SCIENCE

SCIENCE AND SOCIETY

Philosophy of Science

A coherent approach to the nature of scientific knowledge must include both empirical and logical aspects. We begin with a short discussion emphasizing the tentative nature of all scientific knowledge, by R. P. Feynman, *a distinguished contemporary theoretical physicist. The admission of ignorance—the admission that there is no complete and final knowledge—is one of this century's fundamental insights.* P. W. Bridgman *and* H. Poincaré *complement each other in discussions of how scientific theories are coupled to experience. Bridgman, a Nobel prize winner for his work on the physics of very high pressure, originated the concept of an "operational definition" in his attempts to understand the revolutions in physics during the first quarter of this century. In the selection included here he explains and illustrates the process of operational definition and analysis, in terms which are accessible to the layman. This is probably Bridgman's least technical exposition of operationalism. Henri Poincaré, a French mathematical physicist and philosopher, is well known for his insistence on the conventional aspects of knowledge and for being an immediate precursor of Einstein in the development of relativity. His discussion of time, although predating the selection from Bridgman, illustrates some aspects of the operational definition of a single concept, and some of the conceptual difficulties that may be encountered. Had Poincaré pursued his analysis a bit further, he would have been very close indeed to Einstein's insight into the relativity of simultaneity.*

Albert Einstein, the most widely known physicist of this century, gives us a brief, lucid discussion of the logical structure of scientific knowledge. He points out that a scientific theory cannot be an isolated collection of statements, but must have a structure which allows one to pass from some statements to other statements within the theory. In contemporary physics this logical pattern is largely taken from mathematics. Philip Frank illustrates many ideas from all the preceding discussions in his review of one historically important area, geometry, a pivotal subject underlying many modern conceptions in the philosophy of science. This chapter is the most technical in the anthology and was chosen to balance the bulk of qualitative discussion in the other selections. Frank, educated as a physicist, was a member of the Vienna Circle, which played a major role in determining the direction of twentieth century philosophy. A short selection on the nature of physical concepts, excerpted from Max Jammer's historical study of the evolution of the concept of force, furnishes a brief closing summary.

Richard P. Feynman

The Value of Science

From time to time, people suggest to me that scientists ought to give more consideration to social problems—especially that they should be more responsible in considering the impact of science upon society. This same suggestion must be made to many other scientists, and it seems to be generally believed that if the scientists would only look at these very difficult social problems and not spend so much time fooling with the less vital scientific ones, great success would come of it.

It seems to me that we do think about these problems from time to time, but we don't put full-time effort into them—the reason being that we know we don't have any magic formula for solving problems, that social problems are very much harder than scientific ones, and that we usually don't get anywhere when we do think about them.

I believe that a scientist looking at nonscientific problems is just as dumb as the next guy—and when he talks about a nonscientific matter, he will sound as naive as anyone untrained in the matter. Since the question of the value of science is not a scientific subject, this discussion is dedicated to proving my point—by example.

The first way in which science is of value is familiar to everyone. It is that scientific knowledge enables us to do all kinds of things and to make all kinds of things. Of course if we make good things, it is not only to the credit of science; it is also to the credit of the moral

Reprinted with permission from Edward Hutchings, Jr., ed., Frontiers in Science—A Survey *(New York: Basic Books, Inc., 1958), pp. 260–7.*

choice which led us to good work. Scientific knowledge is an enabling power to do either good or bad—but it does not carry instructions on how to use it. Such power has evident value—even though the power may be negated by what one does.

I learned a way of expressing this common human problem on a trip to Honolulu. In a Buddhist temple there, the man in charge explained a little bit about the Buddhist religion for tourists, and then ended his talk by telling them he had something to say to them that they would *never* forget—and I have never forgotten it. It was a proverb of the Buddhist religion:

"To every man is given the key to the gates of heaven; the same key opens the gates of hell."

What then, is the value of the key to heaven? It is true that if we lack clear instructions that determine which is the gate to heaven and which the gate to hell, the key may be a dangerous object to use, but it obviously has value. How can we enter heaven without it?

The instructions, also, would be of no value without the key. So it is evident that, in spite of the fact that science could produce enormous horror in the world, it is of value because it *can* produce *something*.

Another value of science is the fun called intellectual enjoyment which some people get from reading and learning and thinking about it, and which others get from working in it. This is a very real and important point and one which is not considered enough by those who tell us it is our social responsibility to reflect on the impact of science on society.

Is this mere personal enjoyment of value to society as a whole? No! But it is also a responsibility to consider the value of society itself. Is it, in the last analysis, to arrange things so that people can enjoy things? If so, the enjoyment of science is as important as anything else.

But I would like *not* to underestimate the value of the world view which is the result of scientific effort. We have been led to imagine all sorts of things infinitely more marvelous than the imaginings of poets and dreamers of the past. It shows that the imagination of nature is far, far greater than the imagination of man. For instance, how much more remarkable it is for us all to be stuck—half of us upside down—by a mysterious attraction, to a spinning ball that has been swinging in space for billions of years, than to be carried on the back of an elephant supported on a tortoise swimming in a bottomless sea.

I have thought about these things so many times alone that I hope you will excuse me if I remind you of some thoughts that I am sure you have all had—or this type of thought—which no one could ever have had in the past, because people then didn't have the information we have about the world today.

For instance, I stand at the seashore, alone, and start to think. There are the rushing waves . . . mountains of molecules, each stupidly minding its own business . . . trillions apart . . . yet forming white surf in unison.

Ages on ages . . . before any eyes could see . . . year after year . . . thunderously pounding the shore as now. For whom, for what? . . . on a dead planet, with no life to entertain.

Never at rest . . . tortured by energy . . . wasted prodigiously by the sun . . . poured into space. A mite makes the sea roar.

Deep in the sea, all molecules repeat the patterns of one another till complex new ones are formed. They make others like themselves . . . and a new dance starts.

Growing in size and complexity . . . living things, masses of atoms, DNA, protein . . . dancing a pattern ever more intricate.

Out of the cradle onto the dry land . . . here it is standing . . . atoms with consciousness . . . matter with curiosity.

Stands at the sea . . . wonders at wondering . . . I . . . a universe of atoms . . . an atom in the universe.

THE GRAND ADVENTURE

The same thrill, the same awe and mystery, come again and again when we look at any problem deeply enough. With more knowledge comes deeper, more wonderful mystery, luring one on to penetrate deeper still. Never concerned that the answer may prove disappointing, but with pleasure and confidence we turn over each new stone to find uninmagined strangeness leading on to more wonderful questions and mysteries—certainly a grand adventure!

It is true that few unscientific people have this particular type of religious experience. Our poets do not write about it; our artists do not try to portray this remarkable thing. I don't know why. Is nobody inspired by our present picture of the universe? The value of science remains unsung by singers, so you are reduced to hearing —not a song or a poem, but an evening lecture about it. This is not yet a scientific age.

Perhaps one of the reasons is that you have to know how to read the music. For instance, the scientific article says, perhaps, something like this: "The radioactive phosphorous content of the cerebrum of the rat decreases to one-half in a period of two weeks." Now, what does that mean?

It means that phosphorus that is in the brain of a rat (and also in mine, and yours) is not the same phosphorus as it was two weeks ago, but that all of the atoms that are in the brain are being replaced, and the ones that were there before have gone away.

So what is this mind, what are these atoms with consciousness? Last week's potatoes! That is what now can *remember* what was going on in my mind a year ago—a mind which has long ago been replaced.

That is what it means when one discovers how long it takes for the atoms of the brain to be replaced by other atoms, to note that the thing which I call my individuality is only a pattern or dance. The atoms come into my brain, dance a dance, then go out; always new atoms but always doing the same dance, remembering what the dance was yesterday.

THE REMARKABLE IDEA

When we read about this in the newspaper, it says, "The scientist says that this discovery may have importance in the cure of cancer." The paper is only interested in the use of the idea, not the idea itself. Hardly anyone can understand the importance of an idea, it is so remarkable. Except that, possibly, some children catch on. And when a child catches on to an idea like that, we have a scientist. These ideas do filter down (in spite of all the conversation about TV replacing thinking), and lots of kids get the spirit—and when they have the spirit you have a scientist. It's too late for them to get the spirit when they are in our universities, so we must attempt to explain these ideas to children.

I would now like to turn to a third value that science has. It is a little more indirect, but not much. The scientist has a lot of experience with ignorance and doubt and uncertainty, and this experience is of very great importance, I think. When a scientist doesn't know the answer to a problem, he is ignorant. When he has a hunch as to what the result is, he is uncertain. And when he is pretty darn sure of what the result is going to be, he is in some doubt. We have found it of paramount importance that in order to progress we must recognize the ignorance and leave room for doubt. Scientific knowledge is a body of statements of varying degrees of certainty—some most unsure, some nearly sure, none *absolutely* certain.

Now, we scientists are used to this, and we take it for granted that it is perfectly consistent to be unsure—that it is possible to live and *not* know. But I don't know whether everyone realizes that this is true. Our freedom to doubt was born of a struggle against authority in the early days of science. It was a very deep and strong struggle. Permit us to question—to doubt, that's all—not to be sure. And I think it is important that we do not forget the importance of this struggle and thus perhaps lose what we have gained. Here lies a responsibility to society.

We are all sad when we think of the wondrous potentialities human beings seem to have, as contrasted with their small accomplishments. Again and again people have thought that we could do much better. They of the past saw in the nightmare of their times a dream for the future. We, of their future, see that their dreams, in certain ways surpassed, have in many ways remained dreams. The hopes for the future today are, in good share, those of yesterday.

EDUCATION, FOR GOOD AND EVIL

Once some thought that the possibilities people had were not developed because most of those people were ignorant. With education universal, could all men be Voltaires? Bad can be taught at least as efficiently as good. Education is a strong force, but for either good or evil.

Communications between nations must promote understanding: so went another dream. But the machines of communication can be channeled or choked. What is communicated can be truth or lie. Communication is a strong force also, but for either good or bad.

The applied sciences should free men of material problems at least. Medicine controls diseases. And the record here seems all to the good. Yet there are men patiently working to create great plagues and poisons. They are to be used in warfare tomorrow.

Nearly everybody dislikes war. Our dream today is peace. In peace, man can develop best the enormous possibilities he seems to have. But maybe future men will find that peace, too, can be good and bad. Perhaps peaceful men will drink out of boredom. Then perhaps drink will become the great problem which seems to keep man from getting all he thinks he should out of his abilities.

Clearly, peace is a great force, as is sobriety, as are material power, communication, education, honesty and the ideals of many dreamers.

We have more of these forces to control than did the ancients. And maybe we are doing a little better than most of them could do. But what we ought to be able to do seems gigantic compared with our confused accomplishments.

Why is this? Why can't we conquer ourselves?

Because we find that even great forces and abilities do not seem to carry with them clear instructions on how to use them. As an example, the great accumulation of understanding as to how the physical world behaves only convinces one that this behavior seems to have a kind of meaninglessness. The sciences do not directly teach good and bad.

Through all ages men have tried to fathom the meaning of life. They have realized that if some direction or meaning could be given to our actions, great human forces would be unleased. So, very many answers must have been given to the question of the meaning of it all. But they have been of all different sorts, and the proponents of one answer have looked with horror at the actions of the believers in another. Horror, because from a disagreeing point of view all the great potentialities of the race were being channeled into a false and confining blind alley. In fact, it is from the history of the enormous monstrosities created by false belief that philosophers have realized the apparently infinite and wondrous capacities of human beings. The dream is to find the open channel.

What, then, is the meaning of it all? What can we say to dispel the mystery of existence?

If we take everything into account, not only what the ancients knew, but all of what we know today that they didn't know, then I think that we must frankly admit that *we do not know*.

But, in admitting this, we have probably found the open channel.

This is not a new idea; this is the idea of the age of reason. This is the philosophy that guided the men who made the democracy that we live under. The idea that no one really knew how to run a government led to the idea that we should arrange a system by which new ideas could be developed, tried out, tossed out, more new ideas brought in; a trial and error system. This method was a result of the fact that science was already showing itself to be a successful venture at the end of the 18th century. Even then it was clear to socially-minded people that the openness of the possibilities was an opportunity, and that doubt and discussion were essential to progress into the unknown. If we want to solve a problem that we have never solved before, we must leave the door to the unknown ajar.

OUR RESPONSIBILITY AS SCIENTISTS

We are at the very beginning of time for the human race. It is not unreasonable that we grapple with problems. There are tens of thousands of years in the future. Our responsibility is to do what we can, learn what we can, improve the solutions and pass them on. It is our responsibility to leave the men of the future a free hand. In the impetuous youth of humanity, we can make grave errors that can stunt our growth for a long time. This we will do if we say we have the answers now, so young and ignorant; if we suppress all discussion, all criticism, saying, "This is it, boys, man is saved!" and thus doom man for a long time to the chains of authority, confined to the limits of our present imagination. It has been done so many times before.

It is our responsibility as scientists, knowing the great progress and great value of a satisfactory philosophy of ignorance, the great progress that is the fruit of freedom of thought, to proclaim the value of this freedom, to teach how doubt is not to be feared but welcomed and discussed, and to demand this freedom as our duty to all coming generations.

Percy W. Bridgman

Suggestions from Physics

We may gain an insight into complex situations by first understanding simpler situations resembling them. The totality of situations with which we are confronted, including society in its economic, political, esthetic and religious aspects, is enormously more complex than the situations presented by any well defined scientific activity, such as physics or chemistry. For although physics may appear hopelessly complicated to a layman who is trying to understand the most recent technical advances, nevertheless the mere fact that the field of activity is roughly limited is itself evidence that a simplification has been effected. What probably will be questioned is whether there is a close enough connection between the simple situations presented by physics and the complex situations of daily life to warrant the expectation that an analysis of the experience of physics will be helpful in advancing our understanding of the larger problem. It has become the fashion in some quarters during the last few years to depreciate the entire scientific outlook, and we hear much of the "bankruptcy" of science. This scepticism has doubtless arisen from simple misconceptions about the nature of the scientific approach, which has often been thought to have applications to such irrelevant questions as those of value. More particularly, however, it has arisen from plain disappointment because the easy Utopia which brilliant technological advance encouraged the uncritical to think was just around

Reprinted with permission of Robert W. Bridgman from Percy W. Bridgman, The Intelligent Individual and Society *(New York: The Macmillan Company, 1938), pp. 10–47.*

the corner has proved to demand for its actual realization the exercise of intelligent cooperation by all parts of the community. In spite of this popular reaction, I believe that science was never less bankrupt than at the present time, and that in the experience of physics of the last few years one can find suggestions which are nothing short of revolutionary in their implications for the terribly complex social situation.

The reason for this conviction is that physics has found itself confronted with situations in which the attainment of an understanding adequate for even its own restricted purposes has demanded an analysis of the nature and limitations of the mental tools that it uses, and these mental tools are common to our activities in all other fields. Not only is the physicist coming to acquire a better understanding of the nature of those technical tools such as mathematics, which are of somewhat special application in physics, but he has ranged further. In doing this he has uncovered points of view which have obvious bearing on the kind of thinking that is commonly done in every sort of everyday non-technical situation.

In order to make our analysis profitable, it is not necessary to go so far as to maintain that in acquiring the ability to satisfactorily meet the situations presented by physics we have at the same time acquired ability to satisfactorily meet *all* the situations of everyday life. It is enough to observe that a better understanding of the nature and limitations of what we can do in dealing with physical situations does have most important repercussions on all thinking. The conditions imposed by the physical situation must be met by the ultimately valid method in any field, whether or not other conditions prove necessary in addition. I think we shall find that there is no popular current method of approach to social problems, as revealed by what people say and do, which does not appear almost crude and naive when its assumptions and implications are searchingly analyzed in the light of the suggestions of physics. The physical approach, therefore, thoroughly justifies itself. It must not be thought that I maintain that the approach through physics is indispensable, or that thinking in other fields has not already been done which satisfies many of the conditions disclosed by our analysis of the physical situation. This need not detract from the value of the physical approach.

The critical self-consciousness of the physicist probably first began to be awakened to any general extent by the special theory of relativity of Einstein, first formulated in 1905. The paradoxes of that theory have ever since provided a favorite playground for the man in the street, who has not hesitated to let it be known not only that he does not understand them, but that they are contrary to common sense. Velocities which do not add, meter sticks which shorten when set into motion, clocks which run slow when they move, space which is curved, are contrary enough to common experience to make such reactions understandable. Yet the fundamental point of view which should make one willing to admit at least the possibility of such apparent paradoxes is itself simple enough, and the main point can be understood by anyone, without mathematics. It is primarily a question of meanings. One may be at least reconciled to apparent paradox when he recognizes that the relativist does not mean the same thing by the addition of two velocities, for example, as does the man in the street.

Let us examine in detail this matter of the addition of two velocities. What does the relativist mean when he states that a velocity of 170,000 miles per second added to a velocity of 170,000 miles per second gives a velocity of 185,000 miles per second? To the man in the street it is self-evident that a velocity of 170,000 miles per second added to a velocity of 170,000 miles per second gives a velocity of 340,000 miles per second, for it is incontestable that 170,000 plus 170,000 is equal to 340,000. That is, the man in the street means by the sum of two velocities the sum of the two numbers which measure the velocities, and of course he gets the sum by the rules of elementary arithmetic, which he learned in grade school. But now let us examine the justification for what he did. We notice in the first place that he has given no consideration whatever to the fact that he was adding one *velocity* to another, or if he did pay any attention to it, he made the tacit assumption that the fact that he was adding velocities was immaterial. But is this really all there is to it, and shouldn't the fact that *velocities* are being added appear somewhere in our considerations? What may be the meaning anyway of adding one *velocity* to another? The more one thinks about it the more one begins to wonder whether there is perhaps anything that one can do with velocities which corresponds strictly to the arithmetical addition of two numbers. If we had been talking about adding lengths instead of velocities, the situation would have appeared simple enough, for we could have laid off one length, and then laid off the second length in the same straight line as the first, the second length beginning where the first ended, and then what we should have meant by the sum of the two lengths would be the two single lengths combined in this simple way. But we cannot take two velocities and place them end to end like two lengths; in fact velocities are not the sort of thing that we can take up and move about and put down again like lengths.

In some respects the problem of multiplication is simpler than the problem of addition. If we had been asked what we meant by *doubling* a velocity, we should not have been in nearly as much trouble as we found ourselves in on being required to add one velocity to another. For obviously one thing that we might have meant by a velocity of twice 10 miles per hour would be by definition that velocity which makes us pass over twice as many miles in one hour, or 20 miles per hour. This problem, however, is recognizably different from the problem of adding two velocities, for we were required to multiply 10 miles per hour by two, not to multiply 10 miles per hour by 2 miles per hour. It would be difficult indeed to find any sense in the latter, and in fact no attempt is usually made to ascribe any meaning to such a combination of terms; the usual attitude is that this particular combination of terms, each of which has meaning by itself, is without meaning as a combination. In general then, one can have no assurance that one can perform the same sort of operations on velocities that one can on numbers.

Returning to the problem of *adding* one velocity to another, the situation is not quite so hopeless as with regard to multiplying one velocity by another. For, although we are not able to pick up velocities bodily and place them end to end in the same way that we can two lengths, there are nevertheless certain things that we can do which are roughly similar. For example, let us imagine a train one-half mile long with a continuous corridor the entire length of it, and let us imagine that it is traveling at ten miles per hour. What we might mean by this is that an observer on the ground has set up mile posts along the right of way, and that he has a clock at each mile post, and that if the locomotive of the train starts at the zero mile post when the clock there reads 12 M., the locomotive will be opposite the mile post numbered 10 when the clock there reads 1 P.M. Or we could measure the velocity for any proportionately smaller time and, for example, should find the locomotive opposite the first mile post at six minutes after 12 by the clock at the first mile post. Now imagine a man to run down the corridor of the train at five miles per hour. What exactly shall we mean by five miles per hour in this case? We discover on examination that there is no one inevitable thing that we *must* mean, but there are several things which we might mean. One very simple thing that we might mean is that the man has in his pocket a watch which has been checked against any one of the clocks on the mile posts before the train started by the simple process of being set on the mile post beside the clock and being found to keep time with it, and that the man finds that it takes him six minutes on his watch to run the length of the train. And now one thing which we might mean by that velocity which is the sum of the velocity of the man and the train is the velocity with which the man passes the mile posts on the road bed. But how shall we specify this velocity? Shall we read the time when the man is opposite the zero mile post by the clock on that mile post, and the time when he is opposite the first mile post by the clock at that mile post and say the sum of the velocity of man and train is such that a mile is travelled in the difference of these two times? Or shall we measure the combined velocity by asking the man to read on *his* watch when he is opposite the zero mile post and again when he is opposite the first mile post, and say that the sum of the two velocities is such that a mile is passed over in the difference of *these* two times? I think it would be difficult to decide on any *a priori* grounds which one of these two possibilities it would be more appropriate to define as the sum of the two velocities.

Suppose someone should take the position that this is only hair-splitting anyway, and that the two definitions are really the same? What will he do if we ask him to prove it? Unless physicists are entirely wrong in their conception of this situation, he will not be able to find any purely *logical* method of proving that these two sums are the same, but the only thing that he will be able to say is that if we actually try the experiment we shall get the same number by either procedure. But this is in a certain sense not as we would like to have it, because we recognize that although a logical proof may perhaps not be limited as to its accuracy, nevertheless any sort of experimental proof is subject to various sorts of experimental error, so that we can never prove any proposition by actual measurement except with a certain margin of error. Indeed our apprehension turns out to be well grounded, for the physicist has strong reason to believe that although when we use ordinary instruments we shall not be able to establish any difference between the two definitions, nevertheless when we push our measurements to the extreme of precision, a difference will appear.

Granted now that the two results are not the same, which way of defining the sum of the two velocities shall we say is the proper one, and what is the exact result obtained by the method which we decide to be proper? If we still cling to our original idea that the velocities ought to add like numbers, then of course if either process gives 15 miles per hour for the result we shall doubtless say that one is the proper way of adding velocities. But experiment seems to establish that neither way of adding velocities will give exactly 15 miles per hour. This doubtless we shall find enormously disturbing at first, and it may take a considerable amount of experimenting before we are willing to admit that this is really the experimental situation. When we have at last accepted this experimental result we might possibly take the attitude that it is not profitable to try to add velocities anyhow. It is more probable, however, that we will take the attitude that it is advisable to arbitrarily define the sum as that which corresponds to the process which we can perform most simply. Even yet the decision is not perfectly unambiguous, because a process which might be simple if we were equipped with one sort of instrument might be more complicated than some other process if our instruments were of another sort, so that we might define the sum as one or the other thing depending on the state of the instrument market.

This example contains a number of instructive features. Perhaps the most obvious point of all is that we must always be sure of the precise meaning of our words—meanings are often not what they might appear to be at first sight. The meaning of "sum of two velocities," as used by the physicist, was not the same as we had intuitively supposed it to be, whatever that might have been. Furthermore, it turns out on examination that we cannot find any well defined meaning for what we thought we intuitively understood by "sum," whereas the physicist has a definite meaning for his "sum."

It is of great significance that we had such a strong intuitive feeling that we knew what we meant by "sum" of two velocities, and what the numerical value of the sum would be. The situation appeared so simple to us that at first we had no suspicion of the necessity for analysis. I am afraid it appeared simple merely because we were uncritical, perhaps because we assumed without thinking that because velocities were measured in numbers they could be treated in all ways like numbers. At any rate, whatever the explanation for our intuitive uncritical feeling, it is typical of the way we react in many situations. Meanings often appear obvious and issues certain which lose their certainty on a touch of analysis. Debonair unconsciousness of the existence of a problem, or jaunty assurance that we know how to handle a situation merely because it has resemblance to other situations is a very deep-seated human characteristic. The unfortunate consequences of such assurance are very difficult to avoid in the social subjects which are less amenable to clean-cut analysis than the physical sciences.

Having once recognized that "sum" is used in a technical sense, we should immediately be reconciled to the fact that the sum of two velocities is not the arithmetical sum of the two numbers which express the two component velocities, for when we see that "sum" has a meaning distinct from the meaning of the sum of two numbers, our reasons for expecting two velocities to add like two numbers lose their force, and the subject has at least to be reexamined to discover whether expectations based on arithmetical experience are still valid in their new setting. This shows well a common trait of language—the use of a word is frequently extended from an originally simple situation to more complex situations, in which only *some* of the original connotations of the word carry over. Unless one thinks carefully one is very much inclined to make the mistake of carrying over *all* the implications of the simple situation to the extended situation. Thus, in the above example, when we used the same word "sum" in the arithmetical and kinematical cases we were at first inclined to assume that the numerical value of the sum would be found by the same arithmetical procedure in the two cases. Strictly speaking, the same word should not have been used in the two cases; we might speak of the sum of two numbers and the "addit" (or some similar invented word) for that particular combination of two velocities which we have decided is simplest for our purpose. Common usage, however, seems to prefer ambiguity and a small number of words to greater precision and a greater number of words.

Another very important feature of our example was that we had to appeal to experiment in order to decide what the result obtained by adding in a particular conventional sense 10 miles per hour to 5 miles per hour actually is. The discovery by experiment of what the actual result of the combination is constitutes new information which no one has discovered how to anticipate by any purely logical process.

The precise result which experiment finds is also most instructive. Experiment would show that according to either of the definitions proposed above for "sum," the sum of 10 and 5 miles per hour is very closely 15 miles per hour. In fact the result is so nearly 15 miles per hour that it is questionable whether even yet experiment would show unambiguously the difference between the two definitions. Such remains the case as long as the two velocities are small. If experience were confined only to small velocities the question probably would not have arisen as to what convention it would be desirable to adopt for the "sum" of velocities, and we would probably not have suspected the weakness in our naive expectation that of course the sum would be found by adding the corresponding numbers. The reason that the "man in the street" thinks that it is just plain nonsense to imagine that "sum" could mean anything else than arithmetical sum is without doubt to be sought in the fact that his experience has been confined to small velocities, such as the velocity of airplanes or of sound. But when the velocities become very high, and this means when they become comparable with the "velocity" of light, as they do in experiments with electrons or other charged particles in vacuum tubes, then experiment shows that the "sum" is not even approximately the arithmetical sum, but may depart very widely indeed from it. That is, if we leave the range of ordinary experience, as we may do either by enormously increasing the precision of our measurements in the ordinary range of velocities or by enormously increasing the velocities without increasing the precision, then we must be prepared to find that things do not behave in the way we had anticipated from their behavior in the original restricted range. "Extrapolations" can never be made with certainty of correctness, but every extrapolation must be subject to the check of fresh experiment before we can be sure of its validity.

Perhaps the most important feature of all in our example is contained in the method by which we found the meaning of the "sum" of two velocities. This meaning we found by analyzing what we did in combining the two velocities in order to obtain the "sum." This it seems to me is typical of all situations in which meanings are concerned. I believe that one will find that when he wants to assure himself that he understands the meaning of a term or wants to discover what a question means, he makes an analysis of what he does in using the term or answering the question. This sort of analysis I have called "operational." Doubtless there will be many who will question whether this gets to the ultimate roots of the matter, or whether there is not something more to it. However, the question of "ultimate" roots does not necessarily concern us here, and we will be satisfied if the specification of meaning by an analysis of what we do proves to go deep enough to be profitable in the situations of interest to us. The proof that such an analysis does go deep enough to be profitable must be given by the rest of the essay and the exhibition therein contained of the technique in action and the sorts of thing it can accomplish.

I attempt no proof of the statement that an appraisal of meaning demands at least an analysis of what I do; simple observation shows that this analysis is almost the only self-conscious constituent in my own search for meanings, and observation of my fellows convinces me that at least a certain number of them function in the same way and that therefore I may hope that they, at least, will find an exposition like this understandable.

In order to further illustrate the operational method of analysis, let us consider another instructive example taken from relativity theory, that of "simultaneity." Before the advent of relativity theory, two events at two different places were defined as simultaneous if they occurred at the "same time," and it was tacitly assumed that this statement did not need other qualification, or in other words, it was assumed that the "time" of an event had a unique significance. But this tacit assumption was made without an analysis of the operations performed in measuring the time of an event. When the analysis was made in full detail no unique way of measuring time was found, but many ways are possible, so that the method of measurement has to be specified before the meaning of simultaneity is fixed. We have to be prepared to find that two events which are simultaneous by one method of measurement are not simultaneous by another, and such does in fact prove to be the experimental situation. In other words, the assumption of an "absolute" simultaneity, which was made so easily before the analysis, turns out not to correspond to the physical facts. It is obvious that if we try to use the assumption of absolute simultaneity in describing physical situations we shall make errors, but on the other hand, that if we define simultaneity only in terms of physical operations which we have actually performed, and make no statements which we have not checked by experiment, we shall not make mistakes which we shall later have to correct.

There is another very important matter connected with the operational specification of meaning as now employed by the physicist, namely, the operational specification should be as nearly unique as possible. Thus if one defines the length of an object in terms of certain operations performed with a meter stick one is not at liberty at the same time to define the length in terms of the optical operations of a surveyor with a theodolite, in spite of the fact that the two operations may be found to yield the same result. The reason is obvious; the equivalence of the two operations can be proved only by experiment. Experiment is always subject to error and furthermore no experimental result can be assumed to be valid under conditions not yet encountered. We have no way of telling that when experimental accuracy is pushed beyond the limits now possible, or when we encounter new sorts of conditions, such perhaps as intense gravitational fields, the equivalence now found will continue to hold. Since the desire of the physicist is ordinarily not to commit himself with regard to the unknown, this sort of possibility must obviously be ruled out, and length, as every other concept, must be defined in terms of a unique procedure. If two sorts of operation are used, then strictly two different names should be used. It must be confessed, however, that the physicist is not always as meticulous as this, and of course in daily life one is almost never as meticulous as this. In fact, in daily life a quite different point of view is often taken, and philosophers have made objections to the point of view about meanings set forth above which involve exactly this point. Thus it is objected that "length" is unnecessarily restricted by the requirement of uniqueness of operation; for it is an "essential characteristic" of "length" that the same result can be obtained by many different sorts of operation. One can have no quarrel with this point of view if it is clearly recognized. If one wants to emphasize that experience has shown that there are many operations which give approximately the same result, then one may use "length" in this sense, but it is a sense which is not as clean-cut as we can make it, which involves experimental error, and which may later (therefore) be found not to correspond to facts. I think that for his purposes the physicist is justified in defining his terms by unique operations, and making as explicit and self-conscious as he can the place where experiment further enters the situation. Also it seems to me that when a full realization of all the assumptions is demanded one is almost compelled to restrict his defining operations to unique operations. In fact, it appears to me to be of the greatest importance to develop a technique by which distinctions may be made between results which under ordinary conditions are so similar that for most practical purposes it is not necessary to distinguish between them. Language and thought in their evolution as tools for application to everyday situations have made all sorts of compromise and *mésalliances* in the interests of ease of handling, and for clear thinking it is absolutely necessary to have some method of unscrambling them again. I think that one reason that we are so often content in daily life to let a single word stand for a variety of operationally distinguishable things is that we are often concerned with emotions or feelings, and the variety of possible emotional experience is very much more restricted than is the variety of possible visual experience, for example.

The physicist thus has come to see that if he wants his description of nature to rest on a decently secure basis, at least some of his meanings must be found in unique physical operations which he can actually perform. He does not deny that terms with other sorts of meaning can be used, but in such a case he does not expect necessarily a particularly good fit with experience. Suppose, for example, that we persist in talking about "absolute" time. We seek the meaning of "absolute" time in what we do when we apply the term to any particular case. Experiment has shown that there is no complex of *physical* operations at present known which has the property of absoluteness implied in "absolute" time, so that an operational definition in terms of actual physical procedures is impossible. But the philosopher or theologian may find this no difficulty, and may define the absolute time of an event as the time of the event perceived in the mind of God. We would now have to find the meaning of the words "*perceived* in the *mind* of *God*" in terms of things that we do; whatever these things may be they obviously are not the sort of physical things that the physicist does, and it is a matter to be proved whether they have the desired "objective" validity. We will return to this matter in the next chapter.

One very important result of making as articulate an operational analysis as possible is that it may disclose to us possible places where experimental discriminations should be made which had not before occurred to us. Consider, for example, "absolute" time again. The sort of tacit ideal that we have before us in using the word "absolute" is itself not very definite, and may be one thing for the theologian or philosopher and another thing for the physicist. I think most physicists have in the back of their heads when using the word "absolute," not something which cannot be specified in terms of physical operations, as did the theologian and philosopher, but something in which either the operations can be specified in terms which do not refer to accidental, temporary, local situations, or in which the results obtained by the operations are independent of the particular temporary and local situations which entered the specification. Even the ideals tacit in the use of "absolute" are not sharp, but in specific cases the word may or may not be felt to be suitable. Thus if the existence of an all pervading ether could have been established in some way, then velocity measured with respect to the ether would have been the sort of thing that the physicist would have been willing to call absolute. It is curious that there is a uniquely definable velocity, namely velocity with respect to the fixed stars, which is not felt to have the property of absoluteness implicitly wanted. The tacit demands are not sharp with regard to what sort of variation in local and temporary conditions must be covered in order that "absolute" may be applicable. It was of course known for a long while that there were various sorts of experimental time, as sidereal or solar time. Sidereal time might with certain justification have been taken as "absolute" time. Unwillingness to do so must at one time have meant that the possibility was anticipated of making future experimental measurements of something with the properties of the "absolute" time of the theologian. In this sense the meaning for the physicist of "absolute" time was little more than an expectation with regard to future discoveries. But with the development of physics this sort of possibility did not materialize, and this sort of operational meaning for "absolute" time lost its usefulness. Experimentally the situation was satisfactory enough, because the sidereal time of the astronomer was uniquely determined, and could be measured with sufficient accuracy. At least the practical procedure for determining sidereal time was uniquely determined. The operational defination was not very articulate, however. It was not until the development of points of view suggested by relativity theory that it was seen in what significant respects the definition that covered the practical procedure was inarticulate, namely in that it did not specify the motion of the observer with respect to the events whose time was being measured. When attention was thus attracted to the ambiguity of the procedure for measuring time, of course the question at once arose as to whether experiment would show that this was a pertinent factor. The feelings back of the original usage of the word "absolute" were modified until, with the passage of generations, the physicist began to use the word in a new sense, and he would have called simultaneity an "absolute" property of two events if his experiments had shown that the results of the measurement of the times were independent of the *motion* of the observer. Of course the experimental situation has proved to be that the motion of the observer does affect the result, which we now describe by saying that simultaneity is not "absolute," or "there is nothing physical corresponding to absolute time."

With regard to operations the important feature is that if an articulate analysis has been made in the first place of all the specifications necessary to uniquely fix the operations, the possibility would have been recognized that the motion of the observer might make a difference, and experimental search might have been made for it. Actually, of course, experiment and theory play into each other's hands, and it requires unusual intuition to anticipate the possibility of effects for which there is no experimental intimation.

We thus see that an operational analysis suggests almost without argument, to anyone with the background of experience of most physicists, that this concept of absolute time is such that, by its construction, it carries no guarantee that it is adapted to deal with the experimental situation. We cannot, be *sure* that it will *not* fit with experiment, but whether it does or not must in any event be proved by further actual experiment. Of course the physicist may also be a mystic, and he may be so convinced of the objective value of his mysticism that he is sure that the counterpart of his "absolute" time will be found in the experimental world, and he may be inspired to make experimental search for it, and he may thereby make a great discovery, even as great discoveries have been made in the past. But the physicist will at least see that mystical definition is different in kind from definition in terms of actual physical operations, and will recognize that if the mystical defintion is to be applied in actual physical situations the necessity for an additional experimental verification is involved. When the experimental verification has been made, we can discard the mystical definition and substitute a new one in terms of physical operations, which the new experiments have shown us how to perform, but which originally we did not know how to do. The state of mind that uses mystical definitions and is so convinced of their correctness that it is sure that no experimental check is necessary, or which even thinks that the experimental check *must* be met, has been shown by the experience of the last 300 years to be so hopeless for dealing with the world that we shall simply ignore it. Mystical definitions can be adopted, if one likes, as a method for suggesting new experiment, but they must be regarded as of no more significance than any other method of grinding the intellectual crank to obtain suggestions of new things to try.

It will now be perhaps profitable to briefly summarize some of the modifications which the physicist has made in his concepts on the basis of an operational analysis. One which has been much discussed is the fusion of space and time into the single aggregate of "space-time." There has been a great deal of bunkum about this situation. It is of course meaningless to say that time is nothing but a fourth dimension of space, etc., etc. All mention of four dimensions in this connection is purely symbolic. The physical situation is merely that an analysis of the physical operations which one performs in determining the locality or the time of an event discloses that one cannot determine either the locality or the time by itself without paying some attention to the other. For obviously the operation of determining a position cannot be uniquely performed unless one is told when to perform it, nor can the operation of determining a time with a clock be uniquely performed unless one is informed where the clock is situated that one is reading. A further and more detailed analysis shows that the operations of determining locality or time are so tied together that they cannot be separated, so that four "parameters" are necessary to determine an event, namely the three which determine its position and the one which determines its time. "Four" dimensions is the technical mathematical way of describing the fact that four numbers are necessary. There is no connection whatever with an unimaginable geometrical space in which there are four different directions all at right angles to each other.

Our understanding of the fundamental concepts of space and time themselves has been much modified by our awareness of their operational nature. It used to be common to describe these as "necessary forms of thought," the idea being that no thinking could be done except in terms of either space or time. On the other hand, one of the fundamental points of view of the new wave mechanics, much emphasized by Bohr, is that the concepts of space and time are not applicable to small scale events inside the atom. What does this mean? Let us in the first place confine our attention to what is involved in the concept of space. Nearly everyone has had some experience with geometry, and knows that it purports to deal with the properties of space. What do we do when we seek to prove any of the simple theorems of geometry, such for instance as that any two triangles are equal if their three sides are respectively equal? The customary elementary proof was a proof by superposition; that is, one triangle was imagined to be moved into coincidence with the other. But now what sort of a thing is a triangle that it can be moved about? What is it made of, and how do we know that it doesn't change when we move it? Or what do we mean by the points which constitute the apexes of the triangle? We must somehow, in thought at least, be able to identify the points which fix the apexes of the triangle, so that we can know when we have come back to the same points and the same triangle. And what do we mean, anyhow, by coming back to the *same* point? If space itself is amorphous and structureless there can be no way of identifying the points, or setting off anything in space to talk about.

I think one has to realize, then, when one analyzes what one does, that the concept of *empty* space corresponds to nothing pertinent that we can do. We have things in space, or more exactly, we have things, and we are concerned with certain aspects of these things. Certains aspects are called spatial aspects, and what is meant by space involves the aggregate of these spatial aspects. We do not need to go very far into the analysis of exactly what we understand by spatial aspects, but at least one minimum requirement is plainly obvious from our discussion above; the things with which we are concerned and whose spatial aspects constitute space must be such that we can identify parts of them in order to mark what we mean by points of space. What is the smallest sort of a thing that we can use as a marker? This depends of course on our experimental skill, but if we accept present physical theory we must admit that we could never conceivably get a marker smaller than the smallest physical particle, which in our present state of physical knowledge is somewhat indefinite, but is certainly not smaller than the electron. It therefore is absolutely meaningless from the point of view of physical operations which can actually be performed to talk about the *space inside* an electron, and if we have accepted the convention that our physical concepts must be framed in terms of operations that can be actually carried out, we must recognize that "space" inside the electron is meaningless. We have thus found a limit to this supposedly necessary form of thought. Further, since "inside" is a spatial term, we might as well admit that "inside of the electron" is itself a meaningless combination.

You may resent this summary disposal of the meaning of perhaps a cherished term, and reply that even if one cannot put a probe inside the electron one can at any rate *think* about the inside of the electron, and if one can think about it it cannot be meaningless. Of course I shall have to grant that you can think about the inside of the electron if you say you can, but I can at any rate ask you to analyze a little more carefully what you do when you think about it. Haven't you in thought done something more or less equivalent to drawing a circle on paper, which you say "represents" the electron, and thinking about the inside of the circle, or if you are tactually minded, perhaps you have imagined yourself holding something in your hand like an orange, which again you say represents the electron, and realizing from your tactual sensations as you explore the external surface that the thing is convex, and so have recognized that you would get additional tactual sensations if you pushed your finger straight through the surface? If you haven't in thought done something more or less equivalent to one of these things, then I can't talk to you any more because that is the only sort of thing that I can do when I "think" about the inside of the electron, and my whole enterprise of communicating ideas presupposes that you find significance when I say the sort of thing that I find significant. Of course you may not admit at once that what you have done in thinking about the inside of the electron is like my description, but as you think further about it you may come to see that this is "really" what you have done. I do not believe that any argument prevails here; you either see that this is so or you do not.

If, now, you have got as far as this paragraph, you recognize that what you "really" do in talking about the inside of the electron or in saying that the inside has the properties of space is merely that you are saying something about a "model" which you set up to use as a tool in thinking about the electron. It is meaningless to talk about the space "actually" inside the electron, so that we are confronted with a situation to which the ordinary ideas of space do not apply.

There are doubtless many physicists who will not like this conclusion, for they will say that they have made calculations of the mass of the electron by assuming that their model of the electron was "really" correct, and that the mass which they have calculated in this way has checked with experiment. If one wants to say that for this reason it makes sense to talk about the "space" "inside" the electron, and if everyone knows what one means by saying so, then there can be no objection. But personally I feel that this is a rather oblique way of saying what I would prefer to expand into the statement: "One can correctly calculate some of the properties of the electron in terms of a model which has ordinary spatial properties." It seems to me that this expanded statement reproduces more exactly what we actually do, and is therefore to be preferred.

What we have been saying about the electron is no more than

anyone might have said, but didn't, thirty-five years ago. Recently, however, new properties of the electron have been found experimentally, which put the whole situation in a different light. We have been thinking of the electron as the sort of thing that might be used as a marker for the points of space; that is, the electron as a whole was thought of as having an identity which could be used to set up a geometry. But this is a pure assumption as far as experiment goes, because no one has ever followed a single electron around to be sure that it doesn't change into something else or that it is always the same. If our interpretation of recent experiments is correct, the electron is intrinsically such a sort of thing that it cannot be followed about. If you have an electron now, and again a split billionth of a second later have an electron, there is no possible experimental procedure by which you could decide whether the second electron is the "same" as the first electron or not. That is, the physical operations which are necessary to give meaning to "identity" are impossible to apply to the electron, and "identity" is a meaningless term when applied to the electron. But the property of identity is perhaps the most fundamental attribute of what we mean by a "thing," and it is connected with other properties such as existence "in" space. Would you be willing to say that a thing exists in space if you knew that it wasn't even a "thing"? Would you say that virtue exists in space? It appears therefore, that we must recognize not only that "space" is not applicable to the "inside" of the electron, but that the electron as a whole is outside the range of the spatial concept in all its ordinary implications.

A somewhat similar analysis which it is not necessary to follow in such detail, applies to the question of the universal applicability of the concept of time. The operational criterion would demand that we can say that events take place in time only when there is some way by which the time at which the event takes place can be determined. But it requires an instrument to determine what the time of an event is, namely a clock, and a clock is composed of parts and has smallest divisions. It is therefore meaningless in our technical sense to talk about the "time" of events which have to be referred to idealized fractions of the smallest division of the smallest possible clock.

In addition to the concepts of time and space there is another concept which has sometimes been said to be so fundamental that thought itself is not possible without it, namely the concept of causality. The sense in which "causality" is used is not sharp and there are various more or less rough significances associated with it in common usage. We shall not be concerned with an exact analysis of the varieties of usage, but shall pick out what for our purposes is the most important aspect. One aspect of the universal conviction that everything has a cause is the idea that there are regularities in the sequence of events such that if all the antecedents were given the event itself could be predicted. It is the aspect of causality connected with the assumption of predictability that will concern us. What is the basis for our conviction that events are predictable, and that the reason that we so often fail to predict is merely that we were not given all the antecedents, or else that the situation was so complicated as to be beyond our powers? I think that one will find on analysis that the basis for this conviction is eventually experimental. Such experiment is mostly confined to the last 300 years, dating perhaps from the time when the principles of mechanics were applied with such spectacular success to the prediction of the motion of the heavenly bodies. The thesis of the inter-relatedness of all things was so successful that it has come to be accepted as necessary, and the converse to be regarded as unthinkable. But the experiments on which this conviction was based were all large scale experiments. It is common knowledge that in the last few years it has been found that on the atomic and sub-atomic scale of magnitude we have not been able to predict, and furthermore the inability to predict has been made a cardinal principle of wave mechanics and the results of this theory agree with experiment. It is not pertinent to urge that the last word has not yet been spoken, and that perhaps later we shall find how to predict phenomena which at present we have to treat as purely statistical. The significant thing is that as a matter of fact there is a whole domain of phenomena which can be thought about and correctly reproduced by giving up the thesis of complete determinism, that is, of universal causality. The assumption of the principle of causality is not necessary to thought because physicists have been doing valid thinking without it.

It must strike one as hazardous, even presumptuous, to attempt to state in what terms thinking "must" be done. Our thinking is part of our method of adjusting ourselves to our environment. It is hard to believe that if the character of our environment should change our thinking would not have enough flexibility to change itself in some way to adapt itself to the new conditions. In fact, we are devising ways of handling atoms and electrons, which constitute a new order of experience, and doubtless shall be able to devise better methods later with more practice, which shall have less resemblance even than our present methods to traditional modes.

I shall now attempt to make certain more general comments and draw some more general conclusions from what the physicist has learned in thinking about recent situations.

There is in the first place the necessity for making an analysis of one's concepts and procedures if one wants to feel any confidence in the validity of the use he makes of them. If one stops to look at his own mental operations he cannot fail to be struck by the paucity of the first hand contacts which these operations make with the prospective use. The number of mental devices which I use in meeting the situations of everyday life which are my own invention and whose validity I have checked by adequate trial is practically negligible. Nearly all my mental devices I learned from other people, either by watching them and imitating them or else by deliberate instruction. I was taught to talk; I was taught to reason syllogistically. The method of instruction was primarily one of imitation; I watched my instructor and imitated what he did until I had acquired facility to do what he would have done in the same situation. The criterion that I had understood was that I should be able to convince my instructor that I was acting as he would. In particular, I learned the use and the meaning of words by becoming able to use them in the same situations with the some implications and for the same purposes as he. Part of the process of learning consisted in discovering the purposes my instructor had in view when he used certain words and the assumptions he made as to what he could do with the words and what the words were good for. When I had acquired the capability for exact imitation, the process of learning was complete, and I was thereby qualified to take my place in society and in turn to hand on what I had learned to the next generation.

It is obvious that although this process of learning is satisfactory enough as long as the only test of it is the ability to understand and to be understood by people like my instructor, it may be subject to a fatal weakness when I wish to put it to "objective" use if my instructor has been mistaken as to the uses for which the operation is adapted. This is no academic matter, for evidently there are situations in which the common assumptions about the validity of a concept or procedure are not correct. We have already encountered an example of such a situation in the concept of "absolute" time. The tacit assumption was that this concept had a certain correspondence with fact and that measurements of time made in the laboratory would have the properties postulated in the concept. When subjected to the check of accurate experiment it was found that this was a false assumption. Furthermore I think that it will be found on examination that most of the concepts in common use imply assumptions about their objective validity.

It appears, therefore, that circulation as part of the linguistic medium of exchange is no guarantee whatever of the genuineness of the coin. As long as people are content to subject their verbalizations only to the control that other people shall respond to them in the way they demand, there is no automatic method that assures the "objective" validity of the concept that is assumed.

Of course one ought to be able to allay any misgivings that may arise as to whether one's instructor is correct in assuming that he can apply his concept for certain purposes by the simple process of asking his instructor what is the method by which he justified his usage? But the unfortunate fact is that this is a Utopian ideal, as one may see by examining his own qualifications as an instructor. Not only can one almost never actually exhibit the line of argument that would justify a traditional usage, but almost never can one even state whether anyone in history has ever as a matter of fact taken pains to make an examination of the question, much less state what his conclusions were. With so uncritical an attitude it must be to a large extent a matter of sheer luck whether the concept is good for what people assume or not. If there were anything very grossly wrong with it, the chances are that it would have been discovered in the course of a varied use, but if it is a more delicate matter, particularly if it is a question of its applicability in new situations, the chances are that its ineptitude will not have shown up. Still more, if it is the sort of concept that never gets subject to the objective verification that by implication it should be able to meet, but is used only as a verbalism subject to no other control than imitative use, its counterfeit nature will never be disclosed.

Physics contains many examples of this counterfeit verbal currency; much more does daily life. Such situations can be disclosed by a careful enough analysis, and it is absolutely necessary to make such analysis if one is to have confidence in the validity of his thinking. We have already encountered examples above in which we analyzed what we did in applying the concepts of velocity or length or time to concrete situations. Similarly our analysis of social concepts will take the form of analyzing what we do when we apply the concept to concrete social situations. One important result of making such analysis is that it puts us in a position to estimate the validity of the claims of the concept to be adapted to its ostensible purpose.

Our appraisal of validity is something quite apart from the analysis itself, and is something which we will not go into in any detail except to remark that it will depend on the experience of the individual, and that different individuals may give different answers. Suppose for example that a peasant says to us "It will surely rain tomorrow." We and the peasant may both agree in our factual analysis of the operations that give rise to this statement; namely, we may both agree that the factual basis is that the priest is now praying for rain. It is probable, however, that there will not be unanimity as to the objective significance to be attached to this fact.

The purpose and the advantage of as detailed an analysis as we can make is thus that it puts us into a position such that we can apply the lessons of any pertinent experience which we may have had. *For the experience itself there can be no substitute.* The physicist will be reminded of dimensional analysis which enables him by a simple mathematical machinery to capitalize any pertinent physical experience he may have had, but which is absolutely impotent without the experience.

One reason that I have to make so many analyses myself, and cannot use analyses which previous generations may have made, is that previous generations did not record the steps leading to their conclusions. It is usually mental economy for the individual to forget the steps which have led to a conclusion and remember only the conclusion.

As one's experience broadens, one's estimate of the validity of the procedures which are disclosed by analysis is subject to continual revision; the conclusions to be drawn from analysis are not frozen conclusions, but are subject to constant change. Many concepts experience a gradual shift of significance from generation to generation to keep pace with the changes in our estimates of the interpretation to be put on experience. For example, we and an inhabitant of the middle ages might have been able to agree in our factual analysis of the concept of "angel" as of a being whose properties were determined by what the priest said. But we would have been entirely at variance in the significance which we would have ascribed to the discovery that the only way of finding the meaning of an "angel" was through the dictum of a priest. We would regard this discovery as confirmation of our conviction that "angel" is only a symbolic figure, whereas our friend of the middle ages was convinced that the dictum of the priest was a perfectly good way of acquiring knowledge of "objective" fact, and in accordance with that belief he would have accorded to reports of the appearance of angels to this or that saint all the implications which he would accord to reports of the goings and comings of ordinary persons, verifiable by everyday methods.

I believe that many of the terms in social usage carry from previous generations hangovers of implication with regard to their significance, and that a fresh analysis is needed to bring them up to date.

Another observation with regard to our analysis of some of the concepts of physics is that we were never able to refine indefinitely, but that analysis always rests at a certain point where we are willing to accept without question the validity of what we are doing. Thus in analzying the process of determining length, we assume without question that we are able to determine the coincidence between the ends of the object which we are measuring and the marks on the meter stick. The reason that we stop at this point is not primarily physical exhaustion at carrying the analysis so far, although physical exhaustion would doubtless eventually stop us, but rather that we have arrived at a point where the operation is so well known and performable with so little hesitation that we feel that uncertainties which may arise from accepting it are insignificant in comparison with the original uncertainties in the concept that we set out to analyze. There is evidently no sharp rule by which it is possible to determine where the analysis may be allowed to rest. The resting place will be determined both by our purpose and by our experience. As our horizons widen, concepts which at first appear so innocent as to be above the need of analysis become suspect and we have to push our analysis farther back.

Again there is a parallelism with the situation in physics. For a couple of thousand years a hypothetical analysis of matter into the four elements earth, air, fire, and water, was sufficient for all demands put upon it. Modern chemistry then arose and matter was analyzed into 92 elements. This was sufficient until the development of electron physics, and we now have the analysis of atoms into electrons and nuclei, and still further the analysis of nuclei into protons and neutrons. Analysis into the 92 different sorts of atom of the chemist is still adequate for a great many purposes, evidence that the length to which the analysis must be carried is no absolute thing, but is determined by the purpose of the moment. (It is a little difficult at the present to think ourselves back into a frame of mind where the analysis into just four elements would have seemed satisfactory.) It is also typical of the frame of mind of the analyst, even when the analyst is a physicist, that for many years an analysis beyond the atom was thought to be "*intrinsically*" impossible, as shown by the derivation of the word atom itself—"that which cannot be cut." In fact, it is not impossible to find in the scientific literature of the past arguments as to the impossibility of structure beyond the atom which must be judged to have only a verbal significance, made possible only by capitalizing the derivation of the word. Similarly, any discussion of daily life assumes certain things as not needing further analysis, that is, it assumes certain "atoms of discourse" to coin a phrase reminiscent of "the universe of discourse." The unanalyzed atoms of discourse may be of different kinds, and there may be various sorts of reason for not pushing the analysis further. It is intellectual economy not to push the analysis further than necessary for the purpose in hand, and people as a matter of fact do often achieve this sort of intellectual economy. Thus most current social discussions in this country assume without question that human life has a certain intrinsic worth, or that democracy is to be assumed in discussing permissible social change, or that the rate and way in which a population propagates itself is as uncontrollable as the "law" of gravitation. The local and temporary status of these "atoms" is obvious enough when one reflects on the people in other places to whom these things are not atomic. Society uses in its thinking unanalyzed purposes, unanalyzed values, and unanalyzed operations, all of which may on occasion be subject to further analysis.

There is no automatic method of discovering what these atoms of discourse are. Nevertheless as complete awareness as possible of what they are is necessary if social exchange is to be agreeable and profitable. It is a matter of the commonest observation that the atoms of discourse of different people are often different, and the discovery of such differences often provides the resolution of apparently irreconcilable conflict. One of the problems which confront the individual in adapting himself to society is the development of a technique by which he may assure himself without officiousness that he is correctly apprehending the atomic structure of his neighbors' thinking. Conversation languishes under the constant demand "Define your terms," which is usually at heart prompted by the laudable desire to discover the atoms of discourse of our fellow.

In addition to the ordinary atoms of discourse which are not analyzed in ordinary discussions because it is not necessary to do so, there may be other sorts of atom which are unanalyzed because we do not see any way of pushing the analysis further, just as in physics at the present time there are certain particles which we do not know how to pick to pieces. We may distinguish between physical operations which we do not see how to analyze further, and situations in which further analysis is prevented by reaching a logical *impasse* which will continue to block us until our ideas of logic itself experience a revision. Or there are other sorts of thing that we at present do not see how to analyze. For instance, how shall we answer the question "How do you know that you now are having feelings?" or "What do you mean by a feeling?" or how shall we analyze the perception of "later" in time, or of "betweenness" in space? There are other sorts of analysis with which we shall not be concerned here at all, such for example as a physiological analysis of cerebration. It seems to me that analysis such as we are considering here eventually always reaches a stage where it is impotent. I regard this as a brute fact of observation, to be accepted as any other brute fact without the attempt to discover implications of significance in the fact. In any event, too extensive an analysis would eventually defeat itself, because we would presently arrive at a mere description of the actual occurrence, which never repeats, and is unlike every other occurrence. I also regard it as brute fact that in most of the intellectual situations that confront me analysis is a most potent means of clarification, in spite of the fact that there are some situations in which it is impotent.

If one analyzes what he does when he makes an analysis I think he will find that a very important part of the process consists in observing and reporting in as great detail as possible exactly what it is that he does or what it is that happens to him. There is no royal rule by which one may be sure of perceiving details of significant fineness, or of not missing broad general relationships. One person will see in a situation what another will not see at all. Furthermore, there is no method by which one can force another to see the same thing that he does. Ability to see details, as subtle differences of meaning in logical processes, for example, is something which grows with experience, and unless one's fellow has had a certain amount of experience, no amount of verbal activity will avail to communicate the picture. One does not attempt to expound relativity to a South Sea Islander until he has gone to school and acquired a certain minimum background. One can therefore never be sure of finality in his own analyses, but must always be prepared for further revision as his own experience grows and he sees more detail, or comes to realize that detail is significant which previously had seemed of no importance.

Perception of finer detail means that the ultimate atoms of discourse get pushed further back—the pushing back of the atomic domain is not possible until one has acquired the ability to discriminate more searchingly. The man in the street not having made the attempt, usually does not see the possibility of splitting his atoms, and does not understand when someone else tries to show him the possibility. "Common sense" is at least in part characterized by its "atom of discourse"—like Dr. Johnson it sees no possibility of analyzing further the atoms of common experience, such as the objects of daily life. On the other hand, we shall find it possible and I think profitable to ask: "What do you mean by an object?" "Under what conditions do you describe your experience in terms of object?" That is, we find it profitable to analyze the concept of object.

The question arises of what to do when someone else claims to see fine discriminations of meaning in a situation in which I myself can see nothing. The easy, but unprofitable, reaction is denial or scepticism. However, experience with one's own growing power of discrimination should usually prohibit the sceptical reaction. At the same time, one knows that others and one's self also on occasion makes mistakes, and some method is necessary to ensure that this is not happening now. The most obvious method is simply to get the other fellow to try to make us see what he does by whatever method his ingenuity can devise. If this method fails we still have the resource of getting him to make predictions of future happenings in the realm of our own experience of such a nature that we ourselves could not make the prediction. The congenital blind man must be convinced in some such way as this that other people have a sense which he does not. But if there is no method either direct or indirect by which the claim of the other fellow to see details beyond our own capacities can touch us, except his mere statement, then we have no alternative than to describe this claim of his as a curious and unexplained bit of verbal behavior, any deeper significance in which for the present eludes us. When confronted by such a situation we will in all probability allow a little more elasticity in our planning for the future than we otherwise would for the possibility that we may ourselves at some time in the future have a deeper vision in certain situations, but present meaning other than this we cannot ascribe to the "reality" of the "existence" of what he claims to see. The reason that we cannot is contained in the operational meaning of "reality" and "existence."

Enough has probably now been said about the applications of the operational method in physics to give one the hang of the thing, and to prepare us for its application in later chapters to the broader situations of daily life. We shall find that the technique of the operational method becomes more complex than when applied to physics, because the situations themselves are more complex. The complexity of the subject matter arises from the participation of human behavior to a much more important extent than it did in physics. Of course there is no sharp line of division, and there is recognizably some element of human behavior in such a simple physical operation as the measurement of the length of a bar, for measuring length is observably something that *we* do. But our interest in a measurement of length is not primarily because it is human behavior, but it is "impersonal." On the other hand, in many of the situations of daily life the interest is primarily in the human behavior aspect; we want to be able to understand human behavior and predict it, and make our plans in accordance with it. Human behavior itself is a complex thing; part of it is more or less "objective" in character, as when we try to design our houses so that they are likely to withstand the shock of an earthquake, but a good part of it is of significance merely within the circle of society itself, as for instance a great deal of our verbalizing is subject to no other "objective" control than that our fellows shall find significance in it. Conversely, a large part of our environment consists of the verbalizing of our fellows, and it is just as essential for our survival that we become adapted to this verbalization as to more impersonal features of our environment. We are concerned with a verbal world by the side of the "real" "external" world, and this verbal world is capable of an apparently hopelessly greater complexity than the "material" world, being subject to no such control of self-consistency as is the material world. Many of our difficulties I believe have their origin right here in the fact that this verbal world is subject to no control of self-consistency.

The operations which are most obviously characteristic of physics are to a large extent operations with our hands—the sort of thing we do in the laboratory in making measurements. But it is impossible to separate the things we do with our hands from the things we do with our "minds," for it is obvious that there are "mental" operations inextricably mixed up with such a primarily physical thing as measuring a length, and of course there are also operations in physics which are almost entirely "mental," as for example counting, which the physicist, no less than the financier, could not get along without. In fact, the two elements are so inextricably intermingled that it is not profitable to try to effect a separation, if indeed a separation has meaning, and we shall talk about operations as such and assume that we know how to perform them, irrespective of whether analysis might be able to show a preponderance of the "physical" or the "mental." But we shall find that the things which we do in our capacity as social beings require a difference of stress on certain of the "mental" aspects which makes it profitable to examine a little more in detail points which we could slur over as long as we were concerned with purely physical applications. In particular, because our purposes are different, we shall sometimes find it necessary to push our analysis farther into the verbal for social purposes than for purposes of physics. Our atoms of discourse may be different. In the next chapter we consider these matters in some detail. Since, however, many of our operations as physicists are the same as our operations in daily life, such as drawing conclusions by syllogistic reasoning, many of our considerations will be pertinent in both fields.

Henri Poincaré

The Measure of Time

I

So long as we do not go outside the domain of consciousness, the notion of time is relatively clear. Not only do we distinguish without difficulty present sensation from the remembrance of past sensations or the anticipation of future sensations, but we know perfectly well what we mean when we say that, of two conscious phenomena which we remember, one was anterior to the other; or that, of two foreseen conscious phenomena, one will be anterior to the other.

When we say that two conscious facts are simultaneous, we mean that they profoundly interpenetrate, so that analysis can not separate them without mutilating them.

The order in which we arrange conscious phenomena does not admit of any arbitrariness. It is imposed upon us and of it we can change nothing.

I have only a single observation to add. For an aggregate of sensations to have become a remembrance capable of classification in time, it must have ceased to be actual, we must have lost the sense of its infinite complexity, otherwise it would have remained present. It must, so to speak, have crystallized around a center of associations of ideas which will be a sort of label. It is only when they thus have lost all life that we can classify our memories in time as a botanist arranges dried flowers in his herbarium.

Reprinted from Henri Poincaré, Foundations of Science *(Science Press, 1913) and Poincaré,* The Value of Science *(New York: Dover Publications, Inc., 1958).*

But these labels can only be finite in number. On that score, psychologic time should be discontinuous. Whence comes the feeling that between any two instants there are others? We arrange our recollections in time, but we know that there remain empty compartments. How could that be, if time were not a form preexistent in our mind? How could we know there were empty compartments, if these compartments were revealed to us only by their content?

II

But that is not all; into this form we wish to put not only the phenomena of our own consciousness, but those of which other consciousnesses are the theater. But more, we wish to put there physical facts, these I know not what with which we people space and which no consciousness sees directly. This is necessary because without it science could not exist. In a word, psychologic time is given to us and must needs create scientific and physical time. There the difficulty begins, or rather the difficulties, for there are two.

Think of two consciousnesses, which are like two worlds impenetrable one to the other. By what do we strive to put them into the same mold, to measure them by the same standard? Is it not as if one strove to measure length with a gram or weight with a meter? And besides, why do we speak of measuring? We know perhaps that some fact is anterior to some other, but not *by how much* it is anterior.

Therefore two difficulties: (1) Can we transform psychologic time, which is qualitative, into a quantitative time? (2) Can we reduce to one and the same measure facts which transpire in different worlds?

III

The first difficulty has long been noticed; it has been the subject of long discussions and one may say the question is settled. *We have not a direct intuition of the equality of two intervals of time.* The persons who believe they possess this intuition are dupes of an illusion. When I say, from noon to one the same time passes as from two to three, what meaning has this affirmation?

The least reflection shows that by itself it has none at all. It will only have that which I choose to give it, by a definition which will certainly possess a certain degree of arbitrariness. Psychologists could have done without this defintion; physicists and astronomers could not; let us see how they have managed.

To measure time they use the pendulum and they suppose by definition that all the beats of this pendulum are of equal duration. But this is only a first approximation; the temperature, the resistance of the air, the barometric pressure, make the pace of the pendulum vary. If we could escape these sources of error, we should obtain a much closer approximation, but it would still be only an approximation. New causes, hitherto neglected, electric, magnetic or others, would introduce minute perturbations.

In fact, the best chronometers must be corrected from time to time, and the corrections are made by the aid of astronomic observations; arrangements are made so that the sidereal clock marks the same hour when the same star passes the meridian. In other words, it is the sidereal day, that is, the duration of the rotation of the earth, which is the constant unit of time. It is supposed, by a new definition substituted for that based on the beats of the pendulum, that two complete rotations of the earth about its axis have the same duration.

However, the astronomers are still not content with this definition. Many of them think that the tides act as a check on our globe, and that the rotation of the earth is becoming slower and slower. Thus would be explained the apparent acceleration of the motion of the moon, which would seem to be going more rapidly than theory permits because our watch, which is the earth, is going slow.

IV

All this is unimportant, one will say; doubtless our instruments of measurement are imperfect, but it suffices that we can conceive a perfect instrument. This ideal can not be reached, but it is enough to have conceived it and so to have put rigor into the definition of the unit of time.

The trouble is that there is no rigor in the definition. When we use the pendulum to measure time, what postulate do we implicitly admit? *It is that the duration of two identical phenomena is the same*; or, if you prefer, that the same causes take the same time to produce the same effects.

And at first blush, this is a good definition of the equality of two durations. But take care. Is it impossible that experiment may some day contradict our postulate?

Let me explain myself. I suppose that at a certain place in the world the phenomenon α happens, causing as consequence at the end of a certain time the effect α'. At another place in the world very far away from the first, happens the phenomenon β, which causes as consequence the effect β'. The phenomena α and β are simultaneous, as are also the effects α' and β'.

Later, the phenomenon α is reproduced under approximately the same conditions as before, and *simultaneously* the phenomenon β is also reproduced at a very distant place in the world and almost under the same circumstances. The effects α' and β' also take place. Let us suppose that the effect α' happens perceptibly before the effect β'.

If experience made us witness such a sight, our postulate would be contradicted. For experience would tell us that the first duration $\alpha\alpha'$ is equal to the first duration $\beta\beta'$ and that the second duration $\alpha\alpha'$ is less than the second duration $\beta\beta'$. On the other hand, our postulate would require that the two durations $\alpha\alpha'$ should be equal to each other, as likewise the two durations $\beta\beta'$. The equality and the inequality deduced from experience would be incompatible with the two equalities deduced from the postulate.

Now can we affirm that the hypotheses I have just made are absurd? They are in no wise contrary to the principle of contradiction. Doubtless they could not happen without the principle of sufficient reason seeming violated. But to justify a defintion so fundamental I should prefer some other guarantee.

V

But that is not all. In physical reality one cause does not produce a given effect, but a multiude of distinct causes contribute to produce it, without our having any means of discriminating the part of each of them.

Physicists seek to make this distinction; but they make it only approximately, and, however they progress, they never will make it except approximately. It is approximately true that the motion of the pendulum is due solely to the earth's attraction; but in all rigor every attraction, even of Sirius, acts on the pendulum.

Under these conditions, it is clear that the causes which have produced a certain effect will never be reproduced except approximately. Then we should modify our postulate and our definition. Instead of saying: 'The same causes take the same time to produce the same effects,' we should say: 'Causes almost identical take almost the same time to produce almost the same effects.'

Our definition therefore is no longer anything but approximate. Besides, as M. Calinon very justly remarks in a recent memoir: [2]

> One of the circumstances of any phenomenon is the velocity of the earth's rotation; if this velocity of rotation varies, it constitutes in the reproduction of this phenomenon a circumstance which no longer remains the same. But to suppose this velocity of rotation constant is to suppose that we know how to measure time.

Our definition is therefore not yet satisfactory; it is certainly not that which the astronomers of whom I spoke above implicitly adopt, when they affirm that the terrestrial rotation is slowing down.

What meaning according to them has this affirmation? We can only understand it by analyzing the proofs they give of their proposition. They say first that the friction of the tides producing heat must destroy *vis viva.* They invoke therefore the principle of *vis viva,* or of the conservation of energy.

They say next that the secular acceleration of the moon, calculated according to Newton's law, would be less than that deduced from observations unless the correction relative to the slowing down of the terrestrial rotation were made. They invoke therefore Newton's law. In other words, they define duration in the following way: time should be so defined that Newton's law and that of *vis viva* may be verified. Newton's law is an experimental truth; as such it is only approximate, which shows that we still have only a definition by approximation.

If now it be supposed that another way of measuring time is adopted, the experiments on which Newton's law is founded would none the less have the same meaning. Only the enunciation of the law would be different, because it would be translated into another language; it would evidently be much less simple. So that the definition implicitly adopted by the astronomers may be summed up thus: Time should be so defined that the equations of mechanics may be as simple as possible. In other words, there is not one way of measuring time more true than another; that which is generally adopted is only more *convenient.* Of two watches, we have no right to say that the one goes true, the other wrong; we can only saw that it is advantageous to conform to the indications of the first.

2 'Etude sur les diverses grandeurs,' Paris, Gauthier-Villars, 1897.

The difficulty which has just occupied us has been, as I have said, often pointed out; among the most recent works in which it is consided, I may mention, besides M. Calinon's little book, the treatise on mechanics of M. Andrade.

VI

The second difficulty has up to the present attracted much less attention; yet it is altogether analogous to the preceding; and even, logically, I should have spoken of it first.

Two psychological phenomena happen in two different consciousnesses; when I say they are simultaneous, what do I mean? When I say that a physical phenomenon, which happens outside of every consciousness, is before or after a psychological phenomenon, what do I mean?

In 1572, Tycho Brahe noticed in the heavens a new star. An immense conflagration had happened in some far distant heavenly body; but it had happened long before; at least two hundred years were necessary for the light from that start to reach our earth. This conflagration therefore happened before the discovery of America. Well, when considering this gigantic phenomenon, which perhaps had no witness, since the satellites of that star were perhaps uninhabited, I say this phenomenon is anterior to the formation of the visual image of the isle of Española in the consciousness of Christopher Columbus, what do I mean?

A little reflection is sufficient to understand that all these affirmations have by themselves no meaning. They can have one only as the outcome of a convention.

VII

We should first ask ourselves how one could have had the idea of putting into the same frame so many worlds impenetrable to each other. We should like to represent to ourselves the external universe, and only by so doing could we feel that we understood it. We know we never can attain this representation: our weakness is too great. But at least we desire the ability to conceive an infinite intelligence for which this representation would be possible, a sort of great consciousness which should see all, and which should classify all *in its time*, as we classify, *in our time*, the little we see.

This hypothesis is indeed crude and incomplete, because this supreme intelligence would be only a demigod; infinite in one sense, it would be limited in another, since it would have only an imperfect recollection of the past; and it could have no other, since otherwise all recollections would be equally present to it and for it there would be no time. And yet when we speak of time, for all which happens outside of us, do we not unconsciously adopt this hypothesis; do we not put ourselves in the place of this imperfect god; and do not even the atheists put themselves in the place where god would be if he existed?

What I have just said shows us, perhaps, why we have tried to put all physical phenomena into the same frame. But that can not pass for a definition of simultaneity, since this hypothetical intelligence, even if it existed, would be for us impenetrable. It is therefore necessary to seek something else.

VIII

The ordinary definitions which are proper for psychologic time would suffice us no better. Two simultaneous psychologic facts are so closely bound together that analysis can not separate without mutilating them. Is it the same with two physical facts? Is not my present nearer my past of yesterday than the present of Sirius?

It has also been said that two facts should be regarded as simultaneous when the order of their succession may be inverted at will. It is evident that this definition would not suit two physical facts which happen far from one another, and that, in what concerns them, we no longer even understand what this reversibility would be; besides, succession itself must first be defined.

IX

Let us then seek to give an account of what is understood by simultaneity or antecedence, and for this let us analyze some examples.

I write a letter; it is afterward read by the friend to whom I have addressed it. There are two facts which have had for their theater two different consciousnesses. In writing this letter I have had the visual image of it, and my friend has had in his turn this same visual image in reading the letter. Though these two facts happen in impenetrable worlds, I do not hesitate to regard the first as anterior to the second, because I believe it is its cause.

I hear thunder, and I conclude there has been an electric discharge; I do not hesitate to consider the physical phenomenon as anterior to the auditory image perceived in my consciousness, because I believe it is its cause.

Behold then the rule we follow, and the only one we can follow: when a phenomenon appears to us as the cause of another, we regard it as anterior. It is therefore by cause that we define time; but most often, when two facts appear to us bound by a constant relation, how do we recognize which is the cause and which the effect? We assume that the anterior fact, the antecedent, is the cause of the other, of the consequent. It is then by time that we define cause. How save ourselves from this *petitio principii?*

We say now *post hoc, ergo propter hoc;* now *propter hoc, ergo post hoc;* shall we escape from this vicious circle?

X

Let us see, not how we succeed in escaping, for we do not completely succeed, but how we try to escape.

I execute a voluntary act A and I feel afterward a sensation *D*, which a regard as a consequence of the act *A*; on the other hand, for whatever reason, I infer that this consequence is not immediate, but that outside my consciousness two facts *B* and *C*, which I have not witnessed, have happened, and in such a way that *B* is the effect of *A*, that *C* is the effect of *B*, and *D* of *C*.

But why? If I think I have reason to regard the four facts *A*, *B*, *C*, *D*, as bound to one another by a causal connection, why range them in the causal order A *B* C *D*, and at the same time in the chronologic order A *B C D*, rather than in any other order?

I clearly see that in the act A I have the feeling of having been active, while in undergoing the sensation *D*, I have that of having been passive. This is why I regard *A* as the initial cause and *D* as the ultimate effect; this is way I put *A* at the beginning of the chain and *D* at the end; but why put *B* before *C* rather than *C* before *B*?

If this question is put, the reply ordinarily is: we know that it is *B* which is the cause of *C* because we *always* see *B* happen before *C*. These two phenomena, when witnessed, happen in a certain order; when analogous phenomena happen without witness, there is no reason to invert this order.

Doubtless, but take care; we never know directly the physical phenomena *B* and *C*. What we know are sensations *B′* and *C′* produced respectively by *B* and *C*. Our consciousness tells us immediately that

B' precedes C' and we *suppose* that B and C succeed one another in the same order.

This rule appears in fact very natural, and yet we are often led to depart from it. We hear the sound of thunder only some seconds after the electric discharge of the cloud. Of two flashes of lightning, the one distant, the other near, can not the first be anterior to the second, even though the sound of the second comes to us before that of the first?

XI

Another difficulty; have we really the right to speak of the cause of a phenomenon? If all the parts of the universe are interchained in a certain measure, any one phenomenon will not be the effect of a single cause, but the resultant of causes infinitely numerous; it is, one often says, the consequence of the state of the universe a moment before. How enunciate rules applicable to circumstances so complex? And yet it is only thus that these rules can be general and rigorous.

Not to lose ourselves in this infinite complexity let us make a simpler hypothesis. Consider three stars, for example, the sun, Jupiter and Saturn; but, for greater simplicity, regard them as reduced to material points and isolated from the rest of the world. The positions and the velocities of three bodies at a given instant suffice to determine their positions and velocities at the following instant, and consequently at any instant. Their positions at the instant t determine their positions at the instant $t + h$ as well as their positions at the instant $t - h$.

Even more; the position of Jupiter at the instant t, together with that of Saturn at the instant $t + a$, determines the position of Jupiter at any instant and that of Saturn at any instant.

The aggregate of positions occupied by Jupiter at the instant $t + e$ and Saturn at the instant $t + a + e$ is bound to the aggregate of positions occupied by Jupiter at the instant t and Saturn at the instant $t + a$, by laws as precise as that of Newton, though more complicated. Then why not regard one of these aggregates as the cause of the other, which would lead to considering as simultaneous the instant t of Jupiter and the instant $t + a$ of Saturn?

In answer there can only be reasons, very strong, it is true, of convenience and simplicity.

XII

But let us pass to examples less artificial; to understand the definition implicity supposed by the savants, let us watch them at work and look for the rules by which they investigate simultaneity.

I will take two simple examples, the measurement of the velocity of light and the determination of longitude.

When an astronomer tells me that some stellar phenomenon, which his telescope reveals to him at this moment, happened nevertheless fifty years ago, I seek his meaning, and to that end I shall ask him first how he knows it, that is, how he has measured the velocity of light.

He has begun by *supposing* that light has a constant velocity, and in particular that its velocity is the same in all directions. That is a postulate without which no measurement of this velocity could be attempted. This postulate could never be verified directly by experiment; it might be contradicted by it if the results of different measurements were not concordant. We should think ourselves fortunate that this contradiction has not happened and that the slight discordances which may happen can be readily explained.

The postulate, at all events, resembling the principle of sufficient reason, has been accepted by everybody; what I wish to emphasize is that it furnishes us with a new rule for the investigation of simultaneity, entirely different from that which we have enunciated above.

This postulate assumed, let us see how the velocity of light has been measured. You know that Roemer used eclipses of the satellites of Jupiter, and sought how much the event fell behind its prediction. But how is this prediction made? It is by the aid of astronomic laws, for instance Newton's law.

Could not the observed facts be just as well explained if we attributed to the velocity of light a little different value from that adopted, and supposed Newton's law only approximate? Only this would lead to replacing Newton's law by another more complicated. So for the velocity of light a value is adopted, such that the astronomic laws compatible with this value may be as simple as possible. When navigators or geographers determine a longitude, they have to solve just the problem we are discussing; they must, without being at Paris, calculate Paris time. How do they accomplish it? They carry a chronometer set for Paris. The qualitative problem of simultaneity is made to depend upon the quantitative problem of the measurement of time. I need not take up the difficulties relative to this latter problem, since above I have emphasized them at length.

Or else they observe an astronomic phenomenon, such as an eclipse of the moon, and they suppose that this phenomenon is perceived simultaneously from all points of the earth. That is not altogether true, since the propagation of light is not instantaneous; if absolute exactitude were desired, there would be a correction to make according to a complicated rule.

Or else finally they use the telegraph. It is clear that the reception of the signal at Berlin, for instance, is after the sending of this same signal from Paris. This is the rule of cause and effect analyzed above. But how much after? In general, the duration of the transmission is neglected and the two events are regarded as simultaneous. But, to be rigorous, a little correction would still have to be made by a complicated calculation; in practise it is not made, because it would be well within the errors of observation; its theoretic necessity is none the less from our point of view, which is that of a rigorous definition. From this discussion, I wish to emphasize two things: (1) The rules applied are exceedingly various. (2) It is difficult to separate the qualitative problem of simultaneity from the quantitative problem of the measurement of time; no matter whether a chronometer is used, or whether account must be taken of a velocity of transmission, as that of light, because such a velocity could not be measured without *measuring* a time.

XIII

To conclude: We have not a direct intuition of simultaneity, nor of the equality of two durations. If we think we have this intuition, this is an illusion. We replace it by the aid of certain rules which we apply almost always without taking count of them.

But what is the nature of these rules? No general rule, no rigorous rule; a multitude of little rules applicable to each particular case.

These rules are not imposed upon us and we might amuse ourselves in inventing others; but they could not be cast aside without greatly complicating the enunciation of the laws of physics, mechanics and astronomy.

We therefore choose these rules, not because they are true, but because they are the most convenient, and we may recapitulate them as follows: "The simultaneity of two events, or the order of their succession, the equality of two durations, are to be so defined that the enunciation of the natural laws may be as simple as possible. In other words, all these rules, all these definitions are only the fruit of an unconscious opportunism."

Albert Einstein

Physics and Reality

1. GENERAL CONSIDERATION CONCERNING THE METHOD OF SCIENCE

It has often been said, and certainly not without justification, that the man of science is a poor philosopher. Why then should it not be the right thing for the physicist to let the philosopher do the philosopizing? Such might indeed be the right thing at a time when the physicist believes he has at his disposal a rigid system of fundamental concepts and fundamental laws which are so well established that waves of doubt can not reach them; but, it can not be right at a time when the very foundations of physics itself have become problematic as they are now. At a time like the present, when experience forces us to seek a newer and more solid foundation, the physicist cannot simply surrender to the philosopher the critical contemplation of the theoretical foundations; for, he himself knows best, and feels more surely where the shoe pinches. In looking for a new foundation, he must try to make clear in his own mind just how far the concepts which he uses are justified, and are necessities.

The whole of science is nothing more than a refinement of every day thinking. It is for this reason that the critical thinking of the physicist cannot possibly be restricted to the examination of the concepts of his own specific field. He cannot proceed without considering critically a much more difficult problem, the problem of analyzing the nature of everyday thinking.

Reprinted with permission of The Estate of Albert Einstein from Albert Einstein, Out of My Later Years *(New York: Philosophical Library, 1950), pp. 59–65.*

On the stage of our subconscious mind appear in colorful succession sense experiences, memory pictures of them, representations and feelings. In contrast to psychology, physics treats directly only of sense experiences and of the "understanding" of their connection. But even the concept of the "real external world" of everyday thinking rests exclusively on sense impressions.

Now we must first remark that the differentiation between sense impressions and representations is not possible; or, at least it is not possible with absolute certainty. With the discussion of this problem, which affects also the notion of reality, we will not concern ourselves but we shall take the existence of sense experiences as given, that is to say as psychic experiences of special kind.

I believe that the first step in the setting of a "real external world" is the formation of the concept of bodily objects and of bodily objects of various kinds. Out of the multitude of our sense experiences we take, mentally and arbitrarily, certain repeatedly occurring complexes of sense impression (partly in conjunction with sense impressions which are interpreted as signs for sense experiences of others), and we attribute to them a meaning—the meaning of the bodily object. Considered logically this concept is not identical with the totality of sense impressions referred to; but it is an arbitrary creation of the human (or animal) mind. On the other hand, the concept owes its meaning and its justification exclusively to the totality of the sense impressions which we associate with it.

The second step is to be found in the fact that, in our thinking (which determines our expectation), we attribute to this concept of the bodily object a significance, which is to a high degree independent of the sense impression which originally gives rise to it. This is what we mean when we attribute to the bodily object "a real existence." The justification of such a setting rests exclusively on the fact that, by means of such concepts and mental relations between them, we are able to orient ourselves in the labyrinth of sense impressions. These notions and relations, although free statements of our thoughts, appear to us as stronger and more unalterable than the individual sense experience itself, the character of which as anything other than the result of an illusion or hallucination is never completely guaranteed. On the other hand, these concepts and relations, and indeed the setting of real objects and, generally speaking, the existence of "the real world," have justification only in so far as they are connected with sense impressions between which they form a mental connection.

The very fact that the totality of our sense experiences is such that by means of thinking (operations with concepts, and the creation and use of definite functional relations between them, and the coordination of sense experiences to these concepts) it can be put in order, this fact is one which leaves us in awe, but which we shall never understand. One may say "the eternal mystery of the world is its comprehensibility." It is one of the great realizations of Immanuel Kant that the setting up of a real external world would be senseless without this comprehensibility.

In speaking here concerning "comprehensibility," the expression is used in its most modest sense. It implies: the production of some sort of order among sense impressions, this order being produced by the creation of general concepts, relations between these concepts, and by relations between the concepts and sense experience, these relations being determined in any possible manner. It is in this sense that the world of our sense experiences is comprehensible. The fact that it is comprehensible is a miracle.

In my opinion, nothing can be said concerning the manner in which the concepts are to be made and connected, and how we are to coordinate them to the experiences. In guiding us in the creation of such an order of sense experiences, success in the result is alone the determining factor. All that is necessary is *the statement* of a set of rules, since without such rules the acquisition of knowledge in the desired sense would be impossible. One may compare these rules with the rules of a game in which, while the rules themselves are arbitrary, it is their rigidity alone which makes the game possible. However, the fixation will never be final. It will have validity only for a special field of application (i.e., there are no final categories in the sense of Kant).

The connection of the elementary concepts of every day thinking with complexes of sense experiences can only be comprehended intuitively and it is unadaptable to scientifically logical fixation. The totality of these connections—none of which is expressible in notional terms—is the only thing which differentiates the great building which is science from a logical but empty scheme of concepts. By means of these connections, the purely notional theorems of science become statements about complexes of sense experiences.

We shall call "primary concepts" such concepts as are directly and intuitively connected with typical complexes of sense experiences. All other notions are—from the physical point of view—possessed of meaning, only in so far as they are connected, by theorems, with the primary notions. These theorems are partially definitions of the concepts (and of the statements derived logically from them) and partially theorems not derivable from the definitions, which express at least indirect relations between the "primary concepts," and in this way between sense experiences. Theorems of the latter kind are "statements about reality" or laws of nature, i.e. theorems which have to show their usefulness when applied to sense experiences comprehended by primary concepts. The questions as to which of the theorems shall be considered as definitions and which as natural laws will depend largely upon the chosen representation. It really becomes absolutely necessary to make this differentiation only when one examines the degree to which the whole system of concepts considered is not empty from the physical point of view.

STRATIFICATION OF THE SCIENTIFIC SYSTEM

The aim of science is, on the one hand, a comprehension, as *complete* as possible, of the connection between the sense experiences in their totality, and, on the other hand, the accomplishment of this aim *by the use of a minimum of primary concepts and relations.* (Seeking, as far as possible, logical unity in the world picture, i.e. paucity in logical elements.)

Science concerns the totality of the primary concepts, i.e. concepts directly connected with sense experiences, and theorems connecting them. In its first stage of development, science does not contain anything else. Our everyday thinking is satisfied on the whole with this level. Such a state of affairs cannot, however, satisfy a spirit which is really scientifically minded; because, the totality of concepts and relations obtained in this manner is utterly lacking in logical unity. In order to supplement this deficiency, one invents a system poorer in concepts and relations, a system retaining the primary concepts and relations of the "first layer" as logically derived concepts and relations. This new "secondary system" pays for its higher logical unity by having, as its own elementary concepts (concepts of the second layer), only those which are no longer directly connected with complexes of sense experiences. Further striving for logical unity brings us to a tertiary system, still poorer in concepts and relations, for the deduction of the concepts and relations of the secondary (and so indirectly of the primary) layer. Thus the story goes on until we have arrived at a system of the greatest conceivable unity, and of the greatest poverty of concepts of the logical foundations, which are still compatible with the observation made by our senses. We do not know whether or not this ambition will ever result in a definite system. If one is asked for his opinion, he is inclined to answer no. While wrestling with the problems, however, one will never give up the hope that this greatest of all aims can really be attained to a very high degree.

An adherent to the theory of abstraction or induction might call our layers "degrees of abstraction"; but, I do not consider it justifiable to veil the logical independence of the concept from the sense experiences. The relation is not analogous to that of soup to beef but rather of wardrobe number to overcoat.

The layers are furthermore not clearly separated. It is not even absolutely clear which concepts belong to the primary layer. As a matter of fact, we are dealing with freely formed concepts, which, with a certainty sufficient for practical use, are intuitively connected with complexes of sense experiences in such a manner that, in any given case of experience, there is no uncertainty as to the applicability or non-applicability of the statement. The essential thing is the aim to represent the multitude of concepts and theorems, close to experience, as theorems, logically deduced and belonging to a basis, as narrow as possible, of fundamental concepts and fundamental relations which themselves can be chosen freely (axioms). The liberty of choice, however, is of a special kind; it is not in any way similar to the liberty of a writer of fiction. Rather, it is similar to that of a man engaged in solving a well designed word puzzle. He may, it is true, propose any word as the solution; but, there is only *one* word which really solves the puzzle in all its forms. It is an outcome of faith that nature—as she is perceptible to our five senses—takes the character of such a well formulated puzzle. The successes reaped up to now by science do, it is true, give a certain encouragement for this faith.

The multitude of layers discussed above corresponds to the several stages of progess which have resulted from the struggle for unity in the course of development. As regards the final aim, intermediary layers are only of temporary nature. They must eventually disappear as irrelevant. We have to deal, however, with the science of today, in which these strata represent problematic partial successes which support one another but which also threaten one another, because today's systems of concepts contain deep seated incongruities which we shall meet later on.

It will be the aim of the following lines to demonstrate what paths the constructive human mind has entered, in order to arrive at a basis of physics which is logically as uniform as possible.

Philipp Frank

Geometry: An Example of a Science

1. GEOMETRY AS THE IDEAL OF PHILOSOPHY

"Metaphysics has always been the ape of mathematics," wrote C. S. Peirce in 1891,[1] and it is well known that Plato did not admit a student of philosophy to the Academy unless he had had training in geometry.[2] Peirce explained this requirement by continuing: "Geometry suggested the idea of a demonstrative system of absolutely certain philosophical principles, and the ideas of the metaphysicians have at all times been in large part drawn from mathematics." [3] When it was demonstrated by the example of non-Euclidean geometry that even the axioms of geometry were not self-evident and not of "eternal validity," the belief in the self-evidence of metaphysical principles was severely shaken. Peirce wrote: "The metaphysical axioms are imitations of the geometrical axioms; and now the latter have been thrown overboard, without doubt the former will be sent after them." [4]

There is no doubt that the high degree of certainty

Reprinted with permission of the author from Philipp Frank, Philosophy of Science *(Englewood Cliffs, N. J.: Prentice-Hall, Inc., 1957), pp. 48–89.*

[1] In his paper "The Architecture of Theories," *The Monist* (1891).

[2] Plato, *Republic*, Book VI, *The Dialogues of Plato,* translated by Benjamin Jowett (New York: Charles Scribner's Sons, 1871), 525B*ff*. There is a translation of the *Republic* in the Mentor edition. Plato stressed the point that the study of geometry and mathematics is the indispensable preliminary for the approach to philosophy.

[3] Peirce, *op. cit.*

[4] *Ibid.*

which has been reached in geometry has encouraged the hope that a similar certainty could be achieved in other fields of knowledge and, above all, in the synthesis of all knowledge, in philosophy. René Descartes,[5] in his famous *Discourse on Method*, a guiding beacon at the start of modern philosophy (after 1600), described precisely the role that he ascribed to geometry as a guide to philosophy, thus:

> The long chain of simple and easy reasoning by means of which geometers are accustomed to reach the conclusions of their most difficult demonstrations, has led me to imagine that all things, to the knowledge of which man is competent, are mutually connected in the same way, and there is nothing so far removed from us as to be beyond our reach or so hidden that we cannot discover it, provided only we abstain from accepting the false for true, and always preserve in our thoughts the order necessary for the deduction of one truth from another.[6]

Since the procedure in geometry had led to more satisfactory results than that in any other field of science, Descartes drew generalizations from it and advanced four "precepts of logic" which would guide him in finding truth. He described these precepts as follows:

> The *first* was never to accept anything as true which I did not clearly know to be such; that is to say, carefully to avoid precipitancy and prejudice, and to compromise nothing more in my judgment than what was presented to my mind so clearly and distinctly as to exclude all possible grounds for doubt.[7]

To know something "clearly and distinctly" has been called the "Cartesian criterion of truth." In substance, it is not much different from Aristotle's requirement that the general principles of science should be "intelligible" or "intrinsically knowable," in contrast to the vague sense impressions which are "knowable to us" but "intrinsically obscure."

Descartes went on: "The *second*, to divide each of the difficulties under examination into as many parts as possible, and as might be necessary for its adequate solution." [8] This "second precept" of Des-

[5] René Descartes, *Discourse on Method*, translated by John Veitch (Chicago: Henry Regnery Company, 1949), Part I, pp. 17, 18.

[6] *Ibid.*

[7] *Ibid.*

[8] *Ibid.*

cartes' is obviously also a generalization of the actual method used by the geometrician. If the latter is to prove from the axioms of geometry the theorem that the sum of the angles of a triangle is 180°, he proceeds by small steps, each of which is a simple, logical conclusion that seems valid to the most untrained mind. This proceeding by small steps is just what Descartes requires in his "second precept."

The characteristic of geometry that has made it an example for all sciences, and, moreover, for philosophy, can be simply formulated as follows: There are two types of statements in geometry, axioms and theorems. Only the latter can be proved by reasoning; the truth of the axioms must be recognized not by reasoning but by direct intuition, by the eyes of the mind or whatever one may call this ability. This conception of geometry is the one which has set the example for philosophers of all time. At the beginning of modern philosophy we have the words of Blaise Pascal: [9]

> Our knowledge of the first principles, such as *space, time, motion, number,* is as certain as any knowledge we obtain by reasoning. As a matter of fact, this knowledge provided by our hearts and instinct is necessarily the basis upon which our reason has to build its conclusions. . . . If our reason denied its consent to the first principles unless our heart had provided a demonstration, this requirement would be as ridiculous as if our heart would deny its consent to all demonstrations unless they were enforced by added sentiment.[10]

No matter how wide the gaps between different philosophical systems, all have two beliefs in common. First, there are propositions about observable facts which we know with certainty although (or perhaps because) they are not based on induction from sense observations. Second, the existence of such propositions is "proved" by the example of mathematical propositions. For these propositions are known with certainty, and this certainty is not based on empirical facts. There is a great variance between the German idealistic [11] philosopher, Immanuel Kant, and the French ration-

[9] Blaise Pascal (1623–1662), French scientist and philosopher. His interpretation of science attempted to point out that the whole personality is involved in this activity. "The heart," he wrote, "has its reasons which reason does not know."

[10] Blaise Pascal, "The Difference Between the Mathematical and the Intuitive Mind," *Pensées (Thoughts)*, translated by W. S. Trotter (New York: Modern Library, 1941), Sect. 1, p. 1.

[11] According to A. C. Ewing, *Idealism: A Critical Survey* (London: Methuen & Co., 1933), Kant is called an "idealist" because he treated physical objects in a characteristically idealist fashion, reducing them to elements in human experience and leaving to the realist only the unknowable thing-in-itself.

alist,[12] Descartes. Kant, however, stressed even more emphatically than Descartes or Pascal the point that the belief in the possibility of "philosophy proper," or "metaphysics," was ultimately based upon the example of geometry, which proved by its mere existence the possibility of "intelligible principles." To understand Kant's statement we have only to note that he meant by a "synthetical *a priori* judgment" [13] what we have called a statement about observable facts which we perceive by the eyes of the mind without actual sense observation, but which can and should be scientifically checked by actual sense observations. Kant wrote in his *Prolegomena to Any Future Metaphysics:* [14]

> It happens fortunately, that though we cannot assume metaphysics to be an actual science, we can say with confidence that certain pure *a priori* synthetical cognitions, pure mathematics and pure physics, are actual and given; for both contain propositions which are thoroughly recognized as absolutely certain . . . and yet as independent of experience. We have therefore some at least uncontested synthetical knowledge *a priori,* and need not ask whether it be possible for it is actual. . . .

If we consider this common opinion of leading philosophical schools, it seems advisable to investigate geometry from the purely scientific point of view and to find out whether geometry actually consists—on the one hand, of axioms which are determined by "internal intuition," and, on the other, of theorems which are logically derived from them. As a matter of fact, during the whole nineteenth century this was the common opinion among mathematicians. We can observe this by looking into any average textbook of geometry. We may choose, for example, W. W. Bemann and D. E. Smith's *New Plane and Solid Geometry* of 1899.[15] We read: "There are a few geometrical statements so obvious that the truth of them

[12] He has been called a "rationalist" because he believed that true general statements about the material world can be found by the power of reason without sense experience. In this respect, his views were similar to the views of scholastic philosophers of the type of St. Thomas Aquinas.

[13] A judgment is "synthetical" if it cannot be proved by mere logic. It is "*a priori*" if its truth can be demonstrated without sense observations. According to Kant, mathematical judgments (such as $7+5=12$) are "synthetical" *and* "*a priori.*"

[14] Immanuel Kant, *Prolegomena to Any Future Metaphysics,* edited in English by Paul Carus (Chicago: Open Court Publishing Company, 1902), Sect. 4.

[15] Wooster Bemann and David Smith, *New Plane and Solid Geometry* (Boston: Ginn and Company, 1899).

may be taken for granted." The authors distinguish, as does Euclid, two types of such "obvious statements," axioms and postulates. All the profound philosophical terminology of Aristotle and Kant, the predicates of "intrinsically intelligible" and "synthetically *a priori*," appear in this textbook under the very harmess designation of "obivous" and "may be taken for granted."

Around 1900 a new conception of geometry developed which deprived "philosophy in its isolated state" ("metaphysics") of its favorite example, and made a reunion of science and philosophy possible. This change in the conception of geometry was, in fact, a decisive one in the relationship between science and philosophy. It is not an accident that at about the same time great changes in physics occurred, the establishment of the new theories of relativity and quanta, which required a fundamental adjustment in our traditional ideas on science and philosophy.

2. "INTELLIGIBLE PRINCIPLES" AND "OBSERVABLE FACTS" IN GEOMETRY

We are now going to discuss the transition from the traditional nineteenth-century conception, in which science was topped by a piece of "separated philosophy," to the twentieth-century conception, the transition from the role of axioms as "intelligible principles" to their twentieth-century role. The different aspects of science can be characterized by the different places they assign to sense observation, to logical reasoning, and to creative imagination. If we want to undertand this, it is best to attempt a thorough undertanding of one specific science. We shall take as our example *plane geometry*. There is an old saying, "If you understand one leaf of grass, you understand the whole universe." Thus, if we understand the structure of science in plane geometry, we have gained much toward understanding it in other sciences.

It is well to start from a field in which you can apparently "prove" a great deal. In geometry no one will doubt that logical argument plays a large role. If we understand what role logical argument plays in geometry, we shall understand the whole role it plays in science in general. The question is: in geometry how do we "prove" facts which can be checked by sense observation? We start from certain "axioms" which are ordinarily said to be statements that are self-evident. Then we try to derive other statements called "theorems" from the axioms by logical conclusions. In geometry, the most elementary student is presented with the distinction between "intelligible principles" (axioms) and observable facts—he does not need to read Aristotle for this. The impression is given in the ordinary teaching of geometry that there is a certain harmony between what can be proved and what can be observed in experiment. For example, consider the triangle:

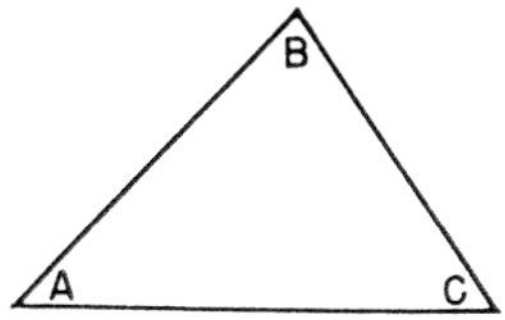

FIGURE 5

We have $A+B+C=180°$ in every triangle. The student learns how to "prove" this. Then he takes a protractor and measures the sum of the angles and, if he is lucky, the sum will be about 180°. He gains the impression that there is a certain established harmony between logical thinking and nature. This idea is really produced by the traditional method of teaching geometry. If the student has once acquired this impression in geometry, he goes further with it in physics. In the latter, he learns some proofs in which logical conclusions and results of experiments are so mixed up that even intelligent students will hardly understand them. One theorem is assumed and another derived from it, but the first is just as uncertain as the other. If this is explained correctly, no confusion results. In geometry it is easier to stress from the beginning what can be proved and what cannot be proved. It is easy to distinguish between what is observed and what is proved. And what is an "intelligible principle"? We can learn all this from geometry.

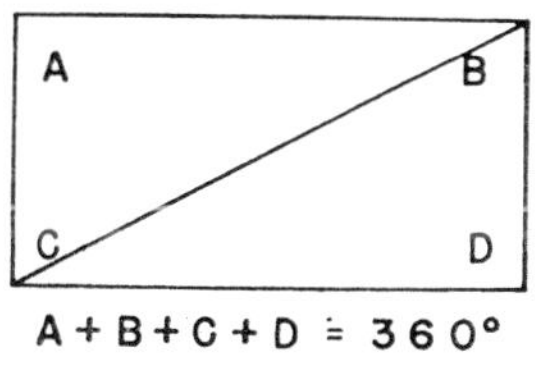

FIGURE 6

Very often a statement does not seem by itself to be "intelligible" or self-evident, but some corollary of it looks very plausible and even self-evident. At first glance, the statement that the sum of the angles of a triangle equals 180° does not look very convincing, but this can be expressed in another form which makes it look much more plausible. If the quadrangle *ABCD* is divided by the diagonal *BC* into two triangles, and if in each of these triangles the sum of the angles is 180°, the sum of the four angles of the quadrangle is 360°. Then we can set the problem in which A, *B*, *C*, and *D* are all equal. In other words, $A = B = C = D$. Then each one is a right angle, and we have a rectangle.

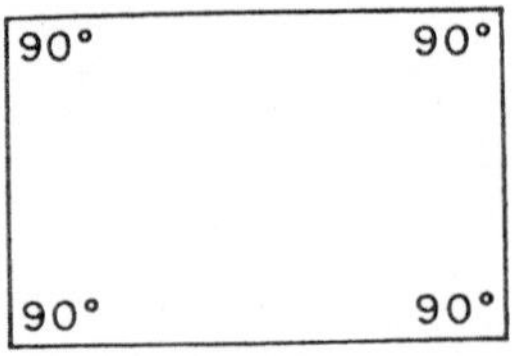

FIGURE 7

Hence, from the statement that "the sum of the angles of a triangle equals 180°," it follows that we can construct rectangles. However, the existence of rectangles is very plausible to us. We would be reluctant to believe that there could be no rectangles or squares. The existence of rectangles makes it possible to build a wall with bricks without gaps. Without rectangles we could not build in our usual way—our whole way of life would be different. We can see that the theorem about the sum of the angles in a triangle is very closely connected with our technical civilization.

On the one hand, we have the impression that these laws of geometry are logically derived; on the other hand, they seem to be laws of technical "know-how." This lends force to the idea that human beings must act in a way that can be derived from intelligible principles. The belief that we can derive empirical facts from intelligible principles is an important part of the web of our ideas. It is very important to examine to what extent this is true or is not true in geometry. Without axioms, there is no geometry; everything in geometry has to start from axioms. Very little space in geometry textbooks is devoted to the question: How do we know that the axioms are true? This question does not belong to mathematics and is not studied in any of the other recognized fields of science. Many teachers of mathematics have volunteered the answer that the question has no meaning. From the purely mathematical point of view this is true, since there is no mathematical method for discussing it. But, as we shall see later, it can be discussed in another way.

3. DESCARTES, MILL, AND KANT

We shall discuss three opinions concerning the foundations of geometry. One goes back to Plato and Aristotle—to the idea of intelligible principles. In other words, we can see quasi-intuitively, with the "eyes of the mind," that the axioms are true. This has perhaps been best described by Descartes, the French mathematician and philosopher.[16] According to him, the statement that certain principles are self-evident means that if you understand them well, you also understand that they are true. He argued: "I can demonstrate properties (by imagining a triangle) which turn out to be really true (by observation); it follows that they come from the essence of the triangle. My mind must be able to grasp this essence. Otherwise I could not demonstrate these properties." This is a school of thought which is called "rationalism"—it holds that by the power of one's mind, one can penetrate to, for example, the essence of the triangle. Descartes wrote:

> I discover innumerable particulars respecting figures, numbers, motion, and the like, which are so evidently true, and so in accord with my nature, that when I now discover them I do not so much appear to learn anything new as to call to memory what was before in my mind, but to which I had not hitherto directed my attention. . . .

In contrast to Descartes' "rationalism," the school of "empiricism" has claimed that there are no principles the validity of which can be confirmed by the power of reason alone. According to the empiricist philosopher, John Stuart Mill, axioms are empirical statements just like any others—they only differ from others in being simpler and in having a wider basis. The rationalist refers to a triangle as an object of our imagination, while the empiricist refers to a triangle as a physical object. Both aspects of a triangle are legitimate in some way, or we could never check principles against facts. Two hundred years after Descartes, John Stuart Mill wrote in his book *A System of Logic* in 1843: [17]

[16] Descartes presented his views on the foundations of geometry first in his *Rules for the Direction of the Mind*, published in 1701 after his death, Rule IV, Rule XIV. In 1644 he published his *Principles of Philosophy*. In Principles 197 through 200 he interprets all phenomena of nature by shape, magnitude, and motion.

[17] John Stuart Mill (1806–1873), British philosopher and economist.

> The peculiar accuracy, supposed to be characteristic of the first principles of geometry, appears to be fictitious. When it is affirmed that the conclusions of geometry are necessary truths, the necessity exists in reality only in this, that they correctly follow from the suppositions from which they are deduced. These suppositions are so far from being necessary that they are not even true; they purposely depart, more or less widely, from the truth. . . . It remains to inquire what is the ground of our belief in axioms—what is the evidence on which they rest. I answer: they are experimental truths, generalizations from observations. The proposition: Two straight lines cannot enclose a space (Euclid's formulation of the axiom that "two points determine one and only one straight line") is an induction from the evidence of our senses.[18]

We see that the axioms of geometry which have been regarded as the most conspicuous instance of Aristotle's "intelligible principles" are, according to the empiricist, Mill, results of sense observations. The conclusions drawn from the principles, on the other hand, are products of our reason. It seems that the rationalist idea and the empiricist idea refer to completely different things, both of which exist. What is the connection between an imaginary triangle and the physical object? The rationalist thinks that he can find the properties of a triangle by "looking with the eyes of his mind upon the triangle." But his mind can obviously look only upon an imagined triangle, and not upon a physical triangle which belongs to the world of material objects. On the other hand, the empiricist thinks that he obtains the properties of a triangle by looking at a physical triangle with his sense organs. How can we then understand that the geometrical propositions are more certain than any result of sense observations?

Immanuel Kant[19] found a way out of this dilemma which must certainly be called ingenious. He asserted that our sense organs, our eyes, do not see the real triangle which exists in the external world. This real triangle, the "thing in itself" as Kant called it, is inaccessible to our sense organs. If we look at a triangle, we see it in a way which is determined by the properties of our minds. What we call in our ordinary language the "seen triangle" is a result of the cooperation of the real triangle and our minds. Our minds are responsible for a "frame" through which we see every external object. This means that what the empiricists call the "real triangle" seen by our sense is actually an "imagined triangle." Therefore, there is no

[18] John Stuart Mill, A *System of Logic* (1843), Book II, Ch. V.

[19] Kant, *op. cit.*

wonder that the eyes of our minds can see its properties. The geometrical properties are actually properties of the imagined triangle, while the properties of the real triangle are unknown, or perhaps even nonexistent. According to Kant, the knowing of properties by our minds is only possible if we assume that these properties are not properties of the real triangle. He said, "By sensuous intuition we can know objects as they *appear* to us (to our senses), not as they are in themselves, and this assumption is absolutely necessary if synthetical propositions *a priori* be granted as possible."

This new idea has been given by Kant and his school the name of "critical idealism." The word "idealism" denotes a world view according to which the results of our sense observations are not pictures of real objects. These objects may not exist at all, or may be very different from the way they appear to us. The first view which denies the reality of the world of our experience is called plain "idealism." The Kantian view asserts that the external world exists in itself, but appears to us in a way that is determined by the nature of our minds. This view is called "critical idealism."

The twentieth century has, in close connection with "science proper," developed a new conception of the place of geometrical axioms which has absorbed some elements of rationalism, empiricism, and critical idealism, but has attempted to eliminate, so far as possible, superfluous concepts.

4. "AXIOMS" AND "THEOREMS"

We shall consider how the theorems of geometry have been proved traditionally; for example, the theorem that the sum of the angles of a triangle is equal to two right angles. We shall see that this is closely connected with the statement that there are similar triangles—in other words, triangles with the same angles but with sides of different lengths. The existence of similar triangles is one of the fundamental ideas with which we approach the external world. It accounts for the possibility of figures which have the same shape but different sizes. On it is based our belief that what is true on a small scale can be repeated on a large scale, and vice versa. We believe this in a very naive way. No student would find it easy to doubt that what his teacher demonstrates as true for triangles on the blackboard is also true for triangles too big to put on the blackboard.

Before proceeding with this discussion, however, let us first "polish up" our knowledge of plane geometry. We may start with the axiom: if we have two points, *A* and *B*, and we have two straight lines which connect these two points, "between these two lines there is no space," in the language of Euclid.[20]

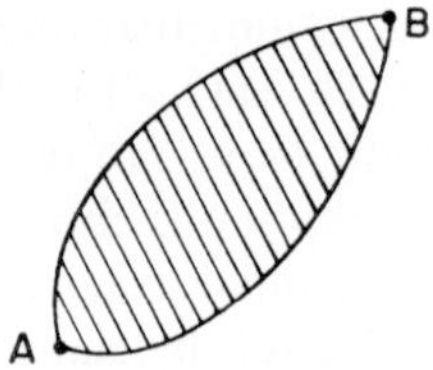

FIGURE 8

In other words, if there are two points, *A* and *B*, there is only one straight line which connects them. This is one of the first axioms in Euclidean geometry.

What is a point? And what is a straight line? In ordinary geometry these are usually defined in a vague way. A point is that which has no part. Intuitively this has a certain meaning, but it is difficult to use. We shall return to these questions later. For the moment we have only a vague idea of points and lines.

However, we can at once ask the question: is this axiom which we have just described self-evident, or is it not self-evident? It is not as self-evident as it looks because it means this: through a point *A*, two straight lines which diverge can never meet again.

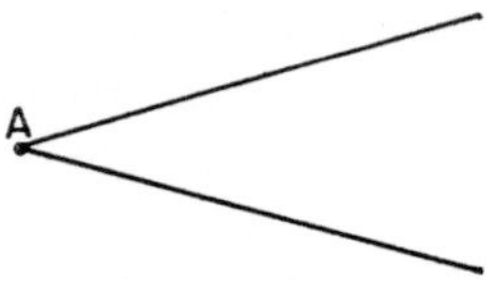

FIGURE 9

If we look into ourselves, it seems at first that this is intuitively clear, but how far does our imagination go toward imagining straight lines? I would say hardly ten feet. Intuitive imagination certainly does not go very far. What we use is actually an inference from the increasing distance between the segments of the lines. We imagine that the distance between them will continue to increase. But this is just a vicious circle; it amounts to saying the same thing—that lines

[20] Euclid, a Greek mathematician, was younger than Plato and older than Archimedes. His main work, *The Elements*, in which he presented his deductive system of geometry was written about 325 B.C.

which are diverging will never meet. If we pursue two "straight lines," along the surface of the earth, they will certainly meet on the other side of the earth. When the earth was thought to be a plane, the situation was clear; but we know now that this is an illusion—that there is no way to distinguish a small section of a sphere of large radius from a plane. So what happens farther and farther along on these two diverging "straight lines" we really do not know; there is no intuitive evidence that they never meet again. Our axiom, then, is an hypothesis about the behavior of straight lines.

There is a more sophisticated difficulty involved: someone may say that a line which comes back on itself is not a straight line, but if we define a straight line as a line which never meets itself, this is a tautological statement—a straight line is a straight line. Are axioms only definitions? If they are only definitions we can never derive physical facts from them. Thus there are two aspects of geometrical axioms—"pure definition" and "hypothesis about physical objects." In this first axiom we see already all the difficulties involved.

Note that from this first axiom we can deduce that two straight lines can have either one point or no points in common.

We shall now proceed to the conception of "congruence." Consider a straight line g, which contains two points A and B, and also another straight line g' containing points A' and B'. What do we mean by saying that the two distances AB and $A'B'$ are "congruent?" The two segments are said to be congruent if they can be brought into coincidence. This presupposes that we know what we mean by transposition—that during motion, roughly speaking, the two distances do not change their size, which means that they remain congruent. Again we have a vicious circle. We have, however, a definite idea of a rigid body; we can define it by its physical properties: elasticity, hardness, etc. Then we can define congruence by the transposition of a rigid body. Two segments are "congruent" if they can be brought into coincidence by being moved as "rigid" rods.

We also have the concept of congruent angles. Two straight lines define an angle in the following figure:

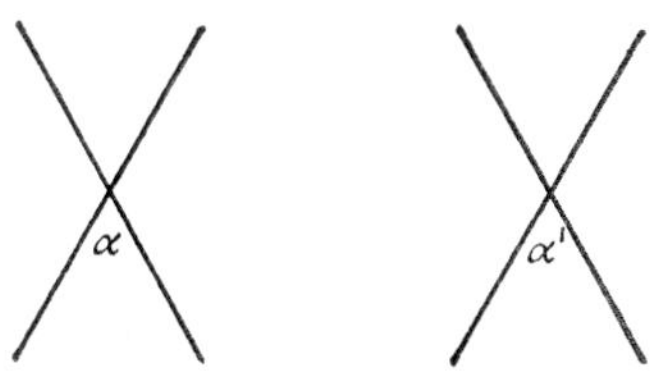

FIGURE 10

Angles are congruent if the straight lines which define them can be brought into coincidence. Two triangles are defined as congruent if all sides and angles are congruent: then the triangles can be brought into coincidence.

Thus we can state the first theorem of congruence. Let ABC and $A'B'C'$ be two triangles:

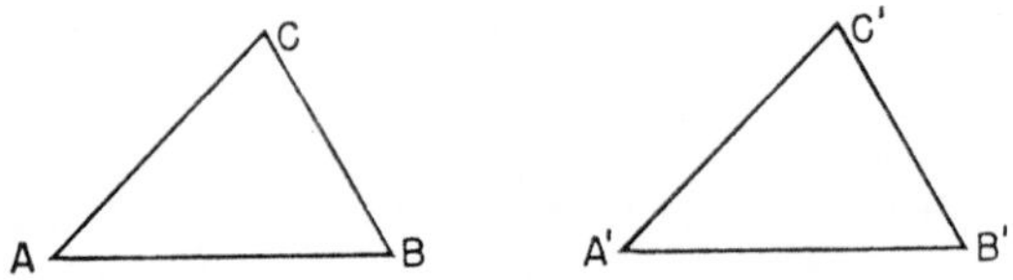

FIGURE 11

Let $AB \equiv A'B'$, angle $CAB(\alpha) \equiv$ angle $C'A'B'$, and $CBA(\beta) \equiv$ angle $C'B'A'$, where the sign $\equiv$ stands for "is congruent with." This means that we could transpose triangle ABC on to triangle $A'B'C'$ so that the line segment AB would coincide with the line segment $A'B'$, the AC with the line $A'C'$, and the line BC with the line $B'C'$. But we know that the lines AC and BC meet at C. The lines $A'C'$ and $B'C'$ meet at C'. But C must coincide with C', since our first axiom states that two straight lines can have only one point (or no point) in common. Thus triangle $ABC \equiv$ triangle $A'B'C'$. This means that we could transport triangle ABC so as to bring it into coincidence with triangle $A'B'C'$. Hence, if $AB \equiv A'B'$ and $\alpha \equiv \alpha'$, $\beta \equiv \beta'$, the triangles are congruent. This is the first theorem of congruence.

5. THE EUCLIDEAN AXIOM OF PARALLELS

We are now much closer to being able to prove that the sum of the angles of a triangle is equal to two right angles, but first we must prove an important theorem about the conditions under which two straight lines do not intersect. Consider a straight line h which is cut at a point A by another straight line g under the angle α. Then consider that h is also cut at another point B by a straight line g' also under the angle α. (See Figure 12.) We wish to prove that the two straight lines g and g', thus drawn, can never meet. How can this be proved? Let us assume that they do meet to the right of h at C. Then we have triangle ABC. Now using the theorem that vertical angles are congruent (which we have not proved), and following the same argument as we have made above, we see that to the left of h there must also be a triangle ABC' congruent to triangle ABC.

Thus, if the two straight lines g and g' meet on one side of h, they must also meet on the other side; but this is impossible, because then there would be two points C and C' connected by two straight lines g and g'; hence the straight lines g and g' can never meet.

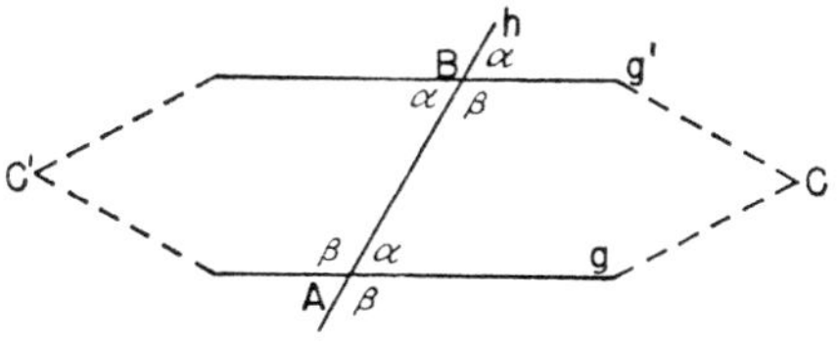

FIGURE 12

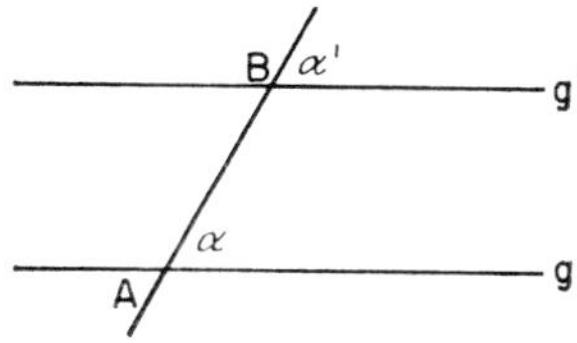

FIGURE 13

Now how can we prove that the sum of the angles of a triangle is 180°? Note that the above proof does not show that it is *only* when two lines g and g' cut the line h under the same angle α that they will never meet. The line g' may also cut the line h under some angle α' (not equal to the angle α under which the line g cuts the line h), and yet g and g' may never meet. In order to derive the theorem about the sum of the angles of a triangle, however, we must make use of the assumption that it is *only* when the lines g and g' cut the line h under the same angle α that they will never meet. (See Figure 13.) Then we say that g' is "parallel" to g. Our assumption is called "Euclid's Axiom," or the "Axiom of Parallels." This states that through a point B outside a straight line g there is one and only one straight line g' which is "parallel" to g. Both g and g' cut h under the same angle α.

We are now ready to prove the theorem about the sum of the angles of any triangle. Consider a triangle ABC and through the vertex C draw the parallel to the base AB. Since g is parallel to g', and AC cuts g and g' under congruent angles α (see Figure 14).

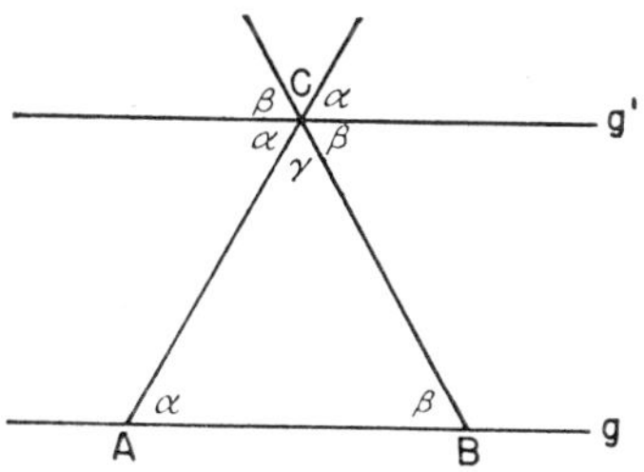

FIGURE 14

BC cuts g and g' under congruent angles β. Since g' is a straight line, angle α plus angle γ plus angle $\beta = 180°$, or two right angles. But these are the same angles as are in the triangle, so that whatever triangle we may be considering, the sum of its angles, $\alpha + \beta + \gamma =$ 180° of two right angles. To reach this conclusion we obviously need the Euclidean axiom. We have proved first that if two straight lines g and g' intersect a transversal h under the same angle α, they can never meet. But in our present proof we have used the theorem that if two straight lines g and g' meet, they must intersect a transversal under the same angle. Otherwise there may be a line g'' which intersects h under a different angle and still will never meet g. To exclude this possibility we must use the "Euclidean Axiom:" the line g' which intersects a transversal under the same angle as the line g is the *only* line which will never meet g.

This is a very important point. The theorem that the sum of the angles of a triangle is equal to 180° presupposes the Euclidean axiom. It plays a particular role for different reasons. We shall see that if this axiom is not accepted, not only the law regarding the sum of the angles of a triangle breaks down, but that much more of our view of the universe breaks down also. I have already mentioned the concept that for every figure there exist similar figures; if we assume the Euclidean axiom, this can be easily proved. Consider a triangle ABC. Through a point D on the side AC draw a parallel to the base AB. If we assume that the prallel axiom is true, then the base angles of the small triangle CDE are equal, respectively, to the base angles of the large triangle ABC, as indicated in Figure 15. Since the sum

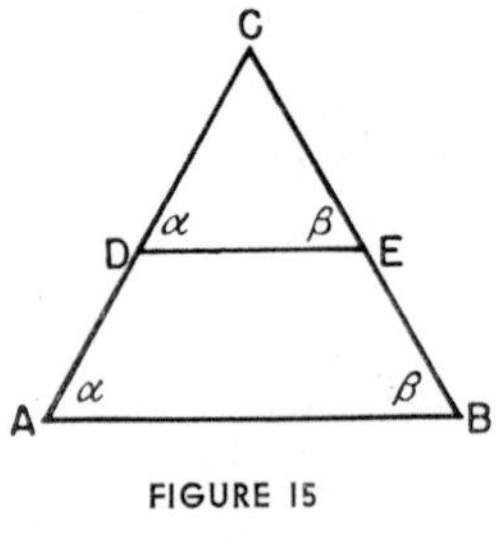

FIGURE 15

of the angles of any triangle is equal to 180°, we get a small triangle CDE with the same angles as the big triangle ABC. These two triangles have the same shape because they have the same angles, but they differ in size. If we do not know that the parallel axiom is true, or if we know that it is not true, we cannot give this proof. Thus, if the parallel axiom is not true, we cannot prove the existence of similar figures. These two things exclude each other.

Can we prove that the parallel axiom is true? Apparently not, or it would not be an axiom. Logically then, we can set up a different axiom. If the angles of a triangle do not equal 180°, what follows from this? One thing we can easily see without much calculation. Consider an isosceles triangle *ABC* (Figure 16). If the sum of the angles is equal to 180°, angle $ABC = 60°$. Now divide the triangle into two equal parts, by dropping a median from the vertex *C*. The question is: Is the sum of the angles in each of the small triangles the same as in the big triangle? The answer is yes, since $60° + 30° + 90° = 180°$. If we assume now that the sum of the angles in a triangle is not 180°, we shall see that the sum of the angles in a small triangle is completely different from the sum in a big triangle. Again consider an isosceles triangle where the base angles equal 60° (Figure 17). Let us assume that the sum of the angles in this triangle is 160°. Then angle *ACB* equals 40°. Divide this triangle into two equal parts, by dropping a median to *AB*. We observe then that the sum of the angles in each of the two small triangles

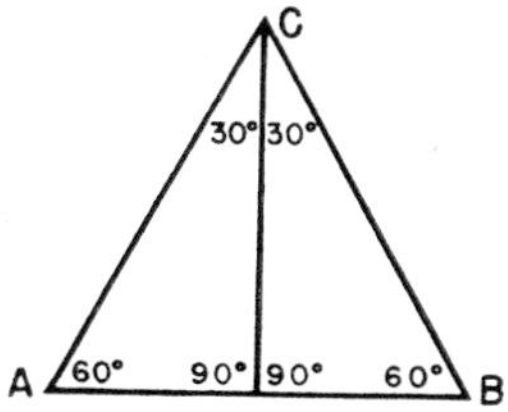

FIGURE 16

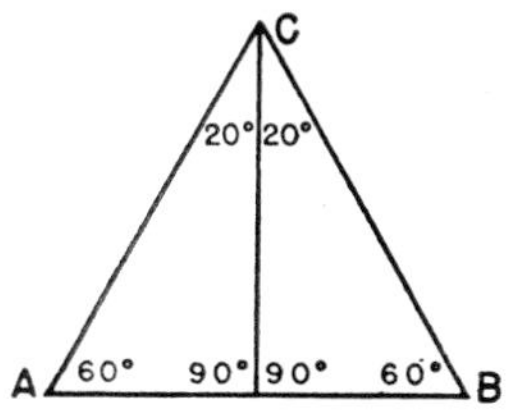

FIGURE 17

is equal to only 170°. If we pursued this, we would see that the smaller a triangle becomes, the nearer the sum of its angles approaches to 180°.

In the case where the sum of the angles of a triangle is less than 180°, let us not describe the sum of the angles itself, but the difference between this sum and 180°—what is called the "defect." In other words, the defect is equal to $[180° - (\alpha + \beta + \gamma)]$. In the big triangle above, the defect is equal to 20°. In the small triangle, the defect is equal to only 10°. Between the area of a triangle and its defect there is a very simple relation. The area of each of the small triangles above is half the area of the big triangle, and the defect of each of the small triangles is half the defect of the big triangle. For very small triangles the defect approaches zero. A very small triangle behaves as if the Euclidean axiom were true. This can be proved in a very general way; here we have only given some examples to illustrate it. If the Euclidean axiom is not true, there are

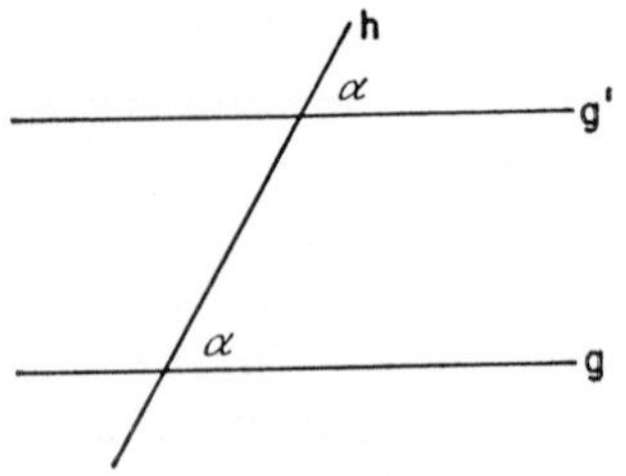

FIGURE 18

no similar triangles, but small triangles behave in a different way from large ones. For this reason it is very difficult to check by measurements whether the sum of the angles of a triangle is generally 180°.

6. NON-EUCLIDEAN GEOMETRY [21]

We shall now consider the possibility of dropping the Euclidean axiom. By what is it to be replaced? If we accept the Euclidean axiom, the geometry built on this axiom is called Euclidean geometry. If we reject the Euclidean axiom, and replace it, the geometry built on its replacement is called a non-Euclidean geometry.

If the Euclidean axiom is rejected, there are two possibilities. This axiom asserts that a straight line which made only the slightest departure from g' (Figure 18), on either side, would intersect with g. One possibility is that there may be *no* line g' which will never intersect g. In other words, all lines which exist will intersect. There is also the possibility that if a straight line is tilted from g', on either side, by a sufficiently small angle ϵ, it will not intersect g. In other words, there may be a "bundle" of lines—symmetric about g' and bounded by the lines which are tilted from g' by the angle ϵ on either side—which will not intersect (Figure 19). This is the second type of non-Euclidean geometry, and it is the only type of non-Euclidean geometry which we shall discuss here. We shall investigate how the world would look if this assertion replaced the Euclidean axiom. One thing is certain—the sum of the angles of a triangle would not be equal to 180°.

[21] Non-Euclidean geometry was advanced by Nikolai I. Lobatchevski and Wolfgang Bolyai, who were in turn stimulated by Karl Friedrich Gauss.

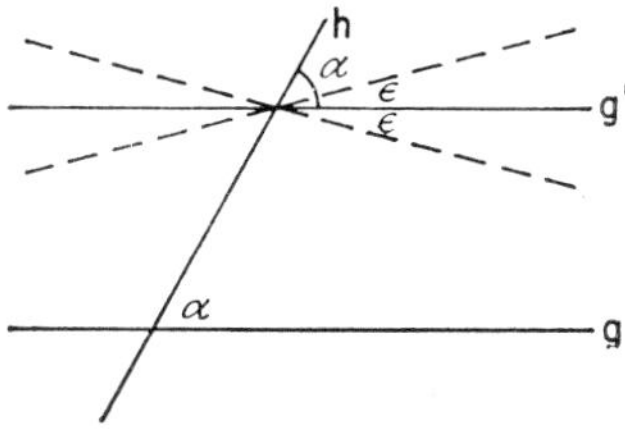

FIGURE 19

The first type of non-Euclidean geometry we have mentioned, which asserts that there are no parallel lines, is known as Riemannian geometry; it also drops the axiom that only one straight line connects two points. The second type, which asserts that there is an infinite number of straight lines which do not intersect *g*, enclosed in a certain angle about *g′*, was built up by Lobatchevski,[22] a Russian mathematician, and too, at about the same time, by the Hungarian, Bolyai.[23] Euclid's axiom is replaced by "Lobatchevski's axiom." The conclusions drawn from this axiom may be further described as follows: Let us draw a straight line *g* and a point A outside *g* (Figure 20). Then we draw through A a transversal *h* normal to *g* and a

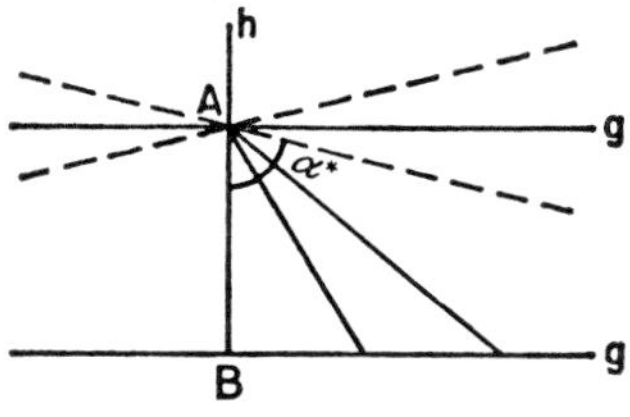

FIGURE 20

straight line *g′* under an angle of 90° to *h*. Then *g′* will not meet *g*. If we draw straight lines from the point A, always making larger and larger angles with *h*, at first these lines will intersect the line *g*. Eventually, however, (if we exclude the case that all straight lines meet each other—the "Riemannian axiom") we will come to a line which makes a certain limiting angle α^* with the transversal *h* and is the first line that will not intersect *g*. In Euclidean geometry $\alpha^* = 90°$. According to Lobatchevski's axiom, the angle α^* is less than 90°. The straight line that includes this angle with *g* is called "parallel" to *g*. In Lobatchevski's geometry, we must distinguish between parallel

[22] Nikolai Ivanovich Lobatchevski (1793–1856), Russian mathematician.
[23] Wolfgang Bolyai (1775–1856), Hungarian mathematician.

lines and nonintersecting lines. All the lines which are contained in the "bundle" around g' are called nonintersecting lines. Only the boundary lines of this "bundle" are called parallel lines. In Lobatchevski's geometry there is a parallel line to the left of the transversal as well as to the right of it. Thus, it is characteristic of Lobatchevski's geometry that there is not one parallel line, but two. All lines between them are nonintersecting, *i.e.*, they do not intersect g.

Let us consider what the sum of the angles of a triangle would be in Lobatchevski's geometry. If we consider a line from A which makes an angle with *AB* which is smaller than α^*, then it will intersect g. We may, however, take a line which makes an angle $\alpha = \alpha^* - \eta$ just a little smaller than α^*. Such a line will intersect g under an angle ϵ which is very small, as small as we like to make it. Thus we see that there are triangles in which the sum of the angles is less than 180°, since $\alpha^* < 90°$ and ϵ may be as small as we wish it to be. This is clear from the beginning if we speak in terms of the defect. In the above triangle, the defect $= 180° - 90° - (\alpha + \epsilon) = 90° - (\alpha + \epsilon)$. Considering that we have made the line from A almost parallel to g, ϵ and η will be infinitesimal and we may consider the defect to be $(90° - \alpha^*)$, a positive number.

How do we know how big $(90° - \alpha^*)$ is? Lobatchevski's axiom obviously does not determine the angle α^*, which a "parallel line" makes with a given line. Under the name "Lobatchevski's axiom" are covered, in fact, an infinite number of axioms. The parallel line to g (called g' in Figure 21) can be almost normal to *AB*, or can make

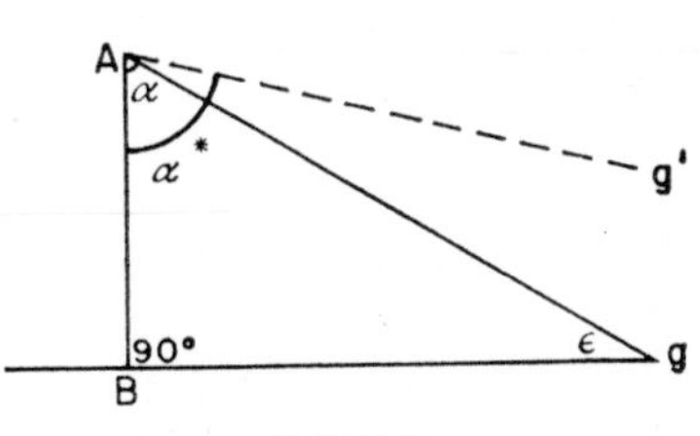

FIGURE 21

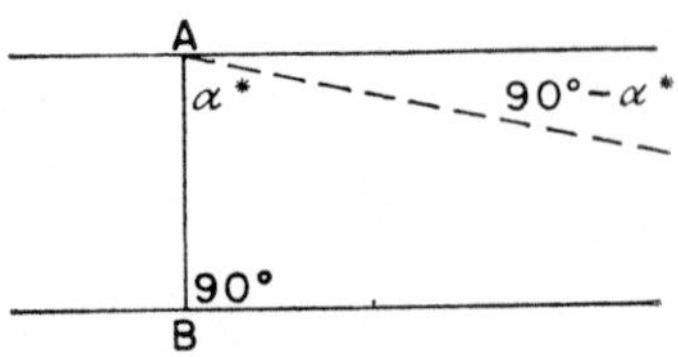

FIGURE 22

any angle with *AB*. We are free to require that for any one specific distance *AB* of A from g the angle α^* may have a value that can be arbitrarily prescribed. To every choice of the angle α^* there corresponds, actually, a special form of the Lobatchevski axiom. If we want a geometry that differs little from Euclidean geometry, we choose that the defect $(90° - \alpha^*)$ be small; if we want a very different geometry, we choose that this defect be large (Figure 22). We can ask the question: At what size does a triangle begin to be noticeably non-Euclidean? When we examine physical triangles made of rigid materials like steel, we have never noticed that the sum of the angles is less than 180°, by measurement, but this does not prove anything. The triangles measured may all have been too small for the defect to be noticeable. We can only say that all the triangles we have measured have been "small" triangles. We may define the concept of a "small triangle" as being small compared with a certain "unit" triangle; we may define a "unit triangle" as a triangle in which the defect is one degree. Instead of giving the value of α^* we can also define a special type of Lobatchevski's geometry by giving the areas of the "unit triangle." If the size of the "unit triangle" were comparable to the dimensions of a galaxy, all physical triangles would be "small," and we would not notice the defect in any of the triangles that we measure. The larger the area of a triangle compared with the "unit triangle," the larger will be the "defect." Therefore, the sum of the angles in a large triangle is less than in a small triangle. A triangle with an area that is very small compared with the area of the "unit triangle" has nearly a zero defect, and the sum of the angles is nearly 180°; with increasing defect, the sum decreases. If we have a small triangle that is similar to a large triangle, both have the same angle-sum of 180°. Since, in Lobatchevski's geometry, large triangles have greater defects than small ones, a large and a small one can never be similar. Therefore, there are no triangles with the same shape but of different sizes. From this, one can easily conclude that there are no geometrical figures of any kind which have the same shape but are of different sizes. By the shape the size is determined. A triangle with the angle-sum of nearly 180° is only possible if it is of very small size.

7. "VALIDITY" OF PROPOSITIONS IN GEOMETRY

We shall now leave the purely mathematical argument for the time being, and ask what the relationship is between geometry and experience. What we have proved up to now has had nothing to do with experience. We have simply shown that if triangles fulfill the Euclidean axioms, there are similar triangles. If, however, triangles fulfill the axioms of Lobatchevski's geometry, there are no similar triangles. These are merely conditional statements; we cannot derive anything from them about physical triangles made of wood or iron. If some axioms are true, certain results are true. All that we know to be true in geometry are these conditional statements. Whatever may happen in the world, these statements remain true. Purely logical statements are true independently of the physical occurrences in the world. The same is true of geometry if we take it in the purely mathematical sense. We can characterize "logical statements" by saying that they are true because of their form, without regard to the meaning of their terms. We can replace all the terms by other terms, and the statements remain nonetheless true. The most familiar example is the logical syllogism: If Socrates is a man and all men are mortal, Socrates is mortal. This statement remains true even if we replace "Socrates," "man," and "mortal" by other terms. For example, if the fox is a mammal and all mammals are vertebrates, the fox is a vertebrate. All statements of geometry are ultimately of this kind.

In the presentation of the elementary textbooks, the statements of geometry are not purely logical statements. They are a mixture of logical and empirical statements. The concept of congruence, for example, is defined by reference to a physical operation, the transfer of rigid bodies. However, we can convert Euclidean geometry by reformulating the axioms into a system of purely logical statements. We shall discuss this reformulation in Section 8. At this point, we shall take it for granted that such a "formalization of geometry" is possible and ask bluntly: Which is true, Euclidean or non-Euclidean geometry? We cannot answer this question from the point of view of mathematics. By mathematical argument, as we have learned, we can only prove that if we assume the Euclidean axiom, it follows that there are similar triangles, and if we reject that axiom, it follows that there are no similar triangles. However, we cannot decide whether it is "true" that there are similar triangles, *i.e.*, whether "Euclidean geometry is true." On the other hand, we are accustomed to applying geometry to physical objects. It needs careful examination to understand how it can be done. Nowhere in the whole system of geometry can there be found a definition of a straight line or a point. Since, however, logical conclusions are independent of the meanings of the terms involved, without defining straight lines and points we can say that if these objects have the properties assumed in the axioms, they also have the properties developed in the theorems. Whatever straight lines and points may be, if we adopt the Euclidean axioms, it follows that there are similar triangles—if Lobatchevski's axioms, no similar triangles—so how can geometry be applied to triangles made of wood or steel? For this purpose, we need obviously, a "geometry" that is entirely different in its structure from the mathematical, formalized geometry of which we have spoken up to now.

We have noted that all the results obtained so far are valid without considering the "meaning" of the geometrical terms. In order to get at the application to physical triangles, we must build up another kind of geometry that considers the meanings of terms like "point," and "straight line." Rudolph Carnap [24] has described, in the introduction to his book, *Formalization of Logic*, "two tendencies in modern logic."

> The one tendency emphasizes form, the logical structure of sentences and deductions, relations between signs and abstractions from their meaning. The other emphasizes just the factors excluded by the first: meaning, interpretation, relations, . . . compatibility and incompatibility as based on meaning, the distinction between necessary and contingent truth, etc. The two tendencies are as old as logic itself and have appeared under many names. Using contemporary terms, we may call them the syntactical and the semantical tendency respectively.

There have been frequent attempts to build up geometry from scratch, not as a logical discipline, but as a science that deals with physical bodies, *e.g.*, wooden and iron triangles. A remarkable attempt of this kind was made by the prominent British mathematician, William Kingdon Clifford, who worked more than most mathematicians have done for the integration of mathematics into our general system of knowledge. Clifford [25] wrote in 1875:

> Geometry is a physical science. It deals with the sizes and shapes and distances of things. . . . We shall study the science of the shapes and distances of things by making one or two very simple and obvious observations. . . . The observations that we make are:
> First, that a thing may be moved about from one place to another without altering its size or shape. Secondly, that it is possible to have things of the same shape but of different sizes.

The "things" about which Clifford speaks here are obivously what are called in physics "rigid bodies." He assumes that the criterion used to make sure a "thing" is rigid is the criterion that is generally used in experimental physics. The "size" and "shape" of

[24] Rudolph Carnap, living American logician and philosopher, *Formalization of Logic* (Cambridge: Harvard Universtiy Press, 1943), Introduction.

[25] William Kingdon Clifford (1845–1879), English mathematician and philosopher. His most important book, *The Common Sense of the Exact Sciences*, was first published in 1875. A new edition was published in New York in 1946 by Alfred A. Knopf, Inc.

a thing are measured by the standard meter in Paris or the standard foot in Washington, using the methods of correction as they are legally prescribed. Then the two observations described by Clifford can be performed using these standards. Clifford continued:

> Applying these [two] observations to triangles we can prove: (a) Two straight lines cannot intersect in more points than one. (b) If two straight lines are drawn in the plane so as not to intersect at all, the angles they make with any third line which meets them will be equal.

We have learned in previous sections (4, 5, and 6) that from the existence of similar triangles we can derive Euclid's axiom of parallels and from this axiom the theorem that a line drawn so as to intersect two parallels will make equal angles with both. In our mathematical argument, we drew these conclusions from "axioms" without using the meaning of the geometrical terms. Clifford started with generalized observations which were, of course, statements about physical facts and conclusions drawn from them which were also statements about physical triangles.

We shall now, in the following sections, discuss the precise relationship between conclusions drawn from axioms without using the meaning of the terms and conclusions drawn from statements about physical facts, where every term denotes a physical object. In twentieth-century science, the "axioms" have been formulated in such a way that in drawing conclusions one actually does not use any information about the meaning of the terms; with the establishment of this completely formalized system of axioms, one draws conclusions about physical triangles by using a peculiar method of coordinating the purely formal, purely logical conclusions with the statements about physical objects.

8. "FORMALIZATION" OF THE AXIOMS

Geometry, as it is treated in elementary textbooks and courses, is not a purely logical system. The meanings of some of the terms, *e.g.*, of "congruence," are defined by means of physical operations, such as the displacement of a rigid body. However, the Euclidean system can be modified so that it becomes purely logical. We shall illustrate this by a very simple example. This means that we must formulate it in such a way that the validity of its statements are dependent only on their form and not on the meaning of the geometrical terms: "straight line," "point," "intersecting," and "connecting."

Previously we laid down the axiom that two points A and *B* can only be connected by one straight line (Axiom I). Then with the help of the following diagrams, we derived the conclusion that two straight lines can only intersect in one or no points. (See Figure 23.) If, in Figure 24, the lines *p* and *p′* intersect not only at A

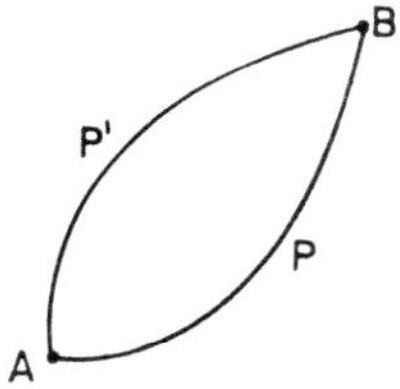

FIGURE 23

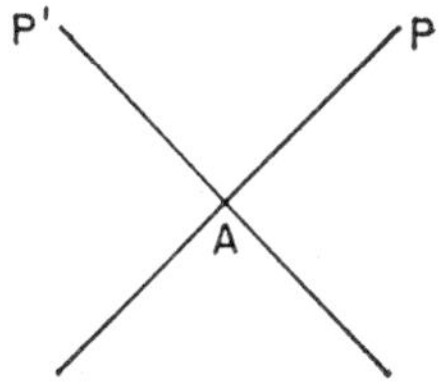

FIGURE 24

but at a second point *B*, we would have Figure 23, which is, according to Axiom I, impossible if *p* and *p′* are different lines. This was an intuitive proof, which depended on visualizing in a certain way straight lines and points and straight lines intersecting. The meanings of straight line and point and intersecting in a physical way, however, are not necessarily involved. We can formulate this proof in such a way that it becomes completely logical; in other words, so that the physical meanings of these terms is not involved.

We shall demonstrate that the geometrical proofs remain valid even if we replace "straight lines" and "points" by "apples" and "oranges." Let us recall "Axiom I": If there are two points, A and *B*, there is only one straight line which connects them. (See Figure 25.) From this we can derive Corollary I:

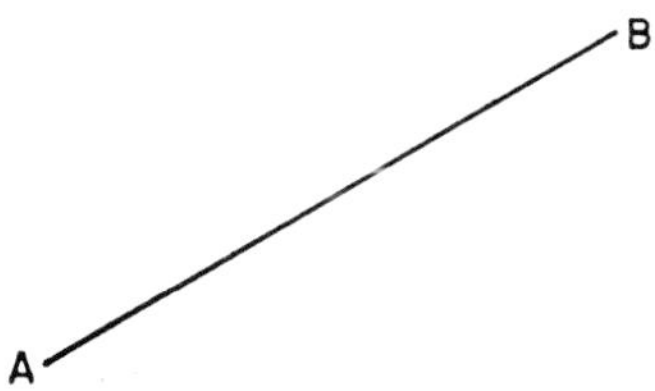

FIGURE 25

Two straight lines, *P* and *P′*, can never intersect in more than one point.

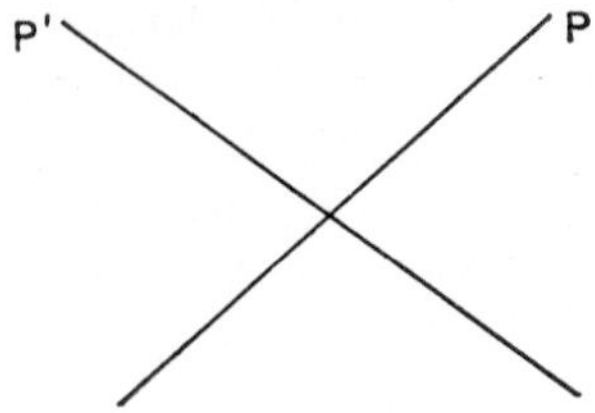

FIGURE 26

Now we must "formalize" these propositions (Axiom I and Corollary I). This means bringing them into such a form that one can clearly see why the meaning of the geometrical terms has no bearing upon the validity of the proofs.

First, we shall eliminate the terms "connect" and "intersect." If a straight line passes through a point, we shall say the "straight line" "coincides with a point." If a point is on a line, we shall say that the "point coincides with a line." Axiom I now becomes: If a straight line *P* coincides with two points, A and *B*, and a straight line *P′* also coincides with the same two points, A and *B*, the *P* and *P′* are not different from each other. If the corollary were not valid, we could assume that a straight line *P* coincides with two points A and *B*, and that a *different* straight line *P′* coincides with the same two points, A and *B*. But the first axiom says that *P* is not different from *P′*. Thus, from the assumption that *P* and *P′* are different, we conclude that *P* is not different from *P′*. This would mean: From a proposition "S is true" it follows that "non-*S* (the negation of S) is true." Therefore, the corollary must be true: Two straight lines, if not identical, can coincide with only one point; or, in other words, cannot intersect in more than one point.

Now we can replace the terms in the above argument as follows: "point" by "apple," "straight line" by "orange," "coincident" with "are on the same plate." Then we shall see that the physical properties of "straight lines," "points," and "coincidence" have nothing to do with the validity of the proof. The first axiom would become: There cannot be on the same plate two apples and more than one orange. And the first corollary: If there are two oranges and one apple on the same plate, then it is impossible that there is still another apple on the plate. If there were a second apple, there would be two apples and two oranges on the same plate. This would contradict Axiom I. Hence, from Axiom I we can obivously conclude the corollary. From this we see that the meanings of "straight line," etc., are not important, that we can draw the same conclusions by changing the meanings of the geometrical terms. In the above argument, we used only the meaning of the term "not," but we could also formalize the logical system so that the meanings of the logical terms would not enter either.

9. FORMALIZATION OF "CONGRUENCE"

The traditional teaching of geometry is still almost the same as it was written by Euclid. In the strictest sense, this is only partly a logical system; it makes use of some empirical notions. Among the basic concepts, the most "physical" seems to be the notion of congruence. The traditional definition says: Two figures are "congruent" if we can bring them into coincidence. This definition clearly refers to the idea that these figures are "rigid bodies" and can be moved without altering their shape or size. It clearly refers to a physical operation, the displacement of rigid bodies.

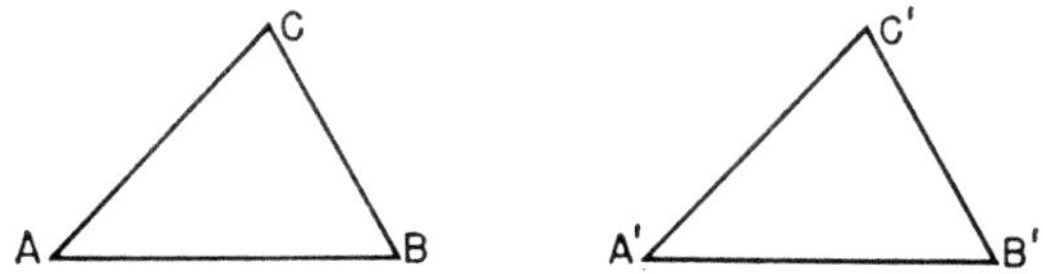

FIGURE 27

Let us consider, for example, the first theorem of congruence. We shall use the symbol $\equiv$ for "congruent." The first theorem of congruence says that if: $AC \equiv A'C'$, $AB \equiv A'B'$, and angle $CAB \equiv C'A'B'$, then $BC \equiv B'C'$. How do we prove this? According to Euclid, two sides are congruent if they can be brought into coincidence. Therefore, according to the conditions given above, AC can be brought into coincidence with $A'C'$ and AB can be brought into coincidence with $A'B'$, simultaneously. Therefore, BC must coincide with $B'C'$ and so $BC \equiv B'C'$. We have used here, intermixed, both logical and empirical arguments.

Now let us use a purely logical proposition. We denote by p, q, and r simple propositions. Then a typical example of a purely logical proposition is this: Assume that if p is true, q follows, and that if q is true, r follows. We can conclude that if p is true, r follows. It doesn't matter whether p, q, and r are statements about points, congruence, coincidence, or whatever.

Toward the end of the nineteenth century, attempts were made to make of geometry such a purely logical system. These attempts were summarized and perfected through the work of David Hilbert [26] in 1898–1899, and published in his book, *The Foundations of Geometry.* The idea was that geometry should be developed in such a way that one could go from the axioms to the theorems without depending on what the concepts in the axioms meant. If we formulate the properties of straight lines in the axioms, and use in the deductions only these properties of straight lines, we do not need to know what a straight line is. We have seen that in traditional geometry, the physical meaning of the predicate "coincidence" is used in order to prove the theorems of congruence. So now let us see how the first theorem of congruence which we have discussed above is proved by Hilbert without using the physical meanings of terms. We can no longer say that two systems are "congruent" if they can be brought into "coincidence." This would refer to a physical operation. We must instead refer to the properties of congruence of axioms. What properties do two segments have if they are congruent? Consider the following diagram.

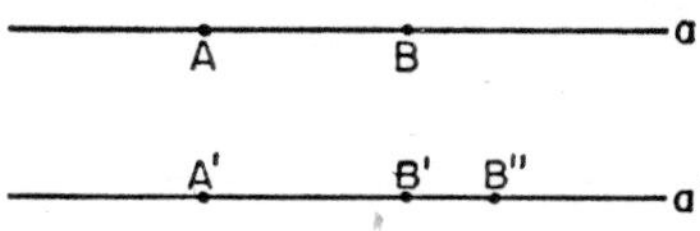

FIGURE 28

We consider a straight line a and two points A and B in this line. Then the first axiom of congruence says: On any straight line a', starting from any one of its points A', and on each side of it respectively, one can always find a point B' such that $A'B' \equiv AB$. This is one of the properties of congruence. A characteristic point is that this axiom does not exclude the possibility that there may also be a point B'', different from B', such that $AB \equiv A'B''$. The axiom does not say that there is only *one* point B' which has the described property. If we define "congruent" by "bringing into coincidence," this would be the case—in Hilbert's geometry the fact that there is only one such point has to be proved. Two more properties of congruence are given in the following axioms: Two segments congruent with a third are congruent with one another; and two angles congruent with a third are congruent with one another. An "angle" is defined as two straight lines, g and h, that meet at a point O. Then we can give the axiom:

[26] David Hilbert (1862–1943), German mathematician. His *Foundations of Geometry* (Leipzig, 1899), inaugurated modern axiomatic method.

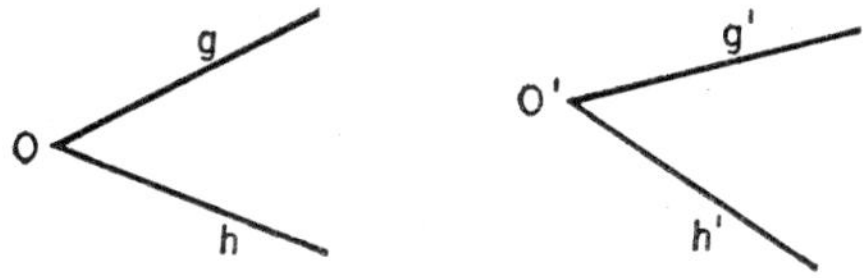

FIGURE 29

Given a line g', issuing from a point O', in any plane which contains it and on each of the two sides of it, there can be found one, and only one, line h' issuing from O' so that the angle $(g'h')$ is congruent with a given angle (gh). Next we introduce an axiom which states, in a certain way, the relationship between the congruence of segments and the congruence of angles. In order to prove the first theorem of congruence, we shall need such a relationship. In order to avoid the physical meaning of congruence, Hilbert advanced this axiom from which we can derive what Euclid derived from the physical meaning (Figure 30). Hilbert's new axiom is: If $AB \equiv A'B'$ and $AC \equiv A'C'$ and angle $CAB \equiv$ angle $C'A'B'$, then angle $ACB \equiv$ angle $A'C'B'$. These axioms as we have just stated them do not bring in any physical operations; they just give properties of congruence.

Now let us proceed to use them to prove the first theorem of congruence. Consider the following diagram:

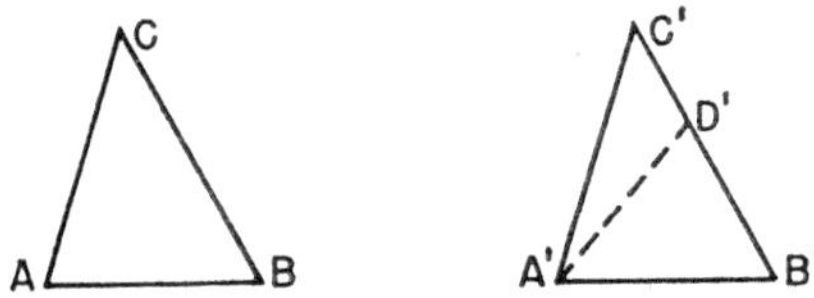

FIGURE 30

It is given that $AB \equiv A'B'$, $AC \equiv A'C'$, and angle $CAB \equiv$ angle $C'A'B'$. According to the "first theorem of congruence," the relation $B'C' \equiv BC$ should hold. If we define "congruence" by "coincidence," the proof is obvious. Hilbert, however, proved it from his axioms as follows: If $B'C'$ were not congruent with BC, then by the first axiom above (Hilbert's) we can always find a point D' such that $B'D' \equiv BC$. (If the point lay beyond C', the argument would be similar.) Now compare triangle ABC with triangle $A'B'D'$. $AB \equiv A'B'$, $BC \equiv B'D'$, and, by Hilbert's axiom, angle ABC is congruent to angle $A'B'D'$. Therefore, also by Hilbert's axiom: Angle $D'A'B'$ is congruent to angle CAB, and angle $A'D'B' \equiv$ angle ACB. Therefore angle $D'A'B' \equiv C'A'B'$, and $A'C'$ must coincide with $A'D'$. We can see, in this way, how, by introducing somewhat more complicated axioms, we can prove the theorems of congruence in a completely logical way without referring to the physical idea of "bringing into coincidence." We did not give any physical interpretation of the terms; we simply stated certain axioms in which the terms occur. From this, it is clear, we cannot tell anything about the external world. It follows only that if some congruence exists, other congruencies exist also, but we do not know "what congruence is."

On the other hand, we learn that geometry provides us with laws about the properties of physical bodies. If we make a triangle from rigid steel, we check, by real measurements, that the sum of the angles is approximately 180°. Now the problem arises: How can the logical system of mathematical geometry, *e.g.*, Hilbert's system of axioms, help us to obtain the physical laws about triangles of steel or wood? This connection will be discussed in the following section.

10. OPERATIONAL DEFINITIONS IN GEOMETRY

We have seen that the system of mathematical geometry, if properly formalized, becomes independent of the meanings of terms such as straight lines and points. The whole system can then be considered as a definition of these terms, inasmuch as it gives all the properties of them. Axiom I, for example, can be formulated as follows: "Points" and "straight lines" are such objects, and "coincidence" is such a property that one and only one straight line can coincide with two given points. This is an "implicit definition" of geometric terms. Axiom I (Section 8) expresses the same thing in a different form. We call it an "implicit definition" of points and straight lines. These definitions are, as every definition is, arbitrary. Whatever happens in the world of experience, no one can prevent us from formulating these definitions. They are neither true nor false; they stipulate rules according to which the geometrical terms, "point," "straight line," "coincidence," etc., are to be *connected with one another*; but they do not stipulate any rules for connecting these terms with physical objects like triangles of wood or steel. If we wish to proceed now to the problem of how to make use of formalized geometry for our orientation in the physical world, we must ask the following question: Are there objects in the physical world which have the properties formulated in the axioms? If so, then they also have the properties formulated in the theorems. We look for a "physical interpretation" of the axioms of geometry.

We could, for example, say that we interpret a straight line in the physical world as the edge of an iron cube. In physics such a body can only be defined by the technological procedures by which such a cube is produced. We have to consider corrections with regard to changes of size and shape caused by changes in temperature and pressure. These procedures include the establishing of the standard meter in Paris and the measurement of our prospective cube by comparison with this standard. Eventually, we obtain the "edge of a rigid body." The ends of the edge are a physical interpretation of "points." In this way, we obtain what P. W. Bridgman has called "operational definitions" of the terms "straight line," "point," etc. These definitions are, obviously, different in kind from the definition of these terms by the axioms of formalized geometry which we may call "axiomatic definitions." We can also give other "operational definitions" of a straight line—we may say that it is the path of a light ray, or of a stretched cord. We may say that it is the shortest distance between two points—in this case, we need an "operational definition" of what is shortest, *i.e.*, a way of measuring length.

If we give a physical interpretation of "point," "straight line," and "intersection," then the axioms and theorems of geometry acquire a completely different character. The axiomatic definitions of "straight line," "point," etc., are arbitrary, but if we substitute for these terms their operational definitions, they become statements about physical things, and have to be checked by experiment: they may be confirmed or refuted. If, then, we make a triangle of wood or steel, measure the sum of its angles, and find it to be about 180°, is this a confirmation of Euclidean geometry? Strictly speaking no; it is a confirmation of a "special physical interpretation of Euclidean geometry." If we find "simple" objects with a certain importance for us which fulfill the axioms of Euclidean geometry, we say that Euclidean geometry is "true" in the sense that it has a certain application for us.

It is impossible to check Euclidean geometry against Lobatchevski's geometry directly by comparing physical interpretations of the axioms. How can we determine whether there are one or more edges of bodies which do not intersect if prolonged far enough? Practically, this is impossible to determine by direct experiment. Perhaps, as in physics, we can check some consequences of them rather than the axioms themselves. For example, from the Euclidean axiom follows the theorem that the sum of the angles in a triangle equals 180°. If we measure it, we may find a small "defect"; the observed sum may be a little less than 180°. We can ascribe the differences to experimental errors. We could also assume, however, that Lobatchevski's geometry is valid for the same physical interpretation. If we admit this possibility, we do not know whether or not the "defect" is really due to errors. It depends upon which specific Lobatchevski geometry is valid (Section 7). We must make a specific assumption with regard to how large the unit triangle is. If our measured triangle is much smaller than the unit triangle, the defect will be very small. If we were to make the base of the measured triangle a million miles long, then we would find a much larger defect. Thus we can see two possibilities of accounting for a small measured difference from 180°: either Euclidean geometry applies and we interpret these differences as "errors," or a specific Lobatchevski geometry applies in such a way that triangles here on earth are very small compared with the unit triangle. If there are two possibilities, we will choose the "simpler"—if we can find an obvious criterion of simplicity.

These remarks have dealt with one and the same physical interpretation of two systems of axioms. We should also consider two different physical interpretations. Then, it might happen that one of these two physical interpretations—say, straight lines shown by light rays in one case, and by the edges of rigid bodies in the other—may confirm Euclidean geometry and the other Lobatchevski's geometry. Thus, experiment can never confirm a system of geometrical axioms, but only a "geometry" *plus* a physical interpretation of it. The problem is always this: If the enlarged system, consisting of the axioms of geometry plus their physical interpretation, fails to check with experiment, we can drop either one or the other part of the enlarged system. We have repeatedly stressed the point that the formalized system of geometry does not tell anything about the world of physical experiments, but consists of "arbitrary" definitions. This fact was formulated by the great French mathematician and philosopher, Henri Poincaré.[27] He claimed that the laws of geometry were not statements about reality at all, but were arbitrary conventions about how to use such terms as "straight line" and "point." This doctrine of Poincaré has become known as "conventionalism." It has angered many scientists because it claims that the statements of geometry, which they have regarded as "truth," are only "conventions." They have emphasized that geometry has been of great practical use to man. This fact was not denied by Poincaré. There are useful conven-

[27] Henri Poincaré (1854–1912), French mathematician, astronomer, and philosopher.

tions and useless conventions. If there were nothing in the physical world which fulfilled the axioms of geometry (*e.g.*, no rigid bodies), that system of conventions would be of no practical interest because it could not be applied to anything. Nevertheless, because of its "if-then" character, geometry would remain true. Thus we can say that such logical structures as geometry are true by themselves, independent of what happens in the world and independent of the meaning of their terms. The meaning of their terms is irrelevant. We might say that geometry is an instrument we have constructed to deal with rigid bodies. If we give the laws of geometry a physical interpretation, they are physical laws just like any other physical laws. We must consider that geometry has a double aspect. As a logical structure, it has no connection with reality, but it has the characteristic of certainty. Once we give it a physical interpretation, it no longer has this characteristic of certainty. Einstein has expressed this as follows: "In so far as geometry is certain, it says nothing about the physical world; and in so far as it says something about our physical experience, it is uncertain." Frequently the question is asked whether our "real space" is Euclidean or non-Euclidean. Some wish to prove that our "real space" is actually Euclidean, and that non-Euclidean space is only a fiction, a product of our imagination or construction. This alternative is not correctly formulated.

We must distinguish between geometry as a logical structure and geometry as a physical interpretation. We must understand the degree to which geometry is conventional. From the purely logical aspect, Euclidean and non-Euclidean geometry are two logical structures which are equally consistent and, therefore, equally "true." The question whether or not our "actual space is Euclidean" means: Are there simple physical interpretations of "point," "straight line," etc., which fulfill the axioms and, therefore, also the theorems of Euclidean geometry?

11. THE TWENTIETH-CENTURY CONCEPTION OF GEOMETRY

When modern science developed, around 1600, there was a certain amount of suspicion with regard to presentations of science which stressed logical systems of terms. Long before the concept of "operational meaning" was thought of, logical systems, as exemplified in medieval scholasticism, had been applied to the world of experience in a rather loose way. It was believed that by formulating a logical system, man had also advanced a theory about the world of experience. In a rather perfunctory way, this belief was not wrong. Some operational definitions were taken for granted, no necessity was felt to formulate them explicitly. Even men like Lobatchevski or Hilbert spoke about straight lines as things of the physical world, as if there were not several different ways of giving an "operational definition" of a straight line. The "edge of a rigid body" has usually been taken for granted as the natural physical interpretation. As we have mentioned, however, the lack of a well-defined link between logical systems and the world of experience was noticed and attacked by the earliest advocates of experimentation as the basis of science. Francis Bacon directed his *Novum Organum* against Aristotle's *Organum, Metaphysics*, and *Physics*, in which the philosopher of ancient science stressed the role of logical systems, without paying sufficient attention to the role of "operational definitions," even though he did pay more attention to the latter than his great predecessor Plato. Francis Bacon wrote: [28]

> The syllogism consists of propositions, propositions of words; words are the signs of notions. If, therefore, the notions be confused and carelessly abstracted from things, there is no solidity in the superstructure. . . . The present system of logic . . . rather assists in confirming and rendering inveterate the errors founded on vulgar notions, than in searching for truth. It is, therefore, more hurtful than useful.

Certainly, the urge to present geometry as a purely logical system has been particularly strong. Geometry has been proud of its "absolute certainty," and this claim could not be based on experimental research. Louis Rougier has said [29] in his book *The Geometrical Philosophy of Henri Poincaré:*

> Geometrical theorems seemed to enjoy a double certainty; the apodictical necessity which arose from demonstration, and the sensual evidence that originated in spatial intuition. They seem to have a double truth: formal truth that originates in the coherent logic of discourse, and material truth originating in the agreement of things with their objects.

According to the usual nineteenth-century presentations of geometry, the theorems were based on formal logical deductions from the axioms, but the truth of the axioms was based upon "spatial intui-

[28] Francis Bacon, *Novum Organum*, I, 14 and I, 11.

[29] Louis Rougier, living French philosopher, *La Philosophie Geometrique de Henri Poincaré* (Paris: F. Alcan, 1920).

tion." The logical derivation of theorems has not been regarded as debatable, but the "spatial intuition of axioms," which is about the same notion as "seeing with the eyes of the mind," has been strongly criticized. Particularly since the middle of the nineteenth century, voices have been raised by those who regarded the axioms as results of experience, even though this would not be compatible with the alleged "certainty" of geometrical theorems.

Two great scientists of the middle of the nineteenth century, Bernhard Riemann[30] and Hermann Helmholtz,[31] made the point that the axioms of geometry were results of physical observation, and that, therefore, the theorems were of no greater certainty than any statements of physics. In his paper *On the Hypotheses of Geometry* Riemann wrote in 1854: "The properties by which space is distinguished from other thinkable three-dimensional continua can only be provided by experience." Around 1900 this view penetrated the vanguard of textbooks, while the average ones were still sticking to the "self-evidence" of axioms. After 1900, some prominent mathematicians published textbooks of geometry in order to bring them into line with the modern view.

The French mathematician, Emile Borel,[32] for example, wrote in his textbook in 1908:

> The goal of geometry is to study those properties of bodies which can be considered independent of their matter, but only with respect to their dimensions and their forms. Geometry measures the surface of a field without bothering to find out whether the soil is good or bad.

The Italian mathematician, Giuseppe Veronese,[33] stated explicitly in his *Elements of Geometry* in 1909: "An axiom is a proposition the content of which is verified experimentally and which is neither contradictory to any other proposition nor deducible from it." The axioms began now to play the role of physical hypotheses. The theorems were, then, also statements about physical facts. The question then arose: What was the difference between an axiom and

[30] Bernhard Riemann (1826–1866), German mathematician, *On the Hypothesis upon Which Geometry is Founded* (1867).

[31] Hermann Helmholtz (1821–1894), German physicist, physiologist, and philosopher.

[32] Emile Borel (1871–   ), French mathematician and statesman.

[33] Giuseppe Veronese (1854–1917), Italian mathematician. He published *Elements of Geometry* (Verona, 1897).

a theorem? The Italian mathematicians, Frederigo Enriques [34] and Umberto Amaldi, answered thus in their *Elements of Geometry* in 1908:

> The first geometrical properties of figures are *evident;* they are suggested to us by immediate sense *observations* of real bodies which have been the sources of our concepts of these figures. From these first intuitive properties, we can derive by logical conclusions other properties, without recourse to further observations. These properties are, in general, less evident.

Thus the authors stressed the very important point that actually no general proposition can be derived from sense observations, but only suggested and verified by observations. Enriques made the point that it is difficult to see that theorems, such as the sum of the angles in a triangle equals 180°, could be suggested by direct observations, while the proposition that there is only one straight line through two points was strongly suggested by observations. The first is a theorem, the latter an axiom. This situation at the turn of the century was described by Einstein in 1921 in the following way: [35]

> Here arises a puzzle that has disturbed scientists of all periods. How is it possible that mathematics, a product of human thought that is independent of experience, fits so excellently the objects of physical reality? Can human reason without experience discover by pure thinking properties of real things?

The twentieth century has favored a solution to this puzzle that is due neither to the pure mathematicians nor to the "pure" philosophers, but to the mathematical physicists. This solution was given in two steps. The first step was the "axiomatic method" or, in other words, the "formalization of the axioms," which was, following the work of some predecessors like Moritz Pasch,[36] finally accomplished by the German mathematician, David Hilbert. He constructed a system of axioms which were actually "axiomatic definitions" of the geometrical terms with all definitions by physical operations excluded.

[34] Frederigo Enriques and Umberto Amaldi, *Elementi di Geometria* (Bologna: Zanichelli, 1905). Enriques was a mathematician who was also a prominent author in the history and philosophy of science.

[35] Albert Einstein (1879–1955). His address "Geometry and Experience" was first given to the Prussian Academy (Berlin) in 1921. An English translation appeared in *Sidelights on Relativity,* translated by G. B. Jeffrey and W. Perrett (New York: E. P. Dutton & Co., Inc., 1921), and (London: Methuen and Co., Ltd.).

[36] Moritz Pasch (1843–1931), German mathematician.

Hilbert, recognized, however, that "this formal system was also a logical analysis of our ability of intuition." He refused to discuss "whether our spatial intuition is *a priori* [seeing with the eyes of the mind] or empirical." We note that in the year 1899 the connection of the formal system of axioms with the properties of physical bodies was still only described by vague and ambiguous terms like "spatial intuition."

The second step was due, above all, to the French mathematician, physicist, and philosopher, Henri Poincaré.[37] Toward the end of the nineteenth century, he attempted to build up a geometry which would embrace the formal-logical as well as the empirical-physical aspect. Hilbert defined the "geometrical terms" by "axiomatic definitions" and referred to their physical interpretations only in such vague terms as "spatial intuition." According to Poincaré, the terms which are defined by a system like Hilbert's are physical things. The claim of the axioms is that there are physical objects in our world, or that physical objects can be manufactured, that fulfill these axioms. If we say, for example, that "light rays" can be substituted for "straight lines," the axioms become "statements of physics." If we want to check whether a triangle of light rays in empty space actually has an angle-sum of two right angles, we face a particular difficulty. If we find that the sum in question is different from two right angles, we can also interpret the result by saying that the "defect" is not due to the nonvalidity of Euclidean geometry, but to the fact that the rays have been deflected by some hitherto unsuspected law of physics. From considerations of this type, Poincaré concluded that we can check whether or not light rays fulfill the Euclidean axioms only if we know all the physical laws about light rays. Otherwise, we can never find out by experiment whether or not Euclidean geometry is valid. We could maintain the validity of the axioms under all circumstances if we assumed the validity of physical laws that compensated any "defect" ascribed to a departure from "Euclidicity."

If we formulate "checking the validity of Euclidean geometry" in this way, it follows, certainly, that there is no experimental method by which it can be decided whether Euclidean or non-Euclidean geometry is true. Einstein wrote: "According to my opinion, Poincaré is right *sub specie aeternitatis* [under the aspect of eternity]." But Einstein[38] thought it would be advisable to give the expression

[37] See footnote 27.
[38] Einstein, *op. cit.*

"test the validity of Euclidean geometry" a narrower meaning. He said:

> But it is my conviction that today one still must use measuring yardsticks and clocks which are defined by Euclidean geometry. This means, one has to start from the hypothesis that the yardsticks and clocks which are manufactured in the traditional way obey within small regions of space and time the laws of Euclidean geometry and Newtonian physics. Then (G) and (*P*) are fixed within certain spatial and temporal limits. Then, you can put the question: If one assumes the validity of the known laws of physics in the whole world, is it possible to uphold Euclidean geometry in the whole world? If the answer is yes, one would say that the validity of the Euclidean geometry is confirmed; if it is no, it is refuted.

One could, for example, make small cubes of rigid steel. According to Einstein's assumption, one could use them to build up small walls without gaps. Then, one could try to see whether he could also build up walls of dimensions of millions of miles without gaps. In this way, the validity of Euclidean geometry could be tested.

The solution of the "puzzle" reached by Poincaré and Einstein has been precisely outlined as follows by Einstein:

> The progress attained by axiomatic geometry consists in the clear separation of the logical form from the factual and intuitive content. According to axiomatic geometry, only the logical-formal is the object of mathematics; but not the intuitive content that is connected with the logical-formal. . . . The statements about physical objects are obtained by coordinating with the empty concepts of axiomatic geometry observable objects of physical reality. In particular: solid bodies behave according to the theorems of three dimensional Euclidean geometry.

The appropriate and general scheme by which the relation between axiomatic geometry and the behavior of physical objects can be treated was developed by P. W. Bridgman.[39] He introduced the concept of "operational definitions" which must be added to the "axiomatic definitions" in order to fulfill the entire task of geometry. Bridgman stressed the point that any term, *e.g.*, "straight line," which occurs in axiomatic geometry must be coordinated with a technical procedure for manufacturing the object described by this term. Every procedure of this kind can be described in terms of our everyday language, hence the name "operational definition." The core of

[39] P. W. Bridgman, *Logic of Modern Physics* (New York: The Macmillan Company, 1927).

the definition is the reduction to "physical operations." We may quote, as a simple example, the definition of "length." Bridgman wrote:

> What do we mean by the length of an object? We evidently know what we mean by length if we can tell what the length of any and every object is. To find the length of an object we have to perform certain physical operations. The concept of length is, therefore, fixed when the operations by which length is measured are fixed. That is, the concept of length involves as much as and nothing more than the set of operations by which length is determined.

The evolution of geometry before and after 1800 gave rise to an advance in the philosophy of science that can hardly be overrated. L. Rougier,[40] who was one of the first among French philosophers to anticipate the trend of twentieth-century ideas on science, wrote in his book *The Geometrical Philosophy of Henri Poincaré:*

> It will turn out that the discovery of non-Euclidean geometry has been the origin of a considerable revolution in the theory of knowledge and, hence, in our metaphysical conceptions about man and the Universe. One can say, briefly, that this discovery has succeeded in breaking up the dilemma within which epistemology has been locked by the claims of traditional logic: the principles of science are either *apodictic truth* [logical conclusions synthetic *a priori*] or *assertoric truth* [facts of sense observation]. Poincaré, taking his inspiration from the work of Lobatchevski and Riemann, pointed out in the particularly significant case of geometry that another solution is possible: the principles may be simply arbitrary conventions.... However, far from being independent of our minds and nature, they exist only by a tacit agreement of all minds and depend strictly upon the factual external conditions in the environment in which we happen to live.

If we consider this evolution of thought in geometry, we can solve two questions which have puzzled scientists and philosophers alike since the birth of non-Euclidean geometry. First, there is the question of whether our "real space" is Euclidean or non-Euclidean. The second is whether or not non-Euclidean geometry is as mentally picturable or as intuitive as Euclidean. The question of "space" can probably be formulated as follows: Is it possible to find physical objects that fulfill the axioms of Euclidean geometry? Since this question, strictly speaking, could never be answered with certainty in the negative, we should ask rather: Do some specific simple objects which

[40] Rougier, *op. cit.*

we, in the language of our daily life, connect with "straight lines" fulfill the Euclidean axioms, such as light rays or the edges of solid cubes? As for the other question, we must consider that there is an ambiguity in the use of the term "intuitive." It can mean "perceivable by sense-observation," but it can also mean "perceivable by the eyes of the mind or by inner intuition." In the first sense, our knowledge of the table on which we write is "intuitive"; in the second sense, the axioms of geometry are "intuitive" to those who believe that their validity is self-evident. This ambiguity plays an even greater role in German philosophy, in which the word "anschaulich," corresponding to "intuitive," is frequently used in the philosophy of science; it has been a favored word and has brought about a great deal of confusion. If we keep to the first meaning of the word "intuitive," which is the only one admissible in science, we shall be adhering to the way in which the great German physiologist, mathematician, physicist, and philosopher, Hermann Helmholtz,[41] defined an "intuitive" presentation of geometry or of any other science. He described this as follows:

> It means to imagine completely the sense impressions which the object [*i.e.*, the physical objects defined by the axioms and operational definitions] would produce in ourselves, according to the known laws of our sense organs, under all conceivable conditions of observations. . . . If the series of sense impressions can be given completely and unambiguously, one must recognize that the object can be *intuitively represented.*

In this sense, non-Euclidean geometry is certainly as intuitive as Euclidean. If we accept, for example, Lobatchevski's axioms, and wish to measure a triangle of light rays in empty space, we can predict the sense impressions we shall have if we measure the angles by means of a protractor or by any of the methods of measurement accepted in physics.

The decisive steps toward a clear understanding of non-Euclidean geometry were taken by Riemann, Helmholtz, and Poincaré, who recognized the essential unity of geometry and physics. However, this understanding did not come into its own until Einstein showed that such a combination of geometry and physics was really necessary for the derivation of phenomena which had actually been observed.

[41] Hermann Helmholtz, *Popular Lectures on Non-scientific Subjects,* translated by E. Atkinson (London: Longmans, Green & Company, 1873).

Max Jammer

The Nature of Scientific Concepts

As a result of modern research in physics, the ambition and hope, still cherished by most authorities of the last century, that physical science could offer a photographic picture and true image of reality had to be abandoned. Science, as understood today, has a more restricted objective: its two major assignments are the description of certain phenomena in the world of experience and the establishment of general principles for their prediction and what might be called their "explanation." "Explanation" here means essentially their subsumption under these principles. For the efficient achievement of these two objectives science employs a conceptual apparatus, that is, a system of concepts and theories that represent or symbolize the data of sense experience, as pressures, colors, tones, odors, and their possible interrelations. This conceptual apparatus consists of two parts: (1) a system of concepts, definitions, axioms, and theorems, forming a hypothetico-deductive system, as exemplified in mathematics by Euclidean geometry; (2) a set of relations linking certain concepts of the hypothetico-deductive system with certain data of sensory experience. With the aid of these relations, which may be called "rules of interpretation" or "epistemic correlations," [1] an association is set up, for instance, between

Reprinted with permission of Harvard University Press from Max Jammer, Concepts of Force *(Cambridge, Mass.: Harvard University Press, 1957), pp. 2–4.*

[1] Rudolf Carnap, who, perhaps in analogy to the Kantian conception of a "transcendental scheme," stressed for the first time the importance of these relations, called them "*phenomenal-physikal-*

a black patch on a photographic plate (a sensory impression) and a spectral line of a certain wavelength (a conceptual element or construct [2] of the hypothetico-deductive system), or between the click of an amplifier coupled to a Geiger counter and the pasage of an electron. The necessity for physical science of possessing both parts as constituents results from its status as a theoretical system of propositions about empirical phenomena. A hypothetico-deductive system without rules of interpretation degenerates into a speculative calculus incapable of being tested or verified; a system of epistemic correlations without a theoretical superstructure of a deductive system remains a sterile record of observational facts, devoid of any predictive or explanatory power.

The adoption of rules of interpretation introduces, to some extent, an arbitrariness in the construction of the system as a whole by allowing for certain predilections in the choice of the concepts to be employed. In other words, arbitrary modifications in the formation of the conceptual counterparts to given sensory impressions can be compensated by appropriate changes in the epistemic correlations without necessarily destroying the correspondence with physical reality. In consequence of this arbitrariness, scientific concepts "are free creations of the human mind and are not, however it may seem, uniquely determined by the external world." [3]

When science attempts to construct a logically consistent system of thought corresponding to the chaotic diversity of sense experience, the selection of concepts as fundamental is not unambiguously determined by their suitability to form a basis for the derivation of observable facts. In the first place, some element of contingency is introduced by the somehow fortuitous sequence of experimentation and observation, an idea recently emphasized by James Bryant Conant: "It seems clear that the development of our modern scientific ideas might have taken a somewhat different course, if the chronological sequence of certain experimental findings had been different. And to some degree, at least, this chronology can be regarded as purely acci-

ische Zuordnungen." See Rudolf Carnap, "Ueber die Aufgaben der Physik," *Kantstudien*, vol. 28 (1923), p. 90. The term "epistemic correlation" is employed by F. S. C. Northrop in his *Logic of the sciences and humanities* (Macmillan, New York, 1947), p. 119.

[2] Cf. Henry Margenau, *The nature of physical reality* (McGraw-Hill, New York, 1950), p. 69.

[3] Albert Einstein and Leopold Infeld, *The evolution of physics* (Simon and Schuster, New York, 1938), p. 33.

dental."[4] In the second place, a certain climate of opinion, conditioned by subconscious motives, is responsible to some extent for the specific character of the basic conceptions or primitive concepts. It is a major task of the historian of science to study this climate of opinion prevailing at a certain period and to expose the extrascientific elements responsible for the finally accepted choice of those concepts that were to play a fundamental role in the construction of the contemporaneous conceptual apparatus. The history of science can often show in retrospect how alternative concepts have, or could have, been employed at the various stages in the development of the physical sciences in a provisionally satisfactory manner.

[4] J. B. Conant, "The citadel of learning," *Yale Review* 45, 56 (1955).

details. In the second case, a greater simplicity of theory [illegible] ... [illegible]

[illegible]

[illegible] satisfactory manner.

[illegible]

History of Science

From the large and complex field of the history of science we choose only a few isolated examples. Too often "history of science" means only a correlation of names, dates, and "discoveries," whereas the really interesting aspects include the development of ideas, the evolution of concepts passing from one individual to another, and the impact of insights won in "natural philosophy" on attitudes and conceptions of human beings in various historical periods. The historian finds that every idea has a prehistory before it is fully developed, that the history of ideas is no smooth linear progression, and that the failures and wrong turns are often more important than the apparent successes. The history of science reveals the scientist as a creator.

Butterfield, a contemporary British historian whose interests extend to the history of science, traces the theory of impulse preceding Galileo's work on mechanics. Contrary to beliefs held until quite recently, the pre-Galilean period was one of substantial scientific activity and Galileo did not arise from an intellectual vacuum. Behind him was a well-established tradition. He gave it a new direction by making additional progress toward a correct law of inertia and by dramatizing the fruitfulness of mathematically describing idealized physical phenomena. Next we leap more than a century to Newton, probably the greatest single individual in the development of science. Little biographical detail on Newton is available. C. C. Gillispie portrays him against the background of his work. Recent work based on the Ports-

mouth papers and other sources is beginning to enlarge our perspective, but our interest in Newton in this anthology extends beyond his purely scientific work and influences. He occupies a pivotal position in the history of ideas of Western civilization. J. H. Randall, Jr. traces some aspects of Newtonian thought in directions far from the mainstream of physical science. The writings of Gillispie and Randall, at Princeton and Columbia Universities, reflect the currently increasing interest in the history of science and the history of ideas.

Herbert Butterfield

The Historical Importance of a Theory of Impetus

It is one of the paradoxes of the whole story with which we have to deal that the most sensational step leading to the scientific revolution in astronomy was taken long before the discovery of the telescope—even long before the Danish astronomer, Tycho Brahe, in the latter part of the sixteenth century, had shown the great improvement that it was still possible to achieve in observations made with the naked eye. When William Harvey in England opened up new paths for physiology by his study of the action of the heart, he alluded once or twice to his use of a magnifying glass, but he carried out his revolutionary work before any serviceable kind of microscope had become available. With regard to the transformation of the science of mechanics, it is remarkable to what an extent even Galileo discusses the ordinary phenomena of everyday life, conjectures what would happen if a stone were thrown from the mast of a moving ship, or plays with pellets on inclined planes in a manner that had long been customary. In fact, we shall find that in both celestial and terrestrial physics—which hold the strategic place in the whole movement—change is brought about, not by new observations or additional evidence in the first instance, but by transpositions that were taking place inside the minds of the scientists themselves. In this connection it is not irrelevant to note that, of all forms of mental activity, the most difficult to induce even in the minds of the young, who may be presumed not to have lost

Reprinted with permission of The Macmillan Company from Herbert Butterfield, The Origins of Science *(New York: The Macmillan Company. Copyright 1957 by G. Bell & Sons), pp. 1–16.*

their flexibility, is the art of handling the same bundle of data as before, but placing them in a new system of relations with one another by giving them a different framework, all of which virtually means putting on a different kind of thinking-cap for the moment. It is easy to teach anybody a new fact about Richelieu, but it needs light from heaven to enable a teacher to break the old framework in which the student has been accustomed to seeing his Richelieu—the framework which is built up sometimes far too rigidly by the Higher Certificate student, and into which he will fit whatever new information he ever afterwards acquires on this subject. But the supreme paradox of the scientific revolution is the fact that things which we find it easy to instil into boys at school, because we see that they start off on the right foot—things which would strike us as the ordinary natural way of looking at the universe, the obvious way of regarding the behaviour of falling bodies, for example—defeated the greatest intellects for centuries, defeated Leonardo da Vinci and at the marginal point even Galileo, when their minds were wrestling on the very frontiers of human thought with these very problems. Even the greatest geniuses who broke through the ancient views in some special field of study—Gilbert, Bacon and Harvey, for example—would remain stranded in a species of medievalism when they went outside that chosen field. It required their combined efforts to clear up certain simple things which we should now regard as obvious to any unprejudiced mind, and even easy for a child.

A particular development of ideas which was already taking place in the later middle ages has come to stand as the first chapter in the history of the transition to what we call the scientific revolution. It is a field of thought upon which an expositor can embark only with the greatest trepidation, in view of the vicissitudes of lecturers at the very beginning of modern times. Students of history will remember how the humanists of the Renaissance, Erasmus included, were accustomed to complaining of the boredom—deriding the sophistries and subtleties—of the scholastic lectures which they had to endure at the university. Occasionally they specified the forms of teaching and lecturing to which they most objected, and as they particularly mentioned those discussions of mechanics with which we have now to concern ourselves, it will no doubt be prudent to make the examination of such teaching as brief as possible. It is curious that these despised scholastic disquisitions should now have come to hold a remarkable key-position in the story of the evolution of the modern mind. Perhaps the lack of mathematics, or the failure to think of mathematical ways of formulating things, was partly responsible for what appeared to be verbal subtleties and an excessive straining of language in these men who were almost yearning to find the way to the modern science of mechanics.

Of all the intellectual hurdles which the human mind has confronted and has overcome in the last fifteen hundred years, the one which seems to me to have been the most amazing in character and the most stupendous in the scope of its consequences is the one relating to the problem of motion—the one which perhaps was hardly disposed of by Galileo, though it received a definitive form of settlement shortly after his time in the full revised statement of what every schoolboy learns to call the law of inertia. On this question of motion the Aristotelian teaching, precisely because it carried such an intricate dovetailing of observations and explanations—that is to say, precisely because it was part of a system which was such a colossal intellectual feat in itself—was hard for the human mind to escape from, and gained a strong hold on medieval scholastic thought. Furthermore, it remains as the essential background of the story—it continues to present the presiding issue—until the time of Galileo himself; in other words, until the first half of the seventeenth century. On the Aristotelian theory all heavy terrestrial bodies had a natural motion towards the centre of the universe, which for medieval thinkers was at or near the centre of the earth; but motion in any other direction was violent motion, because it contradicted the ordinary tendency of a body to move to what was regarded as its natural place. Such motion depended on the operation of a mover, and the Aristotelian doctrine of inertia was a doctrine of rest—it was motion, not rest, that always required to be explained. Wherever this motion existed, and however long it existed, something had to be brought in to account for it.

The essential feature of this view was the assertion or the assumption that a body would keep in movement only so long as a mover was actually in contact with it, imparting motion to it all the time. Once the mover ceased to operate, the movement stopped—the body fell straight to earth or dropped suddenly to rest. Further—a point that will seem very heretical to the present day—it was argued that, provided the resistance of the medium through which the body passed remained a constant, the speed of the body would be proportionate to what we should describe as the force consistently being exerted upon it by the mover. A constant force exerted by the mover over a given length of time produced not any acceleration at all, but a uniform motion for the whole period. On the other hand, if there was any variation in the resistance of the medium—the difference between moving in air and moving in water, for example—the speed would vary in inverse proportion to this, provided the other factors remained constant. And if the resistance were reduced to nought, the speed would be infinite; that is to say, if the movement took place in a vacuum, bodies would move from one place to another instantaneously. The absurdity of this was one of the reasons why the Aristotelians regarded a complete void as impossible, and said that God Himself could not make one.

It is astonishing to what a degree not only this theory but its rivals —even the ones which superseded it in the course of the scientific revolution—were based on the ordinary observation of the data available to common sense. And, as writers have clearly pointed out, it is not relevant for us to argue that if the Aristotelians had merely watched the more carefully they would have changed their theory of inertia for the modern one—changed over to the view that bodies tend to continue either at rest or in motion along a straight line until something intervenes to stop them or deflect their course. It was supremely difficult to escape from the Aristotelian doctrine by merely observing things more closely, especially if you had already started off on the wrong foot and were hampered beforehand with the whole system of interlocking Aristotelian ideas. In fact, the modern law of inertia is not the thing you would discover by mere photographic methods of observation—it required a different kind of thinking-cap, a transposition in the mind of the scientist himself; for we do not actually see ordinary objects continuing their rectilinear motion in that kind of empty space which Aristotle said could not occur, and sailing away to that infinity which also he said could not possibly exist; and we do not in real life have perfectly spherical balls moving on perfectly smooth horizontal planes—the trick lay in the fact that it occurred to Galileo to imagine these. Furthermore, even when men were coming extraordinarily near to what we should call the truth about local motion, they did not clinch the matter—the thing did not come out clear and clean—until they had realised and had made completely conscious to themselves the fact that they were in reality transposing the questions into a different realm. They were discussing not real bodies as we actually observe them in the real world but geometrical bodies moving in a world without resistance and without gravity—moving in that boundless emptiness of Euclidean space which Aristotle had regarded as unthinkable. In the long run, therefore, we have to recognise that here was a problem of a fundamental nature, and it could not be solved by close observation within the framework of the older system of ideas—it required a transposition in the mind.

As often happened with such theories in those days, if not now, the Aristotelian doctrine of motion might seem to correspond in a self-evident manner with most of the data available to common sense, but there were small pockets of fact which did not square with the theory at the first stage of the argument; they were unamendable to the Aristotelian laws at what we should call the ordinary common-sense level. There were one or two anomalies which required a further degree of analysis before they could be satisfactorily adjusted to the system; and perhaps, as some writers have said, the Aristotelian theory came to a brilliant peak in the manner by which it hauled these exceptional cases into the synthesis and established (at a second remove) their conformity with the stated rules. On the argument so far as we have taken it, an arrow ought to have fallen to the ground the moment it lost contact with the bow-string; for neither the bow-string nor anything else could impart a motion which would continue after the direct contact with the original mover had been broken. The Aristotelians explained the continued movement of projectiles by the commotion which the initial movement had produced in the air—especially as the air which was begin pushed and compressed in front had to rush round behind to prevent that vacuum which must never be allowed to take place. At this point in the argument there even occurred a serious fault in observation which harassed the writers on physical science for many centuries. It was thought that the rush of air produced an actual initial acceleration in the arrow after it had left the bow-string, and it is curious to note that Leonardo da Vinci and later writers shared this mistake—the artillerymen of the Renassiance were victims of the same error—though there had been people in the later middle ages who had taken care not to commit themselves on this point. The motion of a projectile, since it was caused by a disturbance in the medium itself, was a thing which it was not possible to imagine taking place in a vacuum.

Furthermore, since the Aristotelian commentators held something corresponding to the view that a constant uniform force only produced uniform motion, there was a second serious anomaly to be explained—it was necessary to produce special reasons to account for the fact that falling bodies were observed to move at an accelerating speed. Once again the supporters of the older teaching used the argument from the rush of air, or they thought that, as the body approached the earth, the greater height of the atmosphere above meant an increase in the downward pressure, while the shorter column of air below would offer a diminishing resistance to the descent. Alternatively they used Aristotle's argument that the falling body moved more jubilantly every moment because it found itself nearer home.

From the fourteenth to the seventeenth century, then, this Aristotelian doctrine of motion persisted in the face of recurrent controversy, and it was only in the later stages of that period that the satisfactory alternative emerged, somewhat on the policy of picking up the opposite end of the stick. Once this question was solved in the modern manner, it altered much of one's ordinary thinking about the world and opened the way for a flood of further discoveries and reinterpretations, even in the realm of common sense, before any very elaborate experiments had been embarked upon. It was as though science or human thought had been held up by a barrier until this moment—the waters dammed because of an initial defect in one's attitude to everything in the universe that had any sort of motion—and now the floods were released. Change and discovery were bound to come in cascades even if there were no other factors working for a scientific revolution. Indeed, we might say that a change in one's attitude to the movement of things that move was bound to result in so many new analyses of various kinds of motion that it constituted a scientific revolution in itself.

Apart from all this there was one special feature of the problem which made the issue momentous. We have not always brought home to ourselves the peculiar character of that Aristotelian universe in which the things that were in motion had to be accompanied by a mover all the time. A universe constructed on the mechanics of Aristotle had the door half-way open for spirits already; it was a universe in which unseen hands had to be in constant operation, and sublime Intelligences had to roll the planetary spheres around. Alternatively, bodies had to be endowed with souls and aspirations, with a "disposition" to certain kinds of motions, so that matter itself seemed to possess mystical qualities. The modern law of inertia, the modern theory of motion, is the great factor which in the seventeenth century helped to drive the spirits out of the world and opened the way to a universe that ran like a piece of clockwork. Not only so—but the very first men who in the middle ages launched the great attack on the Aristotelian theory were conscious of the fact that this colossal issue was involved in the question. One of the early important figures,

Jean Buridan in the middle of the fourteenth century, pointed out that his alternative interpretation would eliminate the need for the Intelligences that turned the celestial spheres. He even noted that the Bible provided no authority for these spiritual agencies—they were demanded by the teaching of the ancient Greeks, not by the Christian religion as such. Not much later than this, Nicholas of Oresme went further still, and said that, on the new alternative theory, God might have started off the universe as a kind of clock and left it to run of itself.

Ever since the earlier years of the twentieth century at latest, therefore, a great and growing interest has been taken in that school of thinkers who so far back as the fourteenth century were challenging the Aristotelian explanations of motion, and who put forward an alternative doctrine of "impetus" which—though imperfect in itself—must represent the first stage in the history of the scientific revolution. And if it is imagined that this kind of argument falls into one of the traps which it is always necessary to guard against—picking out from the middle ages mere anticipations and casual analogies to modern ideas—the answer to that objection will be clear to us if we bear in mind the kind of rules that ought to govern historians in such matters. Here we have a case of a consistent body of teaching which rises in Oxford, is developed as a tradition by a school of thinkers in Paris, and is still being taught in Paris at the beginning of the sixteenth century. It has a continuous history—we know how this teaching passed into Italy, how it was promulgated in the universities of the Renaissance, and how Leonardo da Vinci picked it up, so that some of what were once considered to be remarkable strokes of modernity, remarkable flashes of genius, in his notebooks, were in reality transcriptions from fourteenth-century Parisian scholastic writers. We know how the teaching was developed in Italy later in the sixteenth century, how it was misunderstood on occasion—sometimes only partially appropriated—and how some of Galileo's early writings on motion are reminiscent of this school, being associated with that doctrine of the "impetus" which it is our purpose to examine. It is even known fairly certainly in what edition Galileo read the works of certain writers belonging to this fourteenth-century Parisian school. Indeed, Galileo could have produced much, though not quite all, that we find in his juvenile works on this particular subject if he had lived in the fourteenth century; and in this field one might very well ask what the world with its Renaissance and so forth had been doing in the meantime. It has been suggested that if printing had been invented two centuries earlier the doctrine of "impetus" would have produced a more rapid general development in the history of science, and would not have needed so long to pass from the stage of Jean Buridan to the stage of Galileo.

If the orthodox doctrine of the middle ages had been based on Aristotle, however, it has to be noted that, both then and during the Renaissance (as well as later still), the attacks on Aristotle—the theory of impetus included—would themselves be based on some ancient thinker. Here we touch on one of the generative factors, not only in the formation of the modern world, but also in the development of the scientific revolution—namely, the discovery of the fact that even Aristotle had not reigned unchallenged in the ancient days. All this produced a healthy friction, resulting in the emergence of important problems which the middle ages had to make up their own minds about, so that men were driven to some kind of examination of the workings of nature themselves, even if only because they had to decide between Aristotle and some rival teacher. It also appears that a religious factor affected the rise of that movement which produced the theory of impetus, and, in a curious manner which one tries in vain to analyse away, a religious taboo operated for once in favour of freedom for scientific hypothesis. In the year 1277 a council in Paris condemned a large number of Aristotelian theses, such as the view that even God could not create a void, or an infinite universe, or a plurality of worlds; and that decision—one in which certain forms of partisanship were involved—was apparently extended by the Archbishop of Canterbury to this country. The regions that came within the orbit of these decisions must have been the seat of a certain anti-Aristotelian bias already; and certainly from this time both Oxford and Paris showed the effects of this bias in the field of what we should call physical science. From this time also the discussion of the possibility of the existence of empty space, or of an infinite universe, or of a plurality of worlds takes a remarkable step forward in Paris. And amongst the names concerned in this development are some which figure in the rise of the doctrine of impetus. It has been pointed out furthermore that in the same Parisian tradition there was a tendency towards something in the nature of mathematical physics, though the mathematics of the time were not sufficiently advanced to allow of this being carried very far or to produce anything like the achievement of Galileo in the way of a mathematical approach to scientific problems. We must avoid the temptation, however, to stress unduly the apparent analogies with modern times and the "anticipations" which are so easy to discover in the past—things which often owe a little, no doubt, to the trick-mirrors of the historian. And though it may be useful sometimes, in order to illustrate a point, we must beware of submitting to the fascination of "what might have been."

The people who chiefly concern us, then, are certain fourteenth-century writers, first of all a group at Merton College, Oxford, and, after these, Jean Buridan, Albert of Saxony and Nicholas of Oresme. They are important for other things besides their teaching on the subject of impetus. The contemporaries of Erasmus laughed at the scholastic lecturers for discussing not only "uniform motion" and "difform motion," but also "uniform difform motion"—all carried to a great degree of subtlety—but it transpired in the sixteenth century, when the world was looking for a formula to represent the uniform acceleration of falling bodies, that the solution of the problem had been at their disposal for a long time in the medieval formula for the case of uniformly difform motion. The whole development which we are studying took place amongst people who, in fact, were working upon questions and answers which had been suggested by Aristotle. These people came up against the Aristotelian theory of motion at the very points where we should expect the attack to take place, namely, in connection with the two particularly doubtful questions of the movement of projectiles and the acceleration of falling bodies. If we take a glance at the kind of arguments they used, we can observe the type of critical procedure which would take place even in the middle ages, producing changes on the margin of the current Aristotelian teaching. We are observing also the early stages of the great debate on certain issues that lay at the heart of the scientific revolution itself. Indeed, the arguments which were employed at this early period often reappeared—with reference to precisely the same instances—even in the major works of Galileo, for they passed into general currency in the course of time. And if they seem simple arguments based on the ordinary phenomena available to common sense, we ought to remember that many of the newer arguments brought forward by Galileo himself at a later stage of the story were really of the same type.

According to the view developed by these thinkers, the projectile was carried forward by an actual impetus which it had acquired and which bodies were capable of acquiring, from the mere fact of being in motion. And this impetus was supposed to be a thing inside the body itself—occasionally it was described as an impetuosity that had been imparted to it; ocassionaly one sees it discussed as though it were itself movement which the body acquired as the result of being in motion. In any case this view made it possible for men to contemplate the continued motion of a body after the contact with the original mover had been lost. It was explained that the impetus lay in the body and continued there, as heat stays in a red-hot poker after it has been taken from the fire; while in the case of falling bodies the effect was described as accidental gravity, an additional gravity which the body acquired as a result of being in motion, so that the acceleration of falling bodies was due to the effects of impetus being continually added to the constant fall due to ordinary weight. A constant force exerted on a body, therefore, produced here not uniform motion but a uniform rate of acceleration. It is to be noted, however, that Leonardo da Vinci, like a number of others who accepted the general theory of impetus, failed to follow the Parisian school in the application of their teaching to the acceleration of falling bodies. Whereas the Aristotelians thought that falling bodies rushed more quickly as they got nearer home, the new teaching inverted this, and said that it was rather the distance from the starting-point that mattered. If two bodies fell to earh along he same line BC, the one which had started higher up at A would move more quickly from B to C than the one that started at B, though in this particular part of their course they were both equally distant from the centre of the earth. It followed from the new doctrine that if a cylindrical hole were cut through the earth, passing through the centre, a body, when it reached the centre, would be carried forward on its own impetus for some distance, and indeed would oscillate about the centre for some time—a thing impossible to conceive under the terms of the ancient theory. There was a further point in regard to which the Aristotelians had been unconvincing; for if the continued flight of a projectile were really due not to the thrower but to the rush of air, it was difficult to see why the air should carry a stone so much farther than a ball of feathers—why one should be able to throw the stone the greater distance. The newer school showed that, starting at a given pace, a greater impetus would be communicated to the stone by reason of the density of its material than to a feather; though, of course, a larger body of the same material would not travel farther—a large stone would not be more easy to throw than a small one. Mass was used as the measure of the impetus which corresponded with a given speed.

Since Aristotle found it necessary on occasion to regard the air as a resisting factor, he was open to the charge that one could not then—in the next breath, so to speak—start using the argument that the air was also the actual propellant. The new school said that the air could not be the propellant except in the case of a high wind; and they brought the further objection that if the original perturbation of the air—the rush which occurred when the bowstring started the arrow—had the capacity to repeat itself, pushing the arrow on and on, there could be no reason why it should ever stop; it ought to go on for ever repeating itself, communicating further perturbations to every next region of the atmosphere. Furthermore, a thread tied to a projectile ought to be blown ahead of it, instead of trailing behind. In any case, on the Aristotelian view of the matter it ought to be impossible for an arrow to fly against the wind. Even the apostles of the new theory of impetus, however, regarded a projectile as moving in a straight line until the impetus had exhausted itself, and then quickly curving round to make a direct vertical drop to earth. They looked upon this impetus as a thing which gradually weakened and wore itself out, just as a poker grows cold when taken from the fire. Or, said Galileo, it was like the reverberations which go on in a bell long after it has been struck, but which gradually fade away. Only, in the case of the celestial bodies and the orbs which carried the planets round the sky, the impulse never exhausted itself—the pace of these bodies never slackened since there was no air-resistance to slow them down. Therefore, it could be argued, God might have given these things their initial impetus, and their motion could be imagined as continuing for ever.

The theory of the impetus did not solve all problems, however, and proved to be only the half-way house to the modern view, which is fairly explicit in Galileo though it received its perfect formulation only in Descartes—the view that a body continues its motion in a straight line until something intervenes to halt or slacken or deflect it. As I have already mentioned, this modern law of inertia is calculated to present itself more easily to the mind when a transposition has taken place—when we see, not real bodies, moving under the restrictions of the real world and clogged by the atmosphere, but geometrical bodies sailing away in empty Euclidean space. Archimedes, whose works were more completely discovered at the Renaissance and became very influential especially after the translation published in 1543, appears to have done something to assist and encourage this habit of mind; and nothing could have been more important than the growing tendency to geometrise or mathematise a problem. Nothing is more effective, after people have long been debating and wrangling and churning the air, than the appearance of a person who draws a line on the blackboard, which with the help of a little geometry solves the whole problem in an instant. In any case, it is possible that Archimedes, who taught people to think of the weight of a thing in water and then its weight in air and finally, therefore, its weight when unencumbered by either, helped to induce some men to pick up the problem of motion from the opposite end to the usual one, and to think of the simplest form of motion as occurring when there was no resisting medium to complicate it. So you assumed the tendency in bodies to continue their existing motion along a straight line, and you set about afterwards to examine the things which might clog or hamper or qualify that motion; whereas Aristotle, assuming that the state of rest was natural and that bodies tended to return to it when left to themselves, had the difficult task of providing an active mover that should operate as long as the body continued to have any movement at all.

On the other hand, it may be true to say that Aristotle, when he thought of motion, had in mind a horse drawing a cart, so that his whole feeling for the problem was spoiled by his preoccupation with a misleading example. The very fact that his teaching on the subject of projectiles was so unsatisfactory may have helped to produce the phenomenon of a later age which, when it thought of motion, had rather the motion of projectiles in mind, and so acquired a different feeling in regard to the whole matter.

It is natural that the transition to modern science should often appear to us as a reaction against the doctrines of Aristotle. Because there was a conservative resistance to be combated, the supporters of the new ideas would feel compelled to produce what was sometimes a bitterly anti-Aristotelian polemical literature. Appearances are deceptive, however, and often it is fairer to regard the new ideas as the developing achievement of the successive commentators on Aristotle. These men realised their indebtedness to the ancient master; and they would hold to a great part of his system even if, at one place and another, they were pressing against the frontiers of that system. In answer to the conservatives of their time, the innovators would sometimes argue that Aristotle himself would have been on their side if he had been living in the modern world. The conflicts of the later medieval and early modern centuries ought not to be allowed to diminish our impression of the greatness of this ancient teacher, who provoked so much thought and controversy, and who kept the presiding position for so long. Nor ought we to imagine that Aristotle shared the faults of those people who, in the sixteenth and seventeenth centuries, would be held to be of the "Aristotelian" party merely because they were conservatives.

The work of Pierre Duhem, who, over fifty years ago, brought out the importance of the fourteenth-century teaching on the subject of the "impetus," has not remained free from criticism in the period that has since elapsed. On the one hand the story has been carried behind Jean Buridan and the Parisian school—carried further back to Merton College, Oxford. On the other hand it has been rightly pointed out that the transition from the doctrine of the "impetus" to the modern doctrine of inertia required—from Galileo, for example—greater originality than some writers seem to allow. It is also true that the originality in the fourteenth-century writers extended beyond the problem of motion which we have been considering; and by this time, as we shall see, advance was already taking place in the theoretical discussion of scientific method. It is possible to exaggerate the rôle of these medieval precursors, and so to underestimate the magnitude of the seventeenth-century revolution. But the work of Duhem in the field that we have been considering has been an important factor in the great change which has taken place in the attitude of historians of science to the middle ages. One of the strands of the historical narrative with which we are concerned is the progress which is made on occasion through the development of scholastic thinking itself. In other words, the modern world is in a certain sense a continuation of the medieval one—it is not to be regarded as merely a reaction against it. As a result of this some historians of science have been disposed seriously to qualify the traditional concept of the "Renaissance," and to see, from the eleventh or twelfth century at least, a continuous development of western thought.

C. C. Gillispie

Newton with His Prism and Silent Face

The mind of Sir Isaac Newton was one of the glories of the human race, and one of its mysteries. "How did you make your discoveries?" an admirer is said to have asked. "By always thinking unto them," replied Newton, but did not then say what is even more daunting, that he did most of the creative work in two periods of about eighteen months each, in 1665–66 and 1685–86. In those three years of intensive application, interspersed by twenty years of study and reflection, Newton united knowledge of heaven and earth in the mathematical structure of classical physics. For over two centuries that structure contained the thinking of a science which, no longer struggling to be born, grew exponentially in vigor as in volume. "There could be only one Newton," Lagrange is supposed to have said to Napoleon (who was fishing for a comparison and resented the remark), "there was only one world to discover." Contemporary physics has transcended Newtonian in the reaches of the very small and the very fast. But our own century has only hastened the pace of science. It has not altered the rules or the nature of the enterprise. And surely it will always repay effort to study the mind and personality which founded science in generality and once for all. Fellow beings have the right to share in that triumph, and the duty to respect it. It enhances all humanity.

Born in 1642, the year of Galileo's death, Isaac Newton was a posthumous child in a family of minor Lin-

Reprinted with permission of Princeton University Press from C. C. Gillispie, The Edge of Objectivity *(Princeton, N. J.: Princeton University Press, 1960), pp. 117–50.*

colnshire gentry. His mother remarried, and his childhood was not happy. A girl of the neighborhood remembered him as "a sober, silent, thinking lad," who "was never known scarce to play with the boys at their silly amusements." When he was fourteen his step-father died. His mother set him to farming the manor. This was not a success. She wisely put him back in school, and in 1660 sent him up to Cambridge, where he matriculated in Trinity College. There he worked under the Master, Isaac Barrow, a classicist, astronomer, and authority on optics. "In learning Mathematicks," wrote Fontenelle, Newton's first biographer, "he did not study Euclid, who seemed to him too plain and simple, and not worthy of taking up his time; he understood him almost before he read him, and a cast of his eye upon the contents of the Theorems was sufficient to make him master of them. He advanced at once to the Geometry of Des Cartes, Kepler's Opticks, &c., so that we may apply to him what Lucan said of the Nile, whose head was not known by the Ancients,

> Nature conceals thy infant Stream with care
> Nor lets thee, but in Majesty appear.

Barrow did perceive the quality of that stream. He knew in extraordinary measure the finest of a teacher's joys, a fine student. In 1669 he resigned his Lucasian Chair of Mathematics that Newton might have it. This gracious precedent must alarm any professor who becomes aware that his student is abler than he is. But Barrow himself did not then know the portent of what Newton had secretly begun. In the same year he published a book which was obsolete before the type was set, in consequence of his former student's optical experiments, Newton was not ready to communicate these, or other musings. But in preliminary studies at the age of twenty-three he had sketched the world picture of classical physics.

Athletes of the intellect, theoretical physicists build careers upon the innovations of their youth. The plague was in Cambridge in 1665. To escape it, Newton went down to his mother's manor of Woolthorpe. It is pleasant to be able for once to record the truth of a legend. As he sat in the garden, a falling apple did indeed set his mind

> into a speculation on the power of gravity: that as this power is not found sensibly diminished at the remotest distance from the center of the earth, to which we can rise, neither at the tops of the loftiest buildings, nor even on the summits of the highest mountains; it

appeared to him reasonable to conclude, that this power must extend much farther than is usually thought; why not as high as the moon, said he to himself? and if so, her motion must be influenced by it; perhaps she is retained in her orbit thereby.

The account is Henry Pemberton's, who was much with Newton in old age, and wrote one of the first and best explanations of his system. But Newton's retirement was no desultory meditation at the end of college. He himself left a fragmentary memoir of these months of discovery:

> I found the Method [of fluxions—i.e. the calculus] by degrees in the years 1665 and 1666. In the beginning of the year 1665 I found the method of approximating Series and the Rule for reducing any dignity of any Binomial into such a series [i.e. he had formulated the Binomial Theorem]. The same year in May I found the method of tangents of Gregory and Slusius, and in November had the direct method of fluxions [the differential calculus], and the next year in January had the Theory of colours, and in May following I had entrance into ye inverse method of fluxions [integral calculus]. And the same year I began to think of gravity extending to ye orb of the Moon, and having found out how to estimate the force with w^ch^ [a] globe revolving within a sphere presses the surface of the sphere, from Kepler's Rule of the periodical times of the Planets being in a sesquialterate proportion of their distances from the centers of their Orbs I deducted that the forces wch keep the Planets in their Orbs must [be] reciprocally as the squares of their distances from the centers about wch they revolve: and thereby compared the force requisite to keep the Moon in her Orb with the force of gravity at the surface of the earth, and found them answer pretty nearly. All this was in the two plague years of 1665 and 1666, for in those days I was in the prime of my age for invention, and minded Mathematicks and Philosophy more than at any time since.

The calculus, the composition of light, the law of gravity—the first two were fundamental, the last both fundamental and strategic. As if by instinct, Newton asked not what the forces are that keep the planets in orbit, but what the proportions of those forces are. In part Newton's was a winnowing genius. He took the planetary laws from Kepler. (Kepler had made them serve the tangential drag of sympathetic attractions.) He took from Descartes the argument that curvilinear motion argues a constraint against inertia. (Instead of formulating the quantity of that constraint, Descartes had imagined a mechanism.) He took from Galileo the perception that, though motion is the object of science, the handle to grasp in numbers is change in motion. (Because Galileo was a purist about any hint of animistic or occult qualities he had made falling the source of motion and had never asked the questions which would relate acceleration to a force law. Galileo remains the founder of kinematics, therefore, and left Newton to found dynamics.)

The writings of Christiaan Huygens contain the missing piece. "What Mr. Hugens has published since about centrifugal forces I suppose he had before me," wrote Newton reluctantly (for there is a kind of avarice about discovery which may be one of its springs of action). A Dutchman, Huygens made his career in Paris. He combined his native experimental tradition with Cartesian rationalism, often in criticism against the more naïve physical propositions of the master. The pendulum clock owes its design to his studies, which he addressed rather to specific problems—the laws of impact, conservation of momentum, a wave theory of light—than to establishing some world view. There he remained faithful to the Cartesian conception of science as the mechanistic rationale of material reality.

His analysis of centripetal force (later objections to the term do not diminish the historical value of the argument) considers circular motion as inertial and centrally accelerated. His reader is to imagine a man—a physicist, let us say, for Huygens is an early example of the physicists' genre of instrumental playfulness—attached to the rim of a wheel and holding a plumb bob on a wire. The wheel rotates, and the physicist experiences a tension in the wire indistinguishable from the pull of gravity when it is still. Now let him release his hold, and by a very elegant geometric proof, Huygens showed that the distance from the plumb bob sailing out along the tangent and the physicist on the rim increases as the square of the time of rotation. Let him hold on to it, therefore, and appreciate that the formalism of its angular motion is identical with the law of falling bodies, and that the concept of acceleration includes change in direction as well as velocity. It appears that Newton worked out the same result in ignorance of Huygens' demonstration. But he does not need the credit. For he saw in it what Huygens did not: that by this argument the moon is forever falling around its orbit even as the apple falls, that any acceleration supposes a force, and that if moon and apple move under the same force, then celestial mechanics becomes a sublime instance of inertial motion under a universal force law.

This was the comparison that Newton found "to answer pretty nearly." Nevertheless, he did not then press on to formulate the universal law of gravity. Nor did he generalize the measurement of force by acceleration into the laws of motion. Instead, he kept all these things to himself, laid the work aside, and did not return to it for thirteen years. Various explanations have been advanced for the delay. He was working away from books, and had the wrong figure for the size of the earth—60 miles to the degree instead of 69½. It is said, too, that Newton thought the discrepancy—he says "pretty nearly," not "exactly"—might be caused by other forces at work concurrently with gravity—Descartes' vortices, perhaps, for he was not yet ready to introduce the void as the arena for gravity. What was more important, an essential proof eluded him. He had treated the earth and moon as points, all mass concentrated at the center. The intuition does not compel assent. Nor could Newton then prove the theorem which justifies it. It is a most difficult problem in integration, which he resolved only in time to write the *Principia.* And though posterity is fascinated by the divining power of his intuition, he could hardly come before his contemporaries except in the full force of geometric demonstration.

Meanwhile, in his later twenties, Newton's mind, and now his hands too, were full of optics and of chemistry—alchemy some commentators say, but wrongly, for his chemistry was in the spirit of Boyle's corpuscular philosophy. In 1672 he sent the Royal Society an account of the "oddest if not the most considerable detection, which hath hitherto been made in the operations of nature."

> I procured me (he began) a Triangular glass-Prisme, to try therewith the celebrated *Phaenomena of Colours.* And in order thereto having darkened my chamber, and made a small hole in my windowshuts, to let in a convenient quantity of the Suns light, I place my Prisme at his entrance, that it might thereby be refracted to the opposite wall. It was at first a very pleasing divertisement, to view the vivid and intense colours produced thereby; but after a while applying myself to consider them more circumspectly, I became surprised to see them in an *oblong* form, which, according to the received laws of Refraction, I expected should have been *circular.*

Newton was the first to analyze the spectral band rather than the first to see it. Having ruled out accidents like imperfections in the glass or curving rays, he performed his "Experimentum Crucis." He refracted a ray of each color through a second prism and determined that refrangibility was a constant quantity, specific to the color, greater toward the violet and less toward the red. It follows that white light is composite, "a confused aggregate of rays indued with all sorts of Colours, as they are promiscuously darted from the various parts of luminous bodies." And this was verified by experiments in combining colors:

> These things being so, it can be no longer disputed, whether there be colours in the dark, nor whether they be the qualities of the objects we see, no nor perhaps whether Light be a Body. For, since Colours are the *qualities* of Light, having its Rays for their intire and immediate subject, how can we think those Rays qualities also, unless one quality may be the subject of and sustain another; which in effect is to call it *Substance.* We should not know Bodies for substances, were it not for their sensible qualities, and the Principal of those being now found due to something else, we have as good reason to believe that to be a Substance also.
>
> Besides, whoever thought any quality to be a heterogeneous aggregate, such as Light is discovered to be. But, to determine more absolutely, what Light is, after what manner refracted, and by what modes or actions it produceth in our minds the Phantasms of Colours is not so easie. And I shall not mingle conjectures with certainties.

No summary can do justice to the cogency of Newton's experimental practise, in execution as in design. "When we are for prying into Nature," wrote Fontenelle, "we ought to examine her like Sir Isaac, that is, in as accurate and importunate manner." His first paper is the simplest and most straightforward piece he ever wrote. The vein is frank and youthful, almost innocent. He seems confident that everybody will be as pleased to find out about light and colors as he was. Discovery is exciting. He awaited with confidence the recognition that is one of its rewards.

He proved right about the oddity of his discovery. It went against the instinct of centuries, so deep as to be axiomatic, that light is simple and primary. This made sense of light, and nothing in Newton's own experience forewarned him of the tenacity of intellectual habit. He was not prepared for opposition. Neither was he yet aware of the seamy side of scholarship—though his own ungenerosity to rivals was to become its most illustrious example—which is that reputation accrues at the expense of someone else's status. The scholarly community has developed norms to repress such unworthy chagrins. They were not then strong. The young Newton was a David confronting no Goliath, who would win to the top by force of superiority, in ways not altogether fair, at the cost of growing secretiveness of mind and bitterness of soul. For Newton was a most complicated personality, not at all innocent really, his disillusionment excessive, his dismay extreme, when confronted with what was only human reality and not unjust treatment. "Newton was a nice man to deal with," wrote John Locke (meaning touchy), "and a little too apt to raise in himself suspicions where there is no ground." And John Flamsteed, the Astronomer Royal, with whom he broke, found him "insidious, ambitious, and excessively covetous of praise, and impatient of contradiction ... a good man at the bottom; but, through his natural temper, suspicious."

The incomprehension which greeted his theory of colors was the more frustrating that it raised objections among inferior minds whose applause he craved and who truly could not understand what he meant, so deep and novel was his insight, so new and different his conception of science. Newton undertook to answer each of the criticisms communicated to the Royal Society—from Paris by Adrien Auzout and Father Ignatius Pardies, from Liége by Franciscus Linus, an English Jesuit in exile, from Paris again by no less a person than Huygens, from London and the heart of the Royal Society itself by Robert Hooke, its great experimentalist and author of *Micrographia*, a Baconian cornucopia of observations and experiments. Newton succeeded only with Pardies, who thereby earned the distinction of having understood an argument and changed his mind. As to the rest, the confusion reached deeper than the evidence, right into the question of what science does. For they insisted on seeing colors as modifications of light—the "acts and sufferings of light" Goethe would call colors a century later in a last romantic fling against Newton's "anatomy of light"—and for them optics was not just the science of its behavior, but also the explanation of its nature.

Patiently (at first) Newton tried to explain himself. And the effort was worthwhile. Besides converting the amiable Pardies, he made explicit that limitation of science and that conception of scientific method on which his physics always acted, even when he himself did not. It was in defining what he was saying about light that Newton first laid down the standpoint "Hypotheses non fingo," which seems an almost Baconian repudiation of theory and has so puzzled critics, coming as the phrase does at the end of the *Principia*, that most elegant and comprehensive work of theoretical science in all literature. In one of his replies he addressed himself to the supposition of his critics "in which light is supposed to be a power, action, quality, or certain substance emitted every way from luminous bodies."

In answer to this, it is to be observed that the doctrine which I explained concerning refraction and colours, consists only in certain properties of light, without regarding any hypotheses, by which those properties might be explained. For the best and safest method of philosophizing seems to be, first to inquire diligently into the properties of things, and establishing those properties by experiments and then to proceed more slowly to hypotheses for the explanation of them. For hypotheses should be subservient only in explaining the properties of things, but not assumed in determining them; unless so far as they may furnish experiments. For if the possibility of hypotheses is to be the test of the truth and reality of things, I see not how certainty can be obtained in any science; since numerous hypotheses may be devised, which shall seem to overcome new difficulties. Hence it has been here thought necessary to lay aside all hypotheses, as foreign to the purpose, that the force of the objection should be abstractedly considered, and receive a more full and general answer.

Hooke's objections are the most interesting for the grammar of assent in science. For there has frequently been a stage at which the precepts of science itself—economy, for example, mechanism, realism—have been introduced so literally and at so low a level of abstraction that they have blocked sophistication instead of advancing theory. "*Whiteness* and *blackness*," wrote Hooke, "are nothing but the plenty or scarcity of the undistrubed rays of light" and those "two colours (than the which there are not more compounded in nature) are nothing but the effects of a compounded pulse." He likened Newton's theory that colors "should be originally in the simple rays of light" to saying that the sounds which issue from a musical instrument were originally in the bellows of the organ or the strings of the fiddle. And he criticized the "indefinite variety of primary or original colours" as an inadmissible multiplication of entities. There is, indeed, no better way to summarize the issue than to juxtapose their two definitions of light. Hooke's view was that

Light is nothing but a simple and uniform motion, or pulse of a homogeneous and adopted (that is a transparent) medium, propagated from the luminous body in orbem, to all imaginable distances in a moment of time, and that that motion is first begun by some other kind of motion in the luminous body; such as by the dissolution of sulphureous bodies by the air, or by the working of the air, or the several component parts one upon another, in rotten wood, or putrifying filth, or by an external stroke, as in diamond, sugar, the seawater, or two flints or crystal rubbed together; and that this motion is propagated through all bodies susceptible thereof, but is blended or mixt with other adventitious motions, generated by the obliquity of the stroke upon a refracting body . . . I believe MR. NEWTON will think it no difficult matter, by my hypothesis, to solve all the phaenomena, not only of the prism, tinged liquors, and solid bodies, but of the colours of plated bodies, which seem to have the greatest difficulty.

But Newton found this meaningless. For his definition of light was less capacious: "By light therefore I understand, any being or power of a being, (whether a substance or any power, action, or quality of it) which proceeding directly from a lucid body, is apt to excite vision."

Four years of controversy left Newton bleakly confronting that failure in communication to which his successors have become habituated in the progress of science and specialization. He was not the man to resign himself to this predicament. But his reaction was ambivalent. On the one hand, he affected renunciation: "I was so persecuted with discussions arising from the publication of my theory of light," he wrote to Leibniz, "that I blamed my own imprudence for parting with so substantial a blessing as my quiet to run after a shadow." And to Oldenburg: "I see I have made myself a slave to philosophy, but if I get free of Mr. Linus's business, I will resolutely bid adieu to it eternally, excepting what I do for my private satisfaction, or leave to come out after me; for I see a man must either resolve to put out nothing new, or to become a slave to defend it." And he did refuse to make a treatise of his optical researches until after Hooke's death. So it happened that, though the work was done first, the *Opticks* itself, Newton's most approachable and appealing work, was published last, in 1704.

On the other hand, provoked beyond endurance, he threw off the mask of cautious phenomenalism, violated his own privacy, and, from the inner springs of his being, revealed quite another scientific personality, not the correct empiricist whose theories must just embrace the evidence, not Newton the scientist who may be assimilated to positivism, but Newton the man and the discoverer, the rhapsodist who studied the mystical works of Jakob Boehme even as he studied the mysterious works of God, that secret Newton who was the most daringly speculative thinker about nature known to history, and the most fertile framer of hypotheses. This Newton *must* communicate, even if he has to give his critics what they want:

And therefore, because I have observed the heads of some great virtuosos to run much upon hypotheses, as if my discourses wanted an hypothesis to explain them by, and found, that some, when I could not make them take my meaning, when I spake of the nature of light and colours abstractedly, have readily apprehended it, when I illustrated my discourse by an hypothesis; for this reason I have here thought fit to send you a description of the circumstances of this hypothesis as much tending to the illustration of the papers I herewith send you.

Yet he haughtily makes it clear that he is talking down to them:

I shall not assume either this or any other hypothesis, not thinking it necessary to concern myself, whether the properties of light, discovered by me, be explained by this, or Mr. HOOKE'S, or any other hypothesis. . . . This I thought fit to express, that no man may confound this with my other discourses, or measure the certainty of the one by the other, or think me obliged to answer objections against this script: for I desire to decline being involved in such troublesome and insignificant disputes.

Thus Newton opened his Second Paper on Light and Colours in 1675. The change in tone is distressing. The difference in content is striking. The paper consists of two parts. In the second, Newton shifts his ground—not for the only time—to obviate, and denigrate, certain of Hooke's experimental objections. In the opening part, he proceeds to the hypothesis: "First, it is to be supposed therein, that there is an aethereal medium much of the same constitution with air, but far rarer, subtler, and more strongly elastic."

With this, Newton introduces the aether, not precisely, nor into the structure of physics, but ambiguously, and as a condition for the intelligibility of physics. Having failed with demonstration, he appeals to imagination and gives his own fancy full license:

Perhaps the whole frame of nature may be nothing but various contextures of some certain aethereal spirits, or vapours, condensed as it were by precipitation, much after the manner, that vapours are condensed into water, or exhalations into grosser substances, though not so easily condensible; and after condensation wrought into various forms; at first by the immediate hand of the Creator; and ever since by the power of nature; which, by virtue of the command, increase and multiply, became a complete imitator of the copies set her by the protoplast. Thus perhaps may all things be originated from aether.

Perhaps it is this subtle aether which kicks the motes about in electrostatic situations. "It is to be supposed that the aether is a vibrating medium like air, only the vibrations far more swift and minute." Like water rising in capillary tubes, the aether permeates the pores of solid bodies, "yet it stands at a greater degree of rarity in those pores, than in the free aethereal spaces." It may be the aether—and to this Newton devotes some pages—which will resolve "that puzzling problem" how soul acts on body: "Thus may therefore the soul, by determining this aethereal animal spirit or wind into this or that nerve, perhaps with as much ease as air is moved in open spaces, cause all the motions we see in animals."

Now, this must not be read as animism if one wishes to understand Newton's thought. Aether is not the same thing as soul. It is not some world-spirit creating unity by blending everything into everything. It is not activity taking ontological precedence over matter and motion. It does not permeate matter to unite it with space. On the contrary, the universal impermeability of matter is a cornerstone of Newtonian doctrine, and the aether permeates only the pores between the particles. "That Nature may be lasting," Newton will say much later (even more clearly than Boyle), "the Changes of corporeal Things are to be placed in the various Separations and new Associations and Motions of these permanent Particles." Aether, in other words, is not the Stoic *pneuma,* and not an ineffable refuge of consciousness. It is a subtle fluid, itself particulate in structure. For the fancy Newton is indulging is a scientific fancy, an enrichment but no escape from science. In the same way, to come back from soul to optics, "light is neither aether, nor its vibrating motion, but something of a different kind propagated from lucid bodies." Aether is the medium of light:

> It is to be supposed, that light and aether mutually act upon one another, aether in refracting light, and light in warming aether; and that the densest aether acts most strongly. When a ray therefore moves through aether of uneven density, I suppose it most pressed, urged, or acted upon by the medium on that side towards the denser aether, and receives a continual impulse or ply from that side to recede towards the rarer, and so is accelerated, if it move that way, or retarded, if the contrary.

From the aether itself, Newton moved on in the second part of this, his last reply to Hooke on optics, to its role in the explanation of colors. But now he was concerned less with the prismatic spectrum than with the rings which appear shiftingly in very thin translucent bodies like sheets of mica or soap bubbles. These interference phenomena (as they have since been called) had been described roughly by Hooke in his *Micrographia.* He had objected that neither they nor other instances of diffraction were accounted for in Newton's theory of colors. So clearly was he right that Newton extended the knowledge of the phenomena by a very precise and beautiful series of experiments with a "thin-plate" of air between two optical surfaces, one ground slightly convex, so that by turning one upon the other the rings might be varied and observed from different angles.

The phenomena, Newton saw, argue an element of periodicity in light. In the case of monochromatic light, the rings were alternately light and dark: "If light be incident on a thin skin or plate of any transparent body, the waves, excited by its pasage through the first superficies, overtaking it one after another, till it arrive at the second superficies, will cause it to be there reflected or refracted accordingly as the condensed or expanded part of the wave overtakes it there." But when the rings are colored, it is because in compound light the rays "which exhibit red and yellow" excite "larger pulses in the aether than those, which make blue and violet." By measuring the separation of those rings Newton computed the thickness of the air film corresponding to each ring and color. This was a pesky task, for the boundaries were shadings. Over a century later Thomas Young, employing his new principle of transverse interference, used Newton's measurements to compute the wavelengths of the visible spectrum. His results agreed closely with the figures now accepted.

A cluster of conflicting interpretations rose up in later years to obscure Newton's reasoning. Eighteenth-century atomism committed itself to the corpuscular model of light, and nineteenth-century physics to the wave theory. From both points of view Newton seems inconsistent as between prismatic and thin-plate colors. In fact, however, this is a false problem. Newton did not himself adopt a crude optical atomism—it was fathered on him. It is true that his phraseology does sometimes give occasion for uncritical successors to represent the stream of particles as the Newtonian theory of light. But this was only a manner of speaking. The heart of Newton's theory is the composite nature of light rather than its corpuscular texture. Its part are rays, not corpuscles. It is the *rays* which differ from each other "like as the sands on the shore." What led him to his theory was its structural congruence with philosophical atomism, rather than a literal analogy between the parts of light and the parts of matter. It was, therefore, no inconsistency, but an enlargement of his views, adopted to meet different facts from those encountered in his first paper, when he introduced vibrations as the physical basis of interference phenomena.

The argument has also been represented as a concession to

Hooke's modification theory of color. That was Hooke's view. "After reading this discourse," runs the closing note in the minutes of the Royal Society for 16 December 1675, "Mr. HOOKE said, that the main of it was contained in his *Micrographia*, which Mr. NEWTON had only carried farther in some particulars." Newton's reply was categorical, and delivered only five days later: "I have nothing common with him, but the supposition, that aether is a susceptible medium of vibrations, of which supposition I make a very different use; he supposing it a light itself, which I suppose it is not." And properly appreciated, this distinction should clarify all the ambiguity. For it is the fundamental distinction, that which brings some category of phenomena within the scope of objective science—the same which Galileo established between motion and the moving body, the same which Boyle tried to introduce between substance and change, the same (to go back to the beginnings of objectivity) which Democritus established between atoms and the void. In Newton's work the advancing front of objectivity moves through optics. As always, numbers spelled success. Hooke had indeed observed

> plated bodies exhibiting colours, a phaenomenon, for the notice of which I thank him. But he left me to find out and make such experiments about it, as might inform me of the manner of the production of those colours, to ground an hypothesis on; he having given no further insight to it than this, that the colour depended on some certain thickness of the plate; though what that thickness was at every colour, he confesses in his Micrography, he had attempted in vain to learn; and therefore, seeing I was left to measure it myself, I suppose he will allow me to make use of what I took the pains to find out.

And all the mistake has been to read Newton's optical atomism literally instead of strategically. In a sense, Newton is saying that in some situations it is helpful to consider light as particles, in others as waves, and always as a composite of colored rays each of specific properties—but only in a sense, for before too much prescience is attached to this wisdom, it should be remembered that Newton's waves are longitudinal pulses, not transverse undulations.

After 1676 Newton gave over contending for his theory of colors and withdrew into his alternate posture of renunciation. "I had for some years past," he wrote in 1679, "been endeavouring to bend myself from philosophy to other studies in so much that I have long grutched the time spent in that study unless it be perhaps at idle hours sometimes for a diversion." It is not known in detail how he spent those years. On theology and biblical antiquities certainly, on mathematics probably, on chemistry and on perfecting his optics perhaps, for it is in character that he should have nursed his disenchantment in public and continued his work in private. In 1679 he was recalled to science, but to dynamics this time, by a further letter from Hooke, now become Secretary of the Royal Society. Hooke approached him on two levels. Privately, the letter was an olive branch. Officially, it was the new secretary bespeaking the renewed collaboration of the most potent of his younger colleagues, sulking in his tent.

Newton answered, correctly enough in form, but not very frankly, not at all cordially, affecting ignorance of an "hypothesis of springynesse" (Hooke's law of elasticity) on which Hooke had invited his opinion. So as to disguise without taking the edge off his snub, he threw in as a crumb "a fancy of my own," the solution of a curious problem he had toyed with in one of those idle hours. It concerned the trajectory of a body falling freely from a high tower, supposing the earth permeable and considering only the diurnal rotation. This was in fact a famous puzzle suggested by the Copernician theory, the same problem which Galileo had so curiously and erroneously answered with a semi-circle to the center of the earth. Since then it had been much discussed in obscure and learned places. And having brought it up himself, as if to flex a mental muscle in Hooke's face, Newton gave an answer as wrong as Galileo's. The trajectory, he casually said and drew it, will be a spiral to the center of the earth.

Now, Hooke did not know the right answer. The forces are in fact complex: the force of gravity increases by the inverse square relationship as far as the surface of the earth and thereafter as the first power of the distance. Hooke, along with many others, surmised the former (though he was too feeble a mathematician to handle gravity other than as constant) but was ignorant—as Newton then was—of the latter fact. He did have the happy thought of eliminating Coriolis forces by putting his tower on the equator. But Hooke did not need to solve the problem correctly to perceive that the initial tangential component of motion will not only, as Newton pointed out with an air of correcting vulgar errors, carry the body east of the foot of the tower, but by the same reasoning will insure that one point which the body can never traverse, either on a spiral or on any other path, is the center of the earth. Hooke was not the man to resist this opportunity. He had invited Newton to a private correspondence. He communicated Newton's reply to the Royal Society, and corrected his error publicly.

It would be tedious to follow the ensuing correspondence: the outward forms of courtesy, the philosophical tributes to truth as the goal, the underlying venom, the angry jottings in the margin. Newton "grutched" admitting error far more than the time spent on philosophy. He never did solve the problem. But he left it as the most important unsolved problem in the history of science. For it drew his mind back to dynamics and gravity, back to where he had left those questions thirteen years before. And in the course of these geometrical investigations, he solved the force law of planetary motion: "I found the Proposition that by a centrifugal force reciprocally as the square of the distance a Planet must revolve in an Ellipsis about the center of the force placed in the lowest umbilicus of the Ellipsis and with a radius drawn to that center describe areas proportional to the times." He would prove the point mass theorem only after 1685. But he had proved the law of gravity on the celestial scale, not just approximately for circular orbits as in 1666, but as a rigorous geometric deduction combining Kepler's laws with Huygens' law of centrifugal force. And he told no one, "but threw the calculations by, being upon other studies."

It is one of the ironies attending the genesis of Newton's *Principia* that no one knew beforehand of his work on celestial mechanics. In inviting Newton's correspondence, Hooke may even have thought that he was taking his rival onto his own ground. For the problem of gravity was constantly under discussion. Hooke had certainly surmised that a gravitating force of attraction was involved in the celestial motions, and that it varied in power inversely as the square of the distance. So, too, had Christopher Wren, then one of the most active of the virtuosi, and the young astronomer, Edmund Halley. But none of them was mathematician enough to deduce the planetary motions from a force law.

Far more than Boyle, Hooke was the complete Baconian. The only plausible explanation of his later conduct is that he truly did not understand the necessity for mathematical demonstration. He relied uniquely upon experiment to sort out the good from the bad ideas that crowded out of his fertile imagination. He seems to have been prepared to build even celestial mechanics out of experiments on falling bodies like those improvised to test out Newton's spiral. Nor could he see that the rigorous geomerical demonstrations of the *Principia* added anything to his own idea. They gave the same result. Once again, thought Hooke on seeing the manuscript, Newton had wrapped his intellectual property in figures and stolen it away.

Halley was more sophisticated. He was also an attractive and sympathetic young man. In August 1684 he went up from London to consult Newton. An account of this visit by John Conduitt, who later married Newton's niece, is generally accepted.

> Without mentioning either his own speculations, or those of Hooke and Wren, he at once indicated the object of his visit by asking Newton what would be the curve described by the planets on the supposition that gravity diminished as the square of the distance. Newton immediately answered, *an Ellipse*. Struck with joy and amazement, Halley asked him how he knew it? Why, replied he, I have calculated it; and being asked for the calculation, he could not find it, but promised to send it to him.

While others were looking for the law of gravity, Newton had lost it. And yielding to Halley's urging, Newton sat down to rework his calculations and to relate them to certain propositions *On Motion* (actually Newton's laws) on which he was lecturing that term. He had at first no notion of the magnitude of what he was beginning. But as he warmed to the task, the materials which he had been turning over in his mind in his twenty-five years at Cambridge moved into place in an array as orderly and planned as some perfect dance of figures. Besides proving Halley's theorem for him, he wrote the *Mathematical Principles of Natural Philosophy*. The *Principia*, it is always called, as if there were no other principles. And in a sense there are none. For that book contains all that is classical in classical physics. There is no work in science with which it may be compared.

"I wrote it," said Newton, "in seventeen or eighteen months." He employed an amanuensis who has left an account of his working habits.

> I never knew him to take any recreation or pasttime either in riding out to take the air, walking, bowling, or any other exercise whatever, thinking all hours lost that was not spent in his studies, to which he kept so close that he seldom left his chamber except at term time, when he read in the schools as being Lucasianus Professor. . . . He very rarely went to dine in the hall, except on some public days, and then if he has not been minded, would go very carelessly, with shoes down at heels, stockings untied, surplice on, and his head scarcely combed. At some seldom times when he designed to dine in the hall, [he] would turn to the left hand and go out into the street, when making a stop when he found his mis-

> take, would hastily turn back, and then sometimes instead of going into the hall, would return to his chamber again.

Mostly Newton would have meals sent to his rooms and forget them. His secertary would ask whether he had eaten. "Have I?" Newton would reply.

The Royal Society accepted the dedication, undertook to print the work, and like a true learned organization found itself without funds. The expense, therefore, as well as the editing came upon Halley. He was not a rich man, but he bore both burdens cheerfully, with devotion and tact. He had the disagreeable task of informing Newton that upon receipt of the manuscript Hooke had said of the inverse square law, " you had the notion from him," and demanded acknowledgment in a preface. Upon this Newton threatened to suppress the third book, the climax of the argument, which applied the laws of motion to the system of the world. He was dissuaded, as no doubt he meant to be, but one can understand how his feeling for Hooke turned from irritable dislike to scornful hatred:

> Now is not this very fine? Mathematicians, that find out, settle, and do all the business, must content themselves with being nothing but dry calculators and drudges; and another that does nothing but pretend and grasp at all things, must carry away all the invention, as well of those that were to follow him, as of those that went before. Much after the same manner were his letters writ to me, telling me that gravity, in descent from hence to the centre of the earth, was reciprocally in a duplicate ratio of the altitude, that the figure described by projectiles in the region would be an ellipsis, and that all the motions of the heavens were thus to be accounted for; and this he did in such a way, as if he had found out all, and knew it most certainly. And, upon this information, I must now acknowledge, in print, I had all from him, and so did nothing myself but drudge in calculating, demonstrating, and writing, upon the inventions of this great man. And yet, after all, the first of those three things he told me of is false, and very unphilosophical; the second is as false; and the third was more than he knew, or could affirm me ignorant of by any thing that past between us in our letters.

The provocation was great, as was the strain under which it was given. A few years after completing the *Principia* Netwon suffered a nervous collapse. He wrote very strange letters. One of them accused Locke of trying to embroil him with women—Newton, who was as oblivious to women as if they were occult qualities. Alarmed, his friends had arranged a move to London, to bring him more into company. He gave up solitude in Cambridge with no regrets, became after a few years Master of the Mint, then President of the Royal Society which once he had held at such a haughty distance. Knighted in 1705 he lived out his years until 1727, the incarnation of science in the eyes of his countrymen, a legend in his own lifetime.

But he did very little more science.

The *Principia* is an intractable book. It is doubtful whether any work of comparable influence can ever have been read by so few persons. The scientific community itself required forty years of discussion, rising at times to controversy, to grasp the implications of Newton's achievement and to assume the stance of classical physics. Thereafter the *Principia* scarcely needed to be read. It was enough that it existed. Up to 1900, mechanics, now including celestial mechanics, was a formal development of Newton's laws by more sophisticated and rigorous mathematical techniques. Though of first importance to the technical history of science, classical mechanics had made its contribution to the intellectual history of science in Newton, its founder. Even the other domains of physics, electromagnetism, heat, optics, were conceived with varying success as extensions of Newtonian principles and practice to new ranges of phenomena.

Indeed, no sooner was this development under way than the *Principia* became, if not impossible, at least impracticable to read. For it is expressed in an archaic formalism, not in the new analytical mathematics of the seventeenth century, but in the synthetic geometry of the Greeks. In his mathematical taste, Newton, like Pascal and Galileo, was a purist. He must first have satisfied himself about crucial theorems by his own "fluxions," or calculus. But he demonstrated them as theorems in classical geometry.

The ancients, wrote Newton in the preface, had distinguished between geometry and mechanics, the one rational and abstract, the other having to do with manual arts. As theory, geometry deals with magnitude. As practice, "the manual arts are chiefly conversant in the moving bodies," and mechanics, therefore, is commonly referred to the motion of things. He proposes to unite the two, "and therefore we offer this work as the mathematical principles of natural philosophy. For all the difficulty of philosophy seems to consist in this, from the phenomena of motions to investigate the forces of nature, and then from these forces to demonstrate the other phenomena."

Next Newton defined his terms. They are the basic quantities of classical physics, made explicit for the first time—mass, momentum, and force, the latter from several points of view with special attention to centrally directed forces. His language alone establishes that physics is fundamentally an affair of metrics. Thus for mass: "The quantity of matter is the measure of the same, arising from its density and bulk conjunctly." And of momentum: "The quantity of motion is the measure of the same, arising from the velocity and quantity of matter conjunctly." The definition of force closes with an important qualification:

> I likewise call attractions and impulses, in the same sense, accelerative and motive; and use the words attraction, impulse, or propensity of any sort towards a centre, promiscuously, and indifferently, one for another; considering those forces not physically, but mathematically: wherefore the reader is not to imagine that by those words I anywhere take upon me to define the kind, or the manner of any action, the causes or the physical reason thereof.

An important scholium to the last definition distinguished between absolute and relative time, absolute and relative space. This, of course, was the metaphysical chink into which criticism would bore as it had done into the Aristotelian doctrine of motion. But rather than anticipate, let us leave it for this chapter in Newton's own words at the end of his definitions:

> I do not define time, space, place, and motion, as being well known to all. Only I must observe, that the common people conceive those quantities under no other notions but from the relation they bear to sensible objects. And thence arise certain prejudices, for the removing of which it will be convenient to distinguish them into absolute and relative, true and apparent, mathematical and common.
>
> I. Absolute, true, and mathematical time, of itself and from its own nature, flows equably without relation to anything external, and by another name is called duration; relative, apparent, and common time, is some sensible and external (whether accurate or unequable) measure of duration by the means of motion.
>
> II. Absolute space, in its own nature, without relation to anything external, remains always similar and immovable. Relative space is some movable dimension or measure of the absolute spaces.

Finally, he completes his premises by stating the "Axioms, or Laws of Motion": inertia, the force law, the equivalence of action and reaction.

The *Principia* consists of three books. Book I develops the motion of bodies in unresisting mediums. It is a set of geometric theorems, on the method of limits and exhaustions, on problems of the center of force, on motion in conic sections, on the determination of orbits, on the attraction exerted by spherical bodies, on the motions of mutually attracting bodies, and on other topics. Book II is on the motion of bodies in resisting mediums. Much of it has to do with hydrodynamics, and it might seem a digression. Neither is the discussion always correct. But it was included because, like Galileo before him, only Newton's treatment was austere and mathematical. His purpose was philosophical, not to say polemical. He proposed to refute Cartesianism with its bodies swirling through spatial fluids and show the vortex system to be untenable on strictly mechanical grounds.

Throughout Book II, however, Newton left this an implication to be drawn. So far the structure of his book (like the structure of his space) is Euclidean, a set of mathematical deductions following from a few fundamental definitions and three axioms. But with Book III it becomes rather Archimedean, and the argument is applied to the physical information supplied by astronomy. For he means to compel agreement about universal cosmology, not by metaphysical reasoning, but to compel it with all the force of geometric demonstration. Applying the laws of motion to the solar system, he showed that they contain Kepler's orbits as a celestial consequence. In eternal unpropelled inertial motion, the moon and planets are constrained in their orbits by the universal force of attraction which every body—every particle—in the universe exerts over every other in an amount proportional to the product of the masses divided by the square of the distances. Weight is simply gravity acting on mass. And Newton included a vast array of calculations on fine points of the motion of the moon and tides as illustrations of gravity at work. Like Galileo, he turned to the tides for earthly evidence of his cosmological theory. But he had the principle that Galileo lacked, the answer to the more general, indeed the fundamental, question of what holds the world together? What will unify our science in an infinite universe?

The answer was the law of gravity.

Such was the book which formed the picture of the world in which everyone now alive was brought up. For it is safe to say that relativity and quantum physics have not yet been taken for granted as are Newton's notions of time, space, place, motion, force, and mass. It is easy to summarize the *Principia*. It is less easy to see how it affects our consciousness, though to have been brought up in the Newtonian world certainly does shape that consciousness, as it does to have been brought up an American rather than a Frenchman, a Christian rather than a Moslem. It is an element of culture, and to exist in a culture with no notion whence it came is to invite the anthropologist's inquiry rather than to live as an educated man, aware and in that measure free.

"I am always reading about the Newtonian synthesis," an English professor once said irritably. "What did Newton synthesize?" It is a fair question. On the most immediate level, theory met experiment on equal terms for the first time in Newton. In practise as in principle, Newton achieved the correct relationship between physics as the science of metrics and mathematics as the language of quantity. The problem had bedevilled science ever since Plato and Aristotle had separated the two in opposing but equally defeatist ontologies. Galileo, it is true, had had it right, but in sufficient generality, and Descartes had confused the issue once again. Newton, therefore, had to redistinguish mathematics from physics, and with it space from matter. Thus he was able to unite physics and astronomy in a single science of matter in motion. Finally, by flinging gravity across the void, he reconciled the continuity of space with the discontinuity of matter. This was his resolution of the last of the great Greek philosophical problems which Europe clothed in science, whether the world is a continuum or a concourse of atoms? It is both. In force and motion it is one, in matter the other. And that unites the Platonic-Archimedean tradition with atomism.

People accustomed to think in these separate channels could not easily lose themselves in the great stream of science. But more than habit blocked assent. Newton's science did not answer all the traditional questions. It did not even ask them, and one is tempted to attribute its ready acceptance in England to national pride rather than to superior culture. For to the most refined and subtlest minds on the continent, it seemed that Newton committed two mortal sins in metaphysics. First, the void introduced the existence of the nothing. Second, gravity supposed action at a distance, bodies affecting each other through a mystery rather than a medium. Indeed, the specific complaint which united all Newton's critics was that gravity as attraction was an occult force no better than it should be, a reversion to the innate tendencies which Aristotle put in bodies. It could hardly be expected that Newton should have been understood at once. Science would have to live with these difficulties for a time, after which it would forget them in its own success rather than resolve them—both those which were trivial and those which were profound.

The first objection was only a misunderstanding. The void as Newton used it was not the metaphysical nothing. It was the complement of the aether, that which motion occurs *in*, translational motion in the void and vibrational motion in the aether. The void was introduced for the same reason, not as a positive physical hypothesis, but as a condition for the possibility of physics. The second point, the "cause" of gravity, is more interesting. For it turned on the problem of what it is that science explains. In the lesser person of Hooke, on the lesser issues of optics, Baconianism had already failed to understand the import of Newtonian science. Now it was the turn of Leibniz and the Cartesian school to miss his meaning on the universal plane of gravity.

The web of metaphysical resistance to Newton was complex. On theology he had to survive a cross-fire. It is well known that Newton casually allowed God a hand in the solar system to repair certain irregularities that he thought cumulative. Among people who know little else about Newton, this is, indeed, altogether too well-known, considering what a trivial point it was, and how irrelevant to the structure of his physics. It is more interesting that Newton was a profoundly religious man. Like many later rationalists, he could not credit the Trinity. He was a Unitarian before this position had become respectable. He did certainly believe in the free creation of the world by God and its government under Providence. His was a personal belief, not a principle of physics, any more than was the occasional repair of the solar system. But he was criticized for holding these views (particularly the latter) by the Cartesians, who regarded any finalism as childish. And he was criticized for failing to make providential destiny part of physics by Leibniz, who had united his own system of the word, not by a physical principle like Cartesian extension or Newtonian gravity, but by the metaphysical principle of pre-established harmony. And it was Leibniz who turned the odium traditionally incurred by atomism against Newton, and accused his science of a tendency to lead down the path already trodden by Hobbes to a self-sufficient materialism destructive of natural religion.

Newton's critics, in short, wanted more out of science than he found there. In the Cartesian view, for all its hostility to scholasticism, science moves through nature from definition to rationale; in that of Leibniz, it moves rather from principles to values; and in that of Newton, from descriptions and measurements to abstract generalizations. Strictly speaking, therefore, Newtonian science could never get outside itself, and might be said to be a tautology, or at least to accomplish nothing of human interest or value. The trouble was not in the evidence. No one complained of the mathematics. But taken as an explanation of the universe, the system failed—or rather it was no explanation at all, since no cause could be assigned and no mechanism imagined for its central principle, the principle of attraction. For the concrete, working, mechanical picture of the Cartesian universe, it substituted a set of geometrical theorems.

There is an irony in all this. Countless intellectual historians have followed Leibniz in describing Newton's theory as responsible for the picture of a soulless, deterministic world-machine, that same theory which at the time was rejected by men as discriminating as Huygens and Fontenelle for being overly abstract, insufficiently mechanistic, and subservient to natural theology. Indeed Newton has never been able to give critics what they wanted, a system which saw nature steadily and saw it whole, which accounted at once for the behavior and the cause of phenomena, the "how" and the "why" of nature. He did not know the cause of gravity. Gravity in Newton was a mathematical, not a mechanical force. Nor did he, in fact, believe in action at a distance, or gravity as an innate tendency: "You sometimes speak of gravity as essential and inherent to Matter," he wrote to Bentley. "Pray do not ascribe that Notion to me; for the Cause of Gravity is what I do not pretend to know, and therefore would take more Time to consider of it." But ignorance of the cause is not to deny the effect. "To us it is enough"—so he says in the General Scholium at the end of the *Principia*—"that gravity does really exist, and acts according to the laws which we have explained, and abundantly serves to account for all the motions of the celestial bodies, and of our seas."

To the Cartesians, however, it was not enough.

Growing old, but never mellow, Newton responded to incomprehension in the pattern of his youthful optics. He wrote this "General Scholium" for the second edition (1713) of the *Principia*. The penultimate paragraph works up to the austere rebuke: "But hitherto I have not been able to discover the cause of those properties of gravity from phenomena, and [in the translation newly established by Koyré] I feign no hypotheses. For whatever is not deduced from the phenomena is to be called an hypothesis; and hypotheses, whether metaphysical or physical, whether of occult qualities or mechanical, have no place in experimental philosophy." And then, to make interpretation as difficult as science, the next and last paragraph begins:

> And now we might add something concerning a certain most subtle spirit which pervades and lies hid in all gross bodies; by the force and action of which spirit the particles of bodies attract one another at near distances, and cohere, if contiguous; and electric bodies operate to greater distances, as well repelling as attracting the neighbouring corpuscles; and light is emitted, reflected, refracted, inflected, and heats bodies; and all sensation is excited, and the members of animal bodies move at the command of the will, namely, by the vibrations of this spirit, mutually propagated along the solid filaments of the nerves, from the outward organs of sense to the brain, and from the brain into the muscles.

Again, it is as if there were two Newtons speaking in turn. Once again, the frustrations of the empiricist release the affirmations of the visionary. It must not be supposed that Newton's life in London was only what it seemed, the ceremonial existence, all passion spent, of the elder statesman of science. Behind the scenes, he looked to his polemical interests with an undimmed eye. Hooke died in 1703. In 1704 Newton published the *Opticks*, writing in English now, and very well, as if he meant to be read. The early experiments had been refined and extended. And the book closed with the famous "Queries," that moving and beautiful series of rhetorical speculations about light, heat, and electricity, the aether, the atoms, and God, which Newton left as his legacy of unsolved problems, and to which he added in later editions. (It is seldom noted that in 1672, his very first attempt to explain himself after the mixed reception of his paper on prisms had taken the form of "Queres" addressed to the Royal Society.)

Except in the *Opticks*, Newton chose to retire behind the advocacy of disciples, whom he probably coached. Roger Cotes wrote the preface for the second edition of the *Principia*. Samuel Clarke published a philosophical debate with Leibniz. This discussion developed out of an ignoble squabble over the invention of the calculus, in which the Royal Society acted as umpire in no very just or impartial spirit. Nor can it be said, any more than of the earlier polemics, that all these unworthy quarrels served no higher purpose. They brought the issues before the Republic of Letters as perusal of the theorems of the *Principia* would never have done, if only because those theorems so coldly discourage perusal.

Newton himself spoke out again in the General Scholium. It closes with the renewal of that aethereal hint just given. But what had wounded Newton most deeply was the attribution of infidelity. And his views on divinity do, and should, carry more interest than his hypothesis—for so he had called it himself when first he brought it in—of the aether. God is neither hypothesis nor object of science. He is certainty:

> He endures forever, and is everywhere present; and, by existing always and everywhere, he constitutes duration and space. Since every particle of space is always, and every indivisible moment of duration is everywhere, certainly the Maker and Lord of all things cannot be never and nowhere. . . . Whence also he is all similar, all eye, all ear, all brain, all arm, all power to peceive, to understand, and to act; but in a manner not at all human, in a manner not at all corporeal, in a manner utterly unknown to us. . . . We have ideas of his attributes, but what the real substance of anything is we know not. In bodies, we see only their figures and colours, we hear only the sounds, we touch only their outward surfaces, we smell only the smells, and taste the savours; but their inward substances are not to be known either by our senses, or by any reflex act of our minds; much less, then, have we any idea of the substance of God. We know him only by his most wise and excellent contrivances of things, and final causes; we admire him for his perfections; but reverence and adore him on account of his dominion: for we adore him as his servants; and a god without dominion, providence, and final causes is nothing else but Fate and Nature. . . . And thus much concerning God; to discourse of whom from the appearances of things, does certainly belong to Natural Philosophy.

To discourse, but not to prescribe, nor to presume. For all this speculation on the aether, all this reverence for God, these considerations are interesting for the inspiration of Newton's science, but irrelevant to its validity. Its validity is to be judged—did not Newton say so?—in relation not to Newton, but to nature. Indeed, one of the most elementary though disregarded of distinctions is that between the scientist and his science. Science is created by the scientist, but about nature, not about himself. Once it is created, it has the independence of any work of art. One sometimes reads of the arrogance of science. And Newton was subject to unseemly spells of haughtiness when crossed. But surely—to insist upon the distinction—his science is rather an expression of modesty. That limitation of *allowable* theories to the evidence was no positivist skepticism about truth in the world of things. Rather, it was modesty. Descartes was the one who presumed to prescribe what the world must be. Newton only said how it is, and how it works. And it is right, therefore, to let Newton the scientist, rather than Newton the controversialist, or Newton the theologian, have the last word. It comes from the closing sentence of the final definition at the start of the *Principia*: "But how we are to obtain the true motions from their causes, effects, and apparent differences, and *vice versa,* how from their motions either true or apparent, we may come to the knowledge of their causes and effects, shall be explained more at large in the following treatise. For to this end it was that I composed it."

J. H. Randall, Jr.

The Newtonian World Machine

In the front of an old edition of the works of Rousseau there is an engraving which beautifully illustrates the intellectual spirit of the eighteenth century. Rousseau is seated at his writing-table, facing a pleasant pastoral landscape of green fields, sheep, and graceful willows—that rationally ordered Nature which he and his contemporaries accorded so respectful an admiration. On his desk are two volumes, which, in the absence of any other books, seem designed to sum up the learning of the age—the *Principia Mathematica* of Isaac Newton, and the *Essay concerning Human Understanding* of John Locke.

In truth Newton and Locke were the two luminaries of that brilliant Augustan age in which, under William III and Queen Anne, England assumed for a period of some forty years, from 1680 to 1720, the undisputed intellectual leadership of the world, only to lose it again or at least to share it with first France and then Germany. Theirs are beyond doubt the outstanding names in that epoch which, succeeding to the discoveries and the liberations of the Renaissance and the Reformation, and preceding the rapid change and varied currents of the nineteenth century, made so heroic an attempt to order the world on the basis of the new "Physico–Mathematicall Experimental Learning." The significance of these two men, in spite of their own outstanding achievements, lies not so much in what they themselves did, as in what they stood for to that age, and in the very fact

Reprinted with permission of Houghton Mifflin Company from J. H. Randall, Jr., Making of the Modern Mind *(Boston: Houghton Mifflin Company, 1940), pp. 253–79.*

that they became to an increasing multitude the symbols for certain great ideas. Under their stands the new science for the first time actually entered into every field of human interest, and captured the mind of every educated man. Under such banners was actually effected that outstanding revolution in beliefs and habits of thought which we sometimes mistakenly associate with the Renaissance—that complete break with the spirit of the Middle Ages that prepared the way for the further growth of the next century. The age that hailed them as acknowledged masters, that introduced the spirit of the Renaissance into religion, that placed man squarely in the midst of the new ordered world, that erected a science of man and of social relations, that formulated a complete and rounded philosophical view admirably framed for the middle class which the Industrial and the French Revolutions were so soon to bring into the direct control, and which disseminated these ideas among the whole membership of this class—such an age is fittingly styled the "Age of Enlightenment and Reason." It laid the foundations for our present-day beliefs in every field, and it led on naturally to the two great ideas which the nineteenth century has added to the achievements of its predecessor, evolution and relativity.

In one sense both Newton and Locke were the systematizers of the ideas we have already traced in their formative stage. Newton stands at the end of that row of scientific geniuses who effected the Copernican and the Cartesian revolutions: he finally drew up in complete mathematical form the mechanical view of nature, that first great physical synthesis on which succeeding science has rested, and which has endured unchanged until a present-day revolution bids fair to modify it. Locke stands as apologist and heir of the great seventeenth-century struggles for constitutional liberties and rights and toleration. It is to this expression in systematic form of ideas which had become common property by 1700 that the two owed their immense popularity in the new century. But in another sense both Locke and Newton stand at the threshold of a new era, Newton as the prophet of the science of nature, and Locke as the prophet of the science of human nature. From their inspiration flow the great achievements of the Age of Enlightenment; in their light men went on to transform their beliefs and their society into what we know to-day.

Possessed of a successful scientific method, a combination of mathematics and experiment, and of a guarantee of truth, that "reason" which was both an individual and a universal authority, men set about the task of discovering a natural order that should be both simple and all-embracing. In the words of Fontenelle, the popularizer of Cartesianism, "The geometric spirit is not so bound up with geometry that it cannot be disentangled and carried into other fields. A work of morals, of politics, of criticism, perhaps even of eloquence, will be the finer, other things being equal, if it is written by the hand of a geometer."[1] Isaac Newton effected so successful a synthesis of the mathematical principles of nature that he stamped the mathematical ideal of science, and the identification of the natural with the rational, upon the entire field of thought. Under the inspiration of Locke, the attempt was made to discover and formulate a science of human nature and human society, and to criticize existing religious and social traditions in the light of what seemed rational and reasonable. The two leading ideas of the eighteenth century, Nature and Reason, as outstanding then as Evolution in the last generation, derived their meaning from the natural sciences, and, carried over to man, led to the attempt to discover a social physics. Man and his institutions were included in the order of nature and the scope of the recognized scientific method, and in all things the newly invented social sciences were assimilated to the physical sciences. There grew up the idea of a simple and all-embracing social order in which free play should be left to the activities of every man. It is this great eighteenth-century synthesis in its most important ramifications that we shall now examine, starting with the rational order of the world, as expressed in the Newtonian system of nature, scientific method, and scientific ideals, and proceeding to trace its applications in religion, and in the comprehensive science of human nature that embraced a rational science of the mind, of society, of business, of government, of ethics, and of international relations.

THE SUCCESS OF THE MATHEMATICAL INTERPRETATION OF NATURE

The outstanding fact that colors every other belief in this age of the Newtonian world is the overwhelming success of the mathematical interpretation of nature. We have seen how Galileo found that he could explain and predict motion by applying the language of mathematics to the book of Nature, and how Descartes generalized from his method and its success a universal principle of scientific investigation and a sweeping picture of the universe as a great machine; how both thinkers arrived at the conception of uniform

[1] Fontenelle, *Œuvres Complètes* (1818), *Préface sur l'utilité des mathématiques et de la physique*, I, 34.

natural laws that are essentially mechanical in nature. But Descartes' cosmic picture was a sketch which neither the progress of mathematics nor of physical observation enable him to fill in by the time of his early death. To his disciples he left a system of the world worked out as a provisional hypothesis, which he had not had time to verify by those careful experiments that he increasingly recognized as necessary to determine just what actual phenomena, of the many possible ones that could be deduced from the mechanical principle, really took place. Not to the strict Cartesians, who accepted as final this sketch and did not bother to verify it by the master's method, but to the more original minds who shared Galileo's emphasis on experiment and refrained for a generation from attempting a general hypothesis, were due the discoveries that made Newton's work possible. Especially successful were the triumphs of mathematics in the fields of fluids and gases. Torricelli, Galileo's pupil, in 1643 invented the barometer and weighed the atmosphere, and Pascal confirmed his measurements four years later by his famous experiment of carrying a barometer up a mountain and observing the diminishing atmospheric pressure. To Pascal, too, is due the formulation of the laws of pressure in liquids, while Robert Boyle, who had studied under Galileo, discovered the law of pressure in gases. It is significant that within twenty years these facts had been used in machines for raising water, and that by the end of the century Newcomen's steam engine had begun the application of steam power to industry. To light, too, mathematics was astoundingly applied, and the science of optics, originated by Kepler and Descartes, was systematically developed by the Dutch Huygens and by Newton, who gave it its classic formulation; in 1695, Roemer actually measured the speed of light.

In all this work, mathematics and experimentation were successful allies. The spirit of the new science is exemplified in the foundation of the Royal Society in London in 1662 "for the promoting of Physico-Mathematicall Experimental Learning." This institution for that scientific coöperation so urgently demanded by Descartes, was largely inspired by Bacon's vision of a great scientific establishment; but it wisely followed the mathematical methods of Galileo rather than the purely experimental searching of the Elizabethan. Science rested on experiment, but its main object, for another century at least, was to connect the observed processes of nature with mathematical law. The leading member of the Royal Society, Robert Boyle, shares with Huygens the distinction of being the greatest investigator between Galileo and Newton; he managed to draw together the threads of alchemy and mathematical physics, and his generalization of Galileo's method of mathematical experimentation strongly influenced Newton. Mayow, another member, in 1674 discovered oxygen, although it was a century before Priestley and Lavoisier were able to fit it into a chemical science.

THE MATHEMATICAL SYNTHESIS OF NEWTON

All this experimental work, together with much advance in mathematical theory, took place in the single generation after Descartes' death. But the great formulator of seventeenth-century science, the man who realized Descartes' dream, was born in 1642, the very year of Galileo's death. Though he did not publish his immortal work, the *Philosophiæ Naturalis Principia Mathematica*, till 1687, Newton made his chief discoveries when he was but twenty-three years of age. At that time, he tells us, he discovered:

> first the binomial theorem, then the method of fluxions [the calculus], and began to think of gravity extending to the orb of the moon, and having found out how to estimate the force with which a globe, revolving within a sphere, presses the surface of the sphere, from Kepler's rule I deduced that the forces which keep the planets in their orb must be reciprocally as the squares of their distances from their centres: and thereby compared the force requisite to keep the moon in her orb with the force of gravity at the surface of the earth, and found them to answer pretty nearly. All this was in the two plague years of 1665 and 1666, for in those days I was in the prime of my age for invention and minded Mathematicks and Philosophy more than at any time since.[2]

The thirty years that had passed since Galileo published his *Dialogue on the Two Systems* had seen an enormous intellectual change. Where Galileo was still arguing with the past, Newton ignores old discussions, and, looking wholly to the future, calmly enunciates definitions, principles, and proofs that have ever since formed the basis of natural science. Galileo represents the assault; after a single generation comes the victory. Newton himself made two outstanding discoveries: he found the mathematical method that would describe mechanical motion, and he applied it universally. At last what Descartes had dreamed was true: men had arrived at a complete mechanical intepretation of the world in exact, mathemati-

[2] Quoted in F. S. Marvin, *Living Past*, 179.

cal, deductive terms. In thus placing the keystone in the arch of seventeenth-century science, Newton properly stamped his name upon the picture of the universe that was to last unchanged in its outlines till Darwin; he had completed the sketch of the Newtonian world that was to remain through the eighteenth century as the fundamental scientific verity.

That Newton invented the calculus is perhaps an accident; Leibniz, building on Descartes' analytic geometry, arrived at it independently, while several other mathematicians, like Pascal, seemed almost on the verge of it. Be that as it may, it was inevitable that after the Frenchman had brought algebra and geometry together, men should advance and apply algebra also to motion. Descartes had shown how to find the equation that would represent any curve, and thus conveniently and accurately measure it and enable calculated prediction to be applied to all figures; but the science of mechanics, and with it any measurement of the processes of change in the world, demands a formula for the law of the growth or falling-off of a curve, that is, the direction of its movement at any point. Such a method of measuring movement and continuous growth Newton discovered; he had arrived at the most potent instrument yet found for bringing the world into subjection to man. Since any regular motion, be it of a falling body, an electric current, or the cooling of a molten mass, can be represented by a curve, he had forged the tool by which to attack, not only the figures, but the processes of nature—the last link in the mathematical interpretation of the world. By its means a Lagrange in the eigtheenth or a Clerk-Maxwell in the nineteenth century could bring all measurable phenomena into the unified world of mathematics, and calculate, predict, and control light, heat, magnetism, and electricity.

Newton himself used it to formulate the general laws governing every body in the solar system. Kepler had arrived at the law of planetary motion by induction from observed facts, Galileo had similarly discovered the laws of falling bodies upon the earth. Newton united both in one comprehensive set of principles, by calculating that the deflection of the moon from a straight path, that is, her fall towards the earth, exactly corresponded with the observed force of terrestrial gravitation; and he further showed that on his hypothesis Kepler's law of planetary motion followed mathematically from the law of gravitation. The significance of this lay in the proof that the physical laws which hold good on the surface of the earth are valid throughout the solar system. What Galileo divined, what Descartes believed but could not prove, was both confirmed and made more comprehensive. This meant, on the one hand, that the secrets of the whole world could be investigated by man's experiments on this planet; and on the other, that the world was one huge, related, and uniform machine, the fundamental principles of whose action were known. One law could describe the whirling planet and the falling grass blade; one law could explain the action of every body in the universe. Newton expressed this fundamental principle in a famous rule:

> We are to admit no more causes of natural things than such as are both true and sufficient to explain their appearances. Therefore, to the same natural effects we must, as far as possible, assign the same causes. The qualities of bodies that cannot be diminished or increased, and are found to belong to all bodies within the reach of our experiments, are to be esteemed the universal qualities of all bodies whatsoever. For since the qualities of bodies are only known to us by experiments, we are to hold for universal all such as universally agree with experiments. . . . We are certainly not to relinquish the evidence of experiments for the sake of dreams and vain fictions of our own; nor are we to recede from the analogy of Nature, which uses to be simple, and always consonant with itself. . . .We must, in consequence of this rule, universally allow, that all bodies whatsover are endowed with a principle of mutual gravitation.[3]

Using this principle and his new mathematical tool, Newton proceeded "to subject the phenomena of nature to the laws of mathematics." [4] "I am induced by many reasons to suspect," he says, "that all the phenomena of nature may depend upon certain forces by which the particles of bodies, by some causes hitherto unknown, are either mutually impelled towards each other, and cohere in regular figures, or are repelled and recede from each other." [5] Every event in nature is to be explained by the same kind of reasoning from mechanical principles: the whole program of science is "from the phenomena of motions to investigate the forces of nature, and then from these forces to demonstrate the other phenomena." [6] The world is a vast perpetual motion machine, and every event in it can be deduced mathematically from the fundamental principles of its mechanical action; the discovery of these mathematical relations is

[3] Isaac Newton, *Mathematical Principles of Natural Philosophy*, Bk. III.
[4] *Ibid.*, Author's Preface.
[5] *Ibid.*
[6] *Ibid.*

the goal of science. The universe is one great harmonious order; not, as for Thomas and the Middle Ages, an ascending hierarchy of purposes, but a uniform mathematical system.

> The universal order, symbolized henceforth by the law of gravitation, takes on a clear and positive meaning. This order is accessible to the mind, it is not preëstablished mysteriously, it is the most evident of all facts. From this it follows that the sole reality that can be accessible to our means of knowledge, matter, nature, appears to us as a tissue of properties, precisely ordered, and of which the connection can be expressed in terms of mathematics.[7]

Newton's great mathematical system of the world struck the imagination of the educated class of his time, and spread with amazing swiftness, completing what Descartes had begun. Prior to 1789 some eighteen editions of the difficult and technical *Principia* were called for; British universities were teaching it by the end of the seventeenth century, and Newton was accorded a royal funeral when he died in 1727. In 1734, Bernoulli won the prize of the French Academy of Sciences with a Newtonian memoir; in 1740 the last prize was granted to an upholder of Descartes' physics. Voltaire was struck by Newtonianism during his visit to England in 1726–1728, and popularized him in France in his *English Letters,* in 1734, and his *Elements of the Newtonian Philosophy* in 1738; thenceforth Newton reigned in France as in England. From the presses there poured forth an immense stream of popular accounts for those unable or unwilling to peruse the classic work. His conclusions and his picture of the world were accepted on authority. By 1789 there had appeared about the *Principia* forty books in English, seventeen in French, three in German, eleven in Latin, one in Portuguese, and one in Italian, many of them, like those of Desaguliers, Benjamin Martin, Ferguson's *Lectures for Ladies and Gentlemen,* and Count Alogrotti's *Le Newtonianisme pour les Dames,* running through edition after edition. Newton's name became a symbol which called up the picture of the scientific machine-universe, the last word in science, one of those uncriticized preconceptions which largely determined the social and political and religious as well as the strictly scientific thinking of the age. Newton *was* science, and science was the eighteenth-century ideal.

[7] Léon Bloch, *La Philosophie de Newton,* 555.

Deduction X

THE METHOD OF NEWTONIAN SCIENCE

Hence the method of the new physical science became all important, for men proceeded to apply it in every field of investigation. Just as the success of biology under Darwin led to the importation of the biological method into all the social sciences, and the more recent success of psychology has led to the wider application of its methods, so the social sciences, which, in the absence of any sure method of their own, always borrow from the striking science of the day, were in the Age of Enlightenment almost completely under the domination of the physico-mathematical method. Hence a closer examination of that method is of the utmost importance. Though experiment entered as one of its parts, and became in science increasingly prominent as the century advanced, what was thus borrowed was for the most part overwhelmingly deductive and mathematical: typical is Spinoza, whom we have seen attempting, in his *Ethics*, to deal with men's passions and motives as if they were part of a geometrical system. The new science had not yet led men to give up the medieval Thomistic and Aristotelian ideal of a body of knowledge that could be deductive, universal, and infallible, one great logical system; it had only, as in Descartes and Spinoza, changed its type from the syllogistic logic of Aristotle to the geometrical propositions of Euclid. Such a science must be founded, like geometry, upon a small number of definitely true axioms, from which every law of nature will follow deductively; and it is characteristic of the eighteenth-century scientific ideal that, however much it might turn to experience to suggest these axioms, and to formulate the specific laws governing phenomena, no law was regarded as conclusively established until it could be fitted into such a great universal deductive system. Newton, by proving mathematically that Kepler's inductive law of planetary motion must result from the general principle of gravitation, had given an immense impetus to this ideal. Under the spell of the triumphant mathematical physics men waxed optimistic, and believed that such an infallible and complete science would soon exhaust all experimentation and be able to dispense with every appeal to experience. The world of facts seemed simpler then, and men had not yet learned that experimental research raises more problems than it solves, so it was easy to hope for a speedy return to a non-experimental procedure. With Descartes all save those actually making experimental discoveries in physics believed, throughout the century, that the surest foundation of truth was not any appeal to the fallible testimony of sense experience, so often proved wrong, but rather the clear and distinct intuition of geometrical axioms. We *know* intuitively, with absolute certainty, that the whole is equal to the sum of its parts, and that a straight line is the shortest distance between two points: similarly it was hoped that such intuitive axioms could be discovered in mechanics, in morals, in politics, and in religion. Even Locke, who in some respects stood for a different conception of science, hoped for such a deductive system of religion and of ethics. Rationalism of the geometrical type was the popular intellectual method of the Age of Reason.

We shall trace the influence of this scientific method upon the newly invented social sciences, and observe its influence in every field. Typical of the popular social ideals of the century are Rousseau, who started with such fundamental axioms as that all men are created free and equal, and deduced therefrom a revolutionary system of politics; and the physiocratic economists, who started from the axioms of private property and individual liberty and deduced a geometrical science of business. Such conceptions were overwhelmingly successful in providing a leverage for overthrowing the old ideas and ushering in a régime that provided free scope to the rising middle class; but throughout the nineteenth century they proved incapable of building a new social order, and have worked to this day untold harm and mischief, in their cavalier disregard of the actual facts of human society.

THE RISE OF THE EXPERIMENTAL METHOD

The social sciences remained conservatively deductive; the physical sciences grew increasingly experimental, paving the way for the borrowing of their newer inductive methods in the next century. Galileo had insisted upon experimental analysis of natural events as the basis and the final verification of all mechanical law; even Descartes, more responsible for this rationalism than any other one man, was keenly aware of the necessity of the appeal to experiment in these two places, though he hoped that a completed science would be deductive. Newton himself, inspired by both the mathematical Descartes and the experimental Boyle, effected a harmonious reconciliation of the two elements. His method was, by analysis of observed facts, to arrive at some fundamental principle, then to deduce the mathematical consequences of this principle, and finally by observation and experiment to prove that what follows logically from the principle is in agreement with experience. Indeed, Newton is remarkable for the caution with which he insists that the faith in the mathematical interpretation of nature must be at every step guided and checked by experiment. As against the bold world-picture of Descartes, he insists that such speculative hypotheses have no place in exact science; sound principles must be deduced from the phenomena themselves. "Whatever is not deduced from the phenomena is to be called an hypothesis; and hypotheses, whether metaphysical or physical, whether of occult qualities or mechanical, have no place in experimental philosophy. In this philosophy particular propositions are inferred from the phenomena, and afterwards rendered general by induction."[8] In his fourth rule of philosophizing, he makes it clear that although science is composed of laws stating the mathematical behavior of nature solely, and is thus the exact mathematical formulation of the processes of the natural world, the ultimate test of this formulation must remain agreement with observed fact. "In experimental philosophy we are to look upon propositions collected by general induction from phenomena as accurately or very nearly true, notwithstanding any contrary hypotheses that may be imagined, till such time as other phenomena occur, by which they may either be made more accurate, or liable to exceptions."[9] Thus in Newton himself there is clearly recognized the increasing importance of experimental verification; though most of the applications of his method to realms other than physics tended to overlook this caution.

But the eighteenth century saw also the rise of new scientific investigations in fields that were now for the first time broader than those simplified aspects of nature with which physics deals. Men turned to the amassing of a vast body of concrete descriptive facts about the things in the world, which they were content for the most part to gather and classify; these remained as the indispensable prerequisite for the great hypotheses characteristic of science in the first half of the nineteenth century, hypotheses which only the last generation has brought into the general physico-mathematical system. As Diderot wrote in the initial volume of the *Encyclopédie* in 1775, "Men's minds seem caught in a general movement towards natural history, anatomy, chemistry, and experimental physics."[10] What was loosely called "natural history" became very popular. Men who made

[8] Newton, *Principles*, Motte tr. (1803), II, 314.
[9] *Ibid.*, Bk. III, 4th Rule of Reasoning in Philosophy.
[10] Diderot, *Encyclopédie*, art. "Encyclopédie."

pretensions at scientific learning, like Voltaire, and the various "enlightened rulers" of the day, collected their cabinets of specimens of plants, birds, fossils, rocks, and the like. Naturalists like Buffon, whose great *Natural History* was the mid-eighteenth-century counterpart of our Well's *Outline of History;* Lamarck, Curator of the Paris *Jardin des Plantes;* Cuvier, head of the "School of Facts," and Saint-Hilaire, his colleagues; and Linnæus, the great systematizer of botany, were all indefatigable in collecting and classifying specimens. Geologists like Werner and Hutton and William Smith mapped the rocks and laid the foundations for the epoch-making theories of Lyell in the next age. Here, too, belong the real foundations of experimental chemistry. Cavendish in 1766 reported the discovery of hydrogen, and in 1784 the synthetic production of water; Rutherford in 1772 isolated nitrogen; Priestley in 1774 discovered oxygen; and Lavoisier, by his unremitting use of the delicate balance, founded the science of quantitative chemistry, weighing accurately oxygen and carbonic acid. The ground was cleared for Dalton in the beginning of the next century to place the atomic theory upon a definite and mathematical basis, and usher in modern chemical investigation.

Careful observation of nature and accurate experimentation had at last become as respectable as mathematical physics. "The only good science," wrote Buffon in vindicating such investigation, "is the knowledge of facts, and mathematical truths are only truths of definition, and completely arbitrary, quite unlike physical truths." [11] Hume marks this turning from the spirit of the seventeenth to that of the nineteenth century, when he insists that the contrary of every matter of fact remains possible, and that no amount of deductive reasoning from first principles can decide in advance what course nature actually follows. Only by experimental reasoning can matters of fact be determined; only by experience can man ever learn that fire burns and water is wet, and to such facts all the mathematics in the world helps no whit. Indeed, reason itself is built up from experience. Even a physicist like Holbach has come to feel by 1770 that "the faculty we have of gaining experiences, of remembering them, of calling to mind their effects, constitutes what we designate by the word *reason*. Without experience there can be no reason." [12]

The foremost theoretical exponent of the experimental method in the Age of Reason was Diderot, the editor of the great French *Encyclopédie* that, appearing between 1751 and 1777, was the out-

[11] Buffon, quoted in L. Ducros, *Les Encyclopédistes*, 326.
[12] Holbach, *Système de la Nature* (1770), I, 142.

standing work that popularized all the new scientific ideas. His *Thoughts on the Interpretation of Nature*, in 1754, deserves to rank with Bacon's *Novum Organum* and Descartes' *Discourse on Method* as a classic of scientific method.

> We have three principal means: the observation of nature, reflection, and experiment. Observation gathers facts, reflection combines them, and experiment verifies the result of the combination. . . . We have distinguished two kinds of science, experimental and rational. The one has its eyes bandaged, proceeds feeling its way, seizes everything that falls into its hands, and at last finds precious things and seeks to form from them a torch; but its supposed torch up to the present has served it less than the cautious advance of its rival, and that is as it should be. Experiment infinitely multiplies its movements; it is always in action; it sets about seeking phenomena all the while that reason looks for analogies. Experimental science knows neither what will come nor what will not come of its work, but it never ceases working. On the other hand rational science weighs possibilities, pronounces judgment, and stops short. It boldly says, "Light can not be decomposed." Experimental science hears and remains silent for whole centuries, then suddenly displays the prism and says, "Light has been decomposed." [13]

Diderot rather underemphasized the importance of mathematics even in experimental investigation.

> We are on the point of a great revolution in the sciences. Judging by the inclination that the best minds seem to have for morals, for belles-lettres, for natural history and for experimental physics, I almost dare to predict that before a hundred years are over there will not be three great mathematicians in Europe; that science will stop short where it will have been left by the Bernoullis, the Eulers, the Maupertuis, the Clairauts, the Fontaines, and the D'Alemberts. It will have erected the pillars of Hercules; men will go no further; their works will last through the centuries to come like the pyramids of Egypt, whose bulks, inscribed with hieroglyphics, awaken in us an awful idea of the power and the resources of the men who built them.[14]

Diderot it was who rescued Francis Bacon from the oblivion to which his scorn of mathematics had relegated him for a century, and created the myth that it was he who had really founded modern scientific method. Bacon's vogue dates from the days of this new

[13] Diderot, *Pensées sur l'Interprétation de la Nature*, 15, 23.
[14] *Ibid.*, 4.

interest in experimental investigation. Diderot was himself a convinced Baconian, intensely interested in the practical application of scientific knowledge to the physical welfare of man. Perhaps the chief new note in his *Encyclopédie* is the way in which he brushed aside the traditional intellectual interests and placed the emphasis upon the mechanical arts and crafts. Fascinated by industrial processes, he spent days in the workshops of the craftsmen drawing sketches of every conceivable type of practical technique for the eleven volumes of plates that made such an impression upon his subscribers. His was the spirit of the new industrial revolution just appearing across the Channel.

From this experimental side of the scientific method there sprang a new ideal of science, differing from the reigning mathematical rationalism. Though it did not, save in a few rare and outstanding cases like Hume, capture the imaginations of those who were working out the new social sciences, it was destined, ere the century was out, to effect a new revolution there also and usher in the nineteenth-century spirit and methods in the science of man. This new ideal of science received in the eighteenth century the name of *empiricism*, was adapted by Kant toward the close of the age as *phenomenalism*, and was worshiped in the next century under Comte's term of *positivism*. Of course these three tendencies differed markedly among themselves, but they agreed in a certain fundamental opposition to the rational mathematical ideal we have described as on the whole dominant throughout the eighteenth century, endeavoring to effect a more or less harmonious adjustment with its acknowledgedly successful methods and results.

THE PROBLEM OF KNOWLEDGE AND THE NEW IDEAL OF SCIENCE

Here we reach one of the most perplexing and difficult paradoxes in the history of thought. The conceptions and methods which the special scientific investigators were employing to win vast new continents of facts and laws, whatever their ultimate and theoretical foundation, have indisputably been supremely successful in enabling men to manipulate and control their physical environment. Yet these very methods practically forced reflective men to raise the question of what this new scientific knowledge was really knowledge of, and what its actual relation was to the world it purported to describe. That this knowledge was useful and important and almost indefinitely extensible in degree, has remained incontestable, and men have never allowed these anxieties and perplexities about the nature and foundation of science to deter them from its vigorous prosecution, convinced as they are forced to be that it must possess some very real validity. But the very age that has seen so impressive a growth in scientific knowledge has also been profoundly troubled by the thought that it seems very difficult to understand how in any intelligible sense such a science is possible of attainment by the human mind. This paradox may be somewhat explained if we realize that scientists were attempting to discover a *kind* of knowledge which their very methods made it impossible for them to arrive at: by modern scientific methods of investigation they were trying to reach an absolute system of truth quite independent of any limitations of the mental powers of the essentially imperfect and biological creature that man seems to be. In a word, they were trying to arrive at that complete and perfect understanding and explanation of the universe that only a God could possess, by the methods possible for a being who is not a God but a rational animal. Their ideal was still a *system of revelation,* though they had abandoned the *method* of revelation. They found knowledge, and valid knowledge, to be sure; but it gradually and painfully dawned upon them that the knowledge they could find and have been finding is a different sort of knowledge from that which they thought they were finding. Just what sort of knowledge it is, men are even to-day by no means agreed; but they have been forced to admit that it is neither absolute nor independent of the biologically adaptive nature of the human animal. It has taken over two centuries for an altered scientific method to force an altered conception of the ideal of scientific knowledge, and the end is not yet. But if we are to understand the confusions and vague gropings of men during that period we must try the difficult task of tracing the changes in that ideal of science. Only one thing remained certain, that men really were discovering important and useful knowledge, and that their methods were successful; why they were and what they found is hardly to-day cleared up.

The trouble initially came to light because Galileo and more systematically Descartes, whose methods revealed to them a world of matter in motion governed by mathematical laws, could find no place in that world for the kind of thing that the soul and mind of man seemed to be. Back of them was the long tradition of the Greeks and the Christians, that within the human body there resides a definite entity and thing which observes passively what is going on in the world, as a spectator might sit and gaze upon a motion picture screen, and that knowledge is essentially this securing of a picture of what the world is like. This passive observation constitutes *experience*, and looking upon it the mind perceives the objects and the processes of nature. The goal of science was the attempt, in terms of purpose, to understand why they are as they are; that is, to discover their uses in the economy of nature.

So long as science thus in its content remained Aristotelian, and things were supposed to be just what their picture seemed to the mind to be, no difficulties arose; water was a fluid, wet, formless, of a certain temperature, which did a great many things obviously useful not only for man but also for the other objects it touched. But Galileo revealed a new universe: water now seemed to be nothing but a number of particles of matter whose motion followed definite laws, and whose uses were irrelevant to scientific investigation. If the qualities of wetness and coolness and the like, and the uses of water, were no longer properties of water itself, they must somehow reside, not in the water, but in the mind that perceived the water. Descartes led the way in shoving off these qualities, so inconvenient for the mathematical physicist, into a separate and totally distinct kind of thing, the mind, which he erected into a second type of substance that served as a ready dumping-ground for everything in experience which physics did not read in mechanical nature. Because he was interested in investigating the mathematical properties of nature, and because he believed that in the last analysis knowledge of that nature depended, not upon experience, but upon axioms of geometry and mechanics which the mind intuitively perceived to be true, he was not particularly worried by the fact that this procedure made the world that science described a totally different thing from the picture of experience which the mind actually saw, with all its qualities and uses and purposes. He was concerned with proving that these axioms and the system derived therefrom did really contain the plan on which the world was built; and he tried, unsuccessfully, to show that a wise and good God had created man's mind in such a way that what it intuitively felt to be true could be relied upon in actual experience. His successors, notably Spinoza, abandoned the attempt to *prove* this correspondence, and boldly *assumed* that the order of men's scientific ideas was, in the nature of things, the same as the order of objects in the world. But the chasm between the observing mind, one kind of substance, and the world described by science, a quite different kind, became increasingly apparent. The picture that the mind perceives in experience and the real world that physics depicts seemed totally different; how, then, could the mind be certain that its physics was a genuine knowledge of the world in which man was really living? If the mind perceives only a picture that bears no resemblance to what science persuades it to believe is true, how can it be sure of that science? The bold assertion that the two do correspond seemed a slender foundation upon which to build.

The second generation of Cartesians was too convinced of the necessity of a constant appeal to experience in experiment, and had seen too many ideas that intuitively appealed as certain fall before the test of fact, to stomach such a mere assertion. For them the all-important theoretical problem was how to bridge the chasm between the picture spread before the mind, and the knowledge of physics. John Locke, both a good Cartesian and a confirmed experimentalist, wrote his famous *Essay concerning Human Understanding* about this cardinal problem of the origin, extent, and certainty of science. He waged a brilliant polemic against the Cartesian notion that its origin lay in mathematical axioms, easily showing that such axioms, in the real world, were non-existent, and that first principles must come from the observation of the facts of experience. But because Descartes had relegated all such facts to the mind, taking them out of the world of nature, Locke was led into the momentous step of asserting that experience was essentially *mental*, not physical; that its picture was *in* the mind itself. This naturally created an insoluble problem. How can the mind get outside of itself to a physical and mathematical real world when it is forever shut up inside its own walls? How can we get from sensations to physics? Too honest to claim a solution when there was none, Locke became hopelessly confused in the impossible attempt to reconcile his conception of the method of knowledge as starting inside the mind with his Cartesian ideal of an independent and certain mathematical physics that described nature. His provisional conclusion was that such a science was unattainable, and that man could at best arrive at probable knowledge, a modest light sufficient to guide men's footsteps in conduct.

Thus the eighteenth century was launched upon its career of developing a science which, however practical and useful, seemed, when critically examined, to crumble away into a mere creation of the imagination, which might or might not bear some relation to the world apart from man's mind. The attempts made to bridge the chasm have shown that, if we start with Locke's assumptions, we are bound to end up with Kant, that whatever certainty our science may have, it does not give us any light upon the basic structure of the world; in other words, that the mind of man cannot know reality as it exists, if indeed there be any such world at all apart from man's mind. The only possible method of such science cuts us off from all hope of ever attaining its supposed object, though we may stumble upon valuable light in the attempt. It was not until nineteenth-century biology gave men a quite different conception of the mind and of experience and of knowledge that the difficulty seemed to lessen. If we regard man as a biological creature actively adjusting himself to an environment, and experience not as a picture in the mind but such a process of adjustment, and knowledge, not as a copy of a real world, but as a definite relation between an intelligent organism and its environment, then the problem is transformed, and, set in new terms, seems possible of solution.

It is not necessary here to recount the struggles by which men tried to extricate themselves from their predicament. Suffice it to say that they came gradually to feel that the Cartesian object of science, a knoweldge of the real world as it actually is, was impossible and misdirected; that science must confine itself to what can actually be verified by experience, and that this means that if experience is a moving picture in the mind, then science is a description of that picture, an ordering of mental elements, and their succession in time; that we can never hope to prove mathematically that these elements must succeed each other as they do, but have to rest content with discovering the order in which they do it; in a word, that the fact that we can formulate a mathematical physics of these elements is a happy accident. This program is sometimes known as *phenomenalism*, which emphasizes the belief that objects and events are "appearances" or pictures, not real things; sometimes as *empiricism*, which stresses the origins of knowledge in such an experience; sometimes as *positivism*, which claims that the object of science must be only what we can positively know, the relations between observed phenomena; sometimes as *agnosticism*, which declares that all further knowledge of an independent reality must remain unknown to man.

This scientific ideal has been accepted to the present day by the vast majority of scientific men; but gradually they have come to lose interest in the kind of world Descartes thought his science was describing, and to rest content with a world that is discoverable in experience and a science that does formulate the laws of that experience, seeing there the only reality that need concern an investigator. Hence the upshot has been that, while at first men thought they were changing the *object* of their science, abandoning a real world for a picture world, they now realize that they were rather changing its *nature*, from a mathematically necessary deductive system that would explain the reasons for things, to a mathematically formulated but experimentally derived description of events as they occur in the life of an intelligent animal. In the seventeenth century, science was rational, deducing events from axioms; in the eighteenth, it was empirical, describing the succession of pictures that presented themselves in experience; in the nineteenth, it became experimental, manipulating a biological environment.

THE EMPIRICISTS' ATTACK ON TRADITION

Although this changed conception of the nature of science did not really penetrate into all fields until the days of Hume and Kant, toward the end of the Age of Enlightenment, and even then the popular social sciences conservatively lagged behind with the older method, it did produce certain highly important results. The empiricists who, following Locke, took Europe by storm, were essentially critics: standing face to face with a traditional body of beliefs in which they profoundly disbelieved, particularly in religion, morals, and politics, they used their method to brush aside traditions and clear the ground for newer and better ideas. They were all active reformers; they sought to remove the dead weight of the past by discovering the natural history of the origin and growth in the mind of the ideas connected with objectionable and outworn beliefs and customs. They tried to show up the irrational origin of things which they hated. But when they came to build up new beliefs, they for the most part were forced to have recourse to the rationalistic method again. It took the keen mind of a Hume to make clear that a method that could destroy traditional irrationalities was equally sharp against "natural" and "rational" substitutes. It remained for the nineteenth century to attempt the only possible constructive method, careful and patient experimentation and the verification of hypotheses. But in the Age of Reason "empiricism" was employed by a Voltaire to destroy revealed religion and absolute monarchy and Christian asceticism, and by the same Voltaire "reason" was used to erect a "rational" theology and "natural" rights and a "natural" moral law. This seems a contradiction; and, though it is now easy to see why the eighteenth century universally fell into it, a contradiction it was.

Other consequences of this empiricism were less valuable. Psychology was divorced from biology, and became a barren and fruitless study of mental states and their analysis and integration. Since all knowledge seemed essentially man-made or mind-made rather than real, confidence in the possibility of any principles of morality or religion was weakened. Belief was emphasized, rather than truth, and the good and the true became merely the satisfaction of the needs of man's nature. Problem after problem was approached from the standpoint of a passive psychology rather than of an active, experimental biology.

Though Locke symbolizes this empirical attitude struggling with the older scientific ideal, the Scotchman Hume is undoubtedly, in both its beneficial and its harmful aspects, the greatest apostle of empiricism. He combines a remarkable perception of the nature and method of modern scientific inquiry with the contemporary notion of disillusioned rationalism, in his case half serious and half sceptical, that its object is not the real world but a picture world inside men's heads. At times, indeed, he seems to abandon as meaningless the eighteenth-century distinction between real world and picture world, and to feel that the world that man can experience is real enough for all human purposes. To him, no knowledge for which some antecedent sense impression was not discoverable could claim any validity. The consequences of a ruthless application of this sword can be imagined. Theology, rational morality, Cartesian science, crumbled beneath his touch; and when he was through, he uncompromisingly concluded, "When we run over libraries, persuaded of these principles, what havoc must we make? If we take in our hand any volume; of divinity or school metaphysics, for instance; let us ask, *Does it contain any abstract reasoning concerning quantity or number?* No. *Does it contain any experimental reasoning concerning matter of fact and existence?* No. Commit it then to the flames: for it can contain nothing but sophistry and illusion." [15] But what in these fields appeared purely destructive was in science a potent means of purification. By the same tests, force, energy, causal necessity and all rationalistic explanation of what has to be and of why things are as they are and do as they do, go by the board, and scientists are left only to describe the relations of actual experience. Man can explain nothing, he can only observe and depict.

[15] David Hume, *Enquiry concerning Human Understanding*, Pt. III, sec. 12.

THE SCIENTIFIC IDEALS OF THE AGE OF REASON

But while the empiricism worked itself out to such conclusions, it must not be supposed that it seriously disturbed the imposing edifice of the Newtonian world-machine, even if it did cast doubts upon the existence of that machine apart from human experience. So long as man lived, he lived in such a mechanical world; it really mattered little what the world was to God. Nor did the changing conception of the location of the object of science affect its main outlines. If the world of science was a human world, it still contained whirling planets and unchanging if not unchangeable laws of gravitation and motion. Throughout the eighteenth century all thinkers believed that the scene of human life was set in a great, fixed, geometrical and mechanical order of nature, a mighty machine eternally pursuing the same unchanging round of cyclical processes. And the dominating ideals by which they swore and by which they tested all human concepts were Nature and Reason.

Nature meant, not the world of inanimate objects apart from man, as the term is perhaps most commonly used to-day, but the whole rational order of things, of which man was the most important part.

> Man always deceives himself when he abandons experience to follow imaginary systems. He is the work of Nature. He exists in Nature. He is submitted to her laws. He cannot deliver himself from them. It is in vain his mind would spring forward beyond the visible world: an imperious necessity ever compels his return—for a being formed by Nature, who is circumscribed by her laws, there exists nothing beyond the great whole of which he forms a part, of which he experiences the influence. The beings his imagination pictures as above Nature, or distinguished from her, are always chimeras formed after that which he has already seen, but of which it is utterly impossible he should ever form any correct idea, either as to the place they occupy, or their manner of acting—for him there is not, there can be nothing, out of that nature which includes all beings. . . . The universe, the vast assemblage of everything that exists, presents only matter and motion: the whole offers to our contemplation nothing but an immense, an uninterrupted succession of causes and effects. . . . Nature, therefore, in its most extended signification, is the great whole that results from the assemblage of matter, under its various combinations, with that contrariety of motions, which the universe offers to our view.[16]

[16] Holbach, *Système de la Nature*, ch. I.

Men saw in the world no more chaos, no more confusion, but an essentially rational and harmonious machine.

This was an intoxicating discovery. It was inevitable that men should be struck by the contrast with human society and institutions: in comparison with the simplicity and order of the laws of gravitation, man's laws were anything but harmonious and orderly. If Nature is so much more perfect than human arts, it must be, so men thought, the handiwork of a much more perfect being than man; it must be the harmonious masterpiece of God. Natural laws were regarded as real laws or commands, decrees of the Almighty, literally obeyed without a single act of rebellion. Says Nature to the scientist, in Voltaire, "My poor son, shall I tell you the truth? I have been given a name that does not suit me at all. I am called Nature, and I am really Art" [17]—the art of God. One of Newton's chief disciples sums it up thus:

> Natural science is subservient to purposes of a higher kind, and is chiefly to be valued as it lays a sure foundation for Natural Religion and Moral Philosophy; by leading us, in a satisfactory manner, to the knowledge of the Author and Governor of the universe. . . . To study Nature is to study into His workmanship; every new discovery opens up to us a new part of his scheme. . . . Our views of Nature, however imperfect, serve to represent to us, in the most sensible manner, that mighty power which prevails throughout, acting with a force and efficacy that appears to suffer no diminution from the greatest distances of space or intervals of time; and that wisdom which we see equally displayed in the exquisite structure and just motions of the greatest and the subtilest parts. These, with perfect goodness, by which they are evidently directed, constitute the supreme object of the speculations of a philosopher; who, while he contemplates and admires so excellent a system, cannot but be himself excited and animated to correspond with the general harmony of Nature.[18]

With distinguished scientists, from Newton down, voicing such worship of the perfection of Nature, it is but natural to expect popular thinkers like Alexander Pope in his *Essay on Man* to express this new religion:

> All are but parts of one stupendous whole,
> Whose body Nature is, and God the soul; . . .

[17] Voltaire, *Dictionnaire philosophique*, art. "Nature."

[18] Colin Maclaurin, *An Account of Sir Isaac Newton's Philosophical Discoveries*, 3, 4, 95.

All Nature is but Art, unknown to thee;
All chance, direction, which thou canst not see;
All discord, harmony not understood;
All partial evil, universal good:
And, spite of pride, in erring reason's spite,
One truth is clear, whatever is, is right.[19]

For the eighteenth century, Newton had actually proved this; and Newton was the greatest mind of the ages. Pope sang:

Nature and Nature's laws lay hid in night;
God said, *Let* Newton *be!* and all was Light.[20]

One great difference marks off this Newtonian world from the world of modern science: in such a machine, time counted for nothing. Processes rolled on their way in cyclical fashion, completing themselves, like the orbits of the planets, in recurrent definite intervals; but there was no real change. The world had always been such an order, and always would be; of growth, of development, of evolution, the greatest single new conception introduced by the last century, there was not the slightest idea. For a few radical thinkers, like Holbach, the universe itself was eternal; but from Newton down the vast majority looked upon it as a machine that had been created at a definite point in time. Men could form no conception of how it could have *grown* to be what it was, and they therefore had no difficulty in imagining it to have sprung full-blown from the hand of God 4004 years B.C., as the tradition had it. The very idea of a machine, of a watch, to which it was constantly compared, implied a builder, a watchmaker; and once granted this, he could have made it just as it is at any time. The whole form of Newtonian science practically forced men, as a necessary scientific hypothesis, to believe in an external Creator, just as the very form of nineteenth-century evolutionary science has made that idea all but impossible, and substituted for it the notion of God as immanent, as a soul or spirit dwelling within the universe and developing it through long ages.

Nature was through and through orderly and rational; hence what was natural was easily identified with what was rational, and conversely, whatever, particularly in human society, seemed to an intelligent man reasonable, was regarded as natural, as somehow rooted in the very nature of things. So Nature and the Natural easily

[19] Alexander Pope, *Essay on Man.*
[20] Pope, *Works*, Cambridge ed., 135.

became the ideal of man and of human society, and were interpreted as Reason and the Reasonable. The great object of human endeavor was to discover what in every field was natural and reasonable, and to brush aside the accretions of irrational tradition that Reason and Nature might the more easily be free to display its harmonious order. In religion, the Christian tradition was for the first time seriously criticized in the light of this ideal, and the conception of a Natural or Rational Religion was the dominating idea. In social life, particularly in politics and in business, such notions lent powerful support to the demands of the middle class for freedom from absolute monarchy and mercantilistic restrictions on trade and industry, and formed the banners under which throughout the century business men fought the old régime. Never in human history, perhaps, have scientific conceptions had such a powerful reaction upon the actual life and ideals of men. Whatever differences the reformers may have had in their aims, all agreed in seeking to find a natural and rational order in human affairs and in desiring the existing confusion to be swept aside.

Starting from such premises, the Natural and Rational took on various shades of meaning. Since scientific laws were general and uniform, the Natural in human affairs was first of all the universal, those customs and ideals which could be detected everywhere as the core underlying apparent surface divergencies. It became immensely popular to go to the recently discovered and as yet but half-understood Oriental societies, Persia and especially China, to discern what laws and institutions were common to them and to the West. "Persian" and "Chinese letters" were issued in great profusion, with the aim of criticizing European civilization in the light of such world-wide principles. Thus men were naturally led to an ideal of Cosmopolitanism: they became in truth citizens of the world, and regarded particular national ideas as but "patriotic prejudices" unworthy of the scientist.

This easily passed over into an identification of the Natural with the original and primitive; what existed before man interfered with rational ways of doing things. Most popular writers read this back into the past, and actually believed that in some remote Golden Age men had had a natural religion that commended itself as inherently reasonable, which succeeding ages of scheming priests and monarchs had for their own advantage corrupted into superstition. They believed in an original State of Nature, in which human society had been well-ordered and perfect, until usurpers gained control and introduced silly regulations and foolish schemes that served only to spoil everything. More profound thinkers did not attempt to posit that such a state of nature had ever actually existed; they thought rather that it was something in the present underlying the accretions which man had added. For both classes the implication was that to perfect social arrangements one had only to abolish man-made institutions and allow Nature to function by herself—*laisser-faire* and liberty in all things was its practical import. Such an idea was particularly influential because it was precisely the kind of liberty that the middle class was demanding for itself. Thus the natural was in theory what God had intended the world of man to be, and in practice it was what seemed reasonable to the commercial classes, complete freedom from governmental interference.

This emphasis on the Natural as the original merged into interest in the savage: primitive life among the forests of America or in the South Sea islands was idealized. The Noble Red Man came into his own as the very type of what a free existence should be. Many were the volumes glorifying his rational society, free from all the conventions that hemmed in Europeans, perhaps the most famous being Diderot's *Voyage of Bougainville*, narrating the experiences of that famous French explorer of the Pacific. He found a simple idyllic people—in Diderot's pages—who had no notion of the moral taboos, especially as regards sex, that were the bane of French life. That polished and cultivated age took great delight in reading interminable traveler's romances and dreaming of modifying the society of Paris or London until it resembled the life they thought the Noble Red Man lived.

Again, the Natural was the reasonable and the socially useful, and all that seemed to have no apparent value was unnatural and to be destroyed. It was the ideal, that which men wanted to realize themselves; and it easily passed over into the divine. Nature was God's model for man; nay, it was the very face of God himself.

> "O thou," cries this Nature to man, "who, following the impulse I have given you, during your whole existence, incessantly tend towards happiness, do not strive to resist my sovereign law. Labor to your own felicity; partake without fear of the banquet which is spread before you, with the most hearty welcome; you will find the means legibly written on your own heart. . . . Dare, then, to affranchise yourself from the trammels of superstition, my self-conceited, pragmatic rival, who mistakes my rights; denounce those empty theories, which are usurpers of my privileges; return under the dominion of my laws, which, however severe, are mild in comparison

> with those of bigotry. It is in my empire alone that true liberty reigns. Tyranny is unknown to its soil, slavery is forever banished from its votaries; equity unceasingly watches over the rights of all my subjects, maintains them in the possession of their just claims; benevolence, grafted upon humanity, connects them by amicable bonds; truth enlightens them; never can imposture blind them with his obscuring mists. Return, then, my child, to thy fostering mother's arms! Deserter, trace back thy wandering steps to Nature! She will console thee for thine evils; she will drive from thy heart those appalling fears which overwhelm thee . . . Return to Nature, to humanity, to thyself! . . . Enjoy thyself, and cause others also to enjoy those comforts, which I have placed with a liberal hand for all the children of the earth, who all equally emanate from my bosom. . . . These pleasures are freely permitted thee, if thou indulgest them with moderation, with that discretion which I myself have fixed. Be happy, then, O man!" [21]

The eighteenth century raised its voice as one man in a pæan of praise to Nature.

> O Nature, sovereign of all beings! and ye, her adorable daughters, Virtue, Reason, and Truth! remain forever our revered protectors! it is to you that belong the praises of the human race; to you appertains the homage of the earth. Show us then, O Nature! that which man ought to do, in order to obtain the happiness which thou makest him desire. Virtue! animate him with thy beneficent fire. Reason! conduct his uncertain steps through the paths of life. Truth! let thy torch illumine his intellect, dissipate the darkness of his road. Unite, O assisting deities! your powers, in order to submit the hearts of mankind to your dominion. Banish error from our mind; wickedness from our hearts; confusion from our footsteps; cause knowledge to extend its salubrious reign; goodness to occupy our souls; serenity to occupy our bosoms.[22]

The whole educated world in the eighteenth century was convinced, as never before or since, that the most beneficent and the most divine force in human life, man's supreme achievement and his brightest jewel, is Science. "Without the sciences," wrote Mercier to the Academy of Sciences, "man would rank below the brutes." [23] For the first time in man's long history, it was generally believed that human happiness and human knowledge go hand in hand. Speaking of the early Babylonian astronomers, and seeing there, like

[21] Holbach, *Système de la Nature,* ch. 14.
[22] *Ibid.*
[23] Quoted in L. Ducros, *Les Encyclopédistes,* 315.

his fellows, the rays of the Golden Age, Buffon sounded the spirit of his times: "That early people was very happy, because it was very scientific." [24] And all enlightened men agreed in finding in the pursuit of science the sum of human wisdom: "What enthusiasm is nobler than believing man capable of knowing all the forces and discovering by his labors all the secrets of nature!" [25] The eighteenth century was preëminently the age of faith in science.

SELECTED READING LISTS

The Advance of Mechanical Science: Dampier-Whetham, *H. of Science;* P. Smith, *H. of Modern Culture,* vols. I, II; A. Wolf, *H. of Science, Technology, and Phil. in the 18th cent.;* Sedgwick and Tyler, *Short H. of Science;* Dannemann; Burtt, *Met. Foundations of Mod. Physical Science,* best interpretation of significance: Whitehead, *Science and the Modern World. Cam. Mod. Hist.,* V, c. 23; VIII, c. 1; Lavisse et Rambaud, VI, c. 10; VII, c. 15; by Tannery. *H. des Sciences en France,* in G. Hanotaux, *H. de la Nat. Française,* XIV. See histories of the sciences listed under Ch. X, esp. Berry, Cantor, Mach, Gerland; H. Crew, *Rise of Modern Physics;* F. Rosenberger, *Ges. der Physik.* M. Ornstein, *Role of the Scientific Societies in the 17th cent.* G. N. Clark, *The Seventeenth Century; Science and Invention in the Age of Newton.* Robert Boyle, *Works,* ed. Birch; Life by F. Masson. Huygens, *Oeuvres.* Isaac Newton, *Principia Mathematica,* ed. Cajori; *Opticks.* Lives by D. Brewster, L. T. More, S. Brodetsky; studies by L. Bloch, F. Rosenberger; see Burtt.

The Rise of Experimental Science: In addition to the above E. Gerland and F. Traumüller, *Ges. der physikalischen Experimentierkunst;* L. Hogben, *Science for the Citizen.* Histories of chemistry by E. Thorpe, J. M. Stillman, A. Ladenburg; of geology by K. A. von Zittel, H. A. Woodward; of biology by E. Nordenskiöld, W. A. Locy, L. C. Miall, H. F. Osborne; of medicine by F. H. Garrison, V. Robinson. W. Harvey, *On the Movement of the Heart and the Blood;* W. Gilbert, *On the Magnet;* Boyle's writings. The empirical theory of science: J. Glanvill, *Scepsis Scientifica;* J. Locke, *Essay conc. Human Understanding;* G. Berkeley, *De Motu, Siris;* D. Hume, *Enquiry concerning the Human Understanding;* Diderot, *Thoughts on the Interpretation of Nature.*

Nature and Reason: Carl Becker, *The Heavenly City of the 18th century Philosophers; The Declaration of Independence,* c. 2; W. Marvin, *H. of Eur. Phil.,* c. 23; Höffding, I, 212–35; brief accounts of the influence of the Newtonian ideal. R. B. Mowat, *The Age of Reason;* K. Martin, *French Liberal Thought in the 18th cent.;* D. Mornet, *French Thought in the 18th cent.;* L. Ducros, *Les Encyclopédistes;* E. Cassirer, *Das Zeitalter der Aufklärung.* L. Lévy-Bruhl, *H. of Mod. Phil. in*

[24] Buffon, *Époques de la Nature,* VII.

[25] Buffon, quoted in L. Ducros, *Les Encyclopédistes,* 316.

France; P. Damiron, *H. de la Phil. au 18e s.*; F. A. Lange, *H. of Materialism*; J. Fabre, *Les Pères de la Révolution*; E. Faguet, *Le 18e siècle*; H. Hettner, *Litteraturges. des 18. Jahrh.*; E. Lavisse, *H. de France*, VIII, pt. ii, bk. iii, c. 3; IX, pt. i, bk. iv; VII, pt. ii, bk. vii. Leslie Stephen, *H. of English Thought in the 18th cent.*; John Morley, *Voltaire* (defense of the age), *Diderot, Rousseau, Condorcet*. Colin Maclaurin, *An Account of Sir Isaac Newton's Philosophical Discoveries* (best popularization); Voltaire, *English Letters*, ed. Lanson; *Éléments de la philosophie de Newton*; art. "Nature" in *Phil. Dictionary*; studies by Morley, G. Brandes, N. L. Torrey; G. Pellissier, *Voltaire Philosophe*. H. Robinson, *Bayle the Sceptic*. Buffon, *Natural History*; Holbach, *System of Nature* (most thoroughgoing statement); D'Alembert, *Preliminary Discourse to the Great Encyclopedia*; J. S. Schapiro, *Condorcet and the Rise of Liberalism in France*. G. E. Lessing, lives by T. W. Rolleston, Erich Schmidt. For influence on literature, Boileau, *L'Art Poétique*; A. Pope, *Essay on Criticism, Essay on Man*.

The Problem of Knowledge and Empiricism: John Dewey, *Reconstruction in Philosophy*, chs. 3, 4, gives the best orientation; see also Burtt and Whitehead. Traditional accounts in the histories of philosophy, of which B. A. G. Fuller, H. Höffding, E. Bréhier, and W. Windelband, *Ges. der Neuren Phil.*, are the best. E. Cassirer, *Das Erkenntnisproblem*, full and comprehensive account. J. G. Hibben, *Age of the Enlightenment*. For the German background, see Leibniz, *Selections*, ed. Latta, Montgomery, Duncan, Langley; studies by J. T. Merz, John Dewey, Bertrand Russell. John Locke, *Essay conc. Human Understanding*, esp. bks. II, IV; *Selections*, ed. S. P. Lamprecht. Studies by F. J. E. Woodbridge, in *Essays in Honor of John Dewey, Studies in the H. of Ideas*, III; by A. Hofstader, J. G. Clapp, J. Gibson. George Berkeley, esp. *New Theory of Vision, Principles of Human Knowledge, Three Dialogues*; F. J. E. Woodbridge, *Realism of Berkeley*, in *Stud. Hist. Ideas*, I. For developed empiricism, David Hume, esp. *Treatise of Human Nature, Enquiry concerning the Human Understanding; Selections*, ed. Hendel. Studies by John Laird, C. W. Hendel; S. P. Lamprecht, in *Stud. Hist. Ideas*, II; Thomas Huxley. Condillac, *Traité des Sensations, Essai sur les Origines des Connaissances Humaines*. Helvétius, *De l'Esprit, De l'Homme*.

Science and Society

Science interacts with many aspects of our society and culture. The most celebrated recent analysis of this interaction is C. P. Snow's description of a dichotomy of "two cultures," the older humanistic culture rooted in literature and art and the new culture derived from contemporary science. The controversy generated by Snow's contention is itself an indication that a problem exists, even if one does not agree with all the features of his analysis. Both Juster and Holton raise issues related to this controversy. In The Phantom Tollbooth, *a children's book in the same sense that* Alice in Wonderland *is a children's book, we have an allegorical statement of the problem: in one city words are considered most important, whereas the other city ranks numbers uppermost. Norton Juster is an architect and design critic at the Pratt Institute. Gerald Holton, Professor of Physics at Harvard University, has provided penetrating insights into some of the questions raised by Snow. He has also made major contributions to the education of the nonscientist in an age of science. His discussion disentangles one aspect of the relation between science and society from confusing social and political factors. In clarifying this relationship, he also deals with some often held false images of science.*

Marjorie Nicolson's discussion of Milton and the telescope serves as an example of interaction between science and the arts; in this case, literature. She attempts to show that Milton's knowledge of Galileo's astronomical discoveries influenced his writing of Paradise Lost.

Other writers have considered different aspects of Milton's responses to the science of his day. Professor of English at Columbia University, Marjorie Nicolson has been interested in many facets of the influence of science on English literature.

J. B. Conant's lecture echoes many of the other articles here. A chemist and former President of Harvard University, he is concerned with science as a human activity, created by people and affecting their lives, not only on the technical level, but also through the climate of ideas and ethics.

Robert K. Merton, a sociologist at Columbia University, has had a long standing interest in various aspects of the sociology of science. In this selection he asks a specific question concerning the influence of society on science (as opposed to the more frequently asked questions about the influence of science on society). Using methods of contemporary sociology, he tries to establish a connection between the development of science, especially in the seventeenth century, and the Puritan ethic. As might be expected, the subject is not free from controversy, and there are individuals who challenge Merton's thesis and conclusions. This paper should not be mistaken, however, as having anything to do with the broad range of discussion that concerns itself with interactions between scientific knowledge and religious beliefs. It deals with a sociological and not a religious question.

Finally we return to P. W. Bridgman, whose concern in this selection is one he expresses frequently in his later writings. He is convinced that some of the intellectual attitudes and modes of thought characteristic of the finest scientific tradition can be legitimately extended to guide conduct and decision in other human fields. But he feels that relatively little effective transfer is being made. Since scientists and others have held to naive views concerning the applicability of scientific "methods" in other fields, there exists an extensive litera-

ture debunking undue veneration of the sacred scientific cow. We have not included a sample of this relevant material, but anyone interested in the serious and sophisticated problems raised by Bridgman *would also do well to acquaint himself with writings that evaluate the limitations of science.*

Norton Juster

Faintly Macabre's Story

"Once upon a time, this land was barren and frightening wilderness whose high rocky mountains sheltered the evil winds and whose barren valleys offered hospitality to no man. Few things grew, and those that did were bent and twisted and their fruit was as bitter as wormwood. What wasn't waste was desert, and what wasn't desert was rock, and the demons of darkness made their home in the hills. Evil creatures roamed at will through the countryside and down to the sea. It was known as the land of Null.

"Then one day a small ship appeared on the Sea of Knowledge. It carried a young prince seeking the future. In the name of goodness and truth he laid claim to all the country and set out to explore his new domain. The demons, monsters, and giants were furious at his presumption and banded together to drive him out. The earth shook with their battle, and when they had finished, all that remained to the prince was a small piece of land at the edge of the sea.

" 'I'll build my city here,' he declared, and that is what he did.

"Before long, more ships came bearing settlers for the new land and the city grew and pushed its boundaries farther and farther out. Each day it was attacked anew, but nothing could destroy the prince's new city. And grow it did. Soon it was no longer just a city; it was a kingdom, and it was called the kingdom of Wisdom.

Reprinted with permission of Epstein and Carroll Associates from Norton Juster, The Phantom Tollbooth *(New York: Epstein & Carroll, Inc. Copyright 1961 by Norton Juster), pp. 71–7.*

"But, outside the walls, all was not safe, and the new king vowed to conquer the land that was rightfully his. So each spring he set forth with his army and each autumn he returned, and year by year the kingdom grew larger and more prosperous. He took to himself a wife and before long had two fine young sons to whom he taught everything he knew so that one day they might rule wisely.

"When the boys grew to young-manhood, the king called them to him and said: 'I am becoming an old man and can no longer go forth to battle. You must take my place and found new cities in the wilderness, for the kingdom of Wisdom must grow.'

"And so they did. One went south to the Foothills of Confusion and built Dictionopolis, the city of words; and one went north to the Mountains of Ignorance and built Digitopolis, the city of numbers. Both cities flourished mightily and the demons were driven back still further. Soon other cities and towns were founded in the new lands, and at last only the farthest reaches of the wilderness remained to these terrible creatures—and there they waited, ready to strike down all who ventured near or relaxed their guard.

"The two brothers were glad, however, to go their separate ways, for they were by nature very suspicious and jealous. Each one tried to outdo the other, and they worked so hard and diligently at it that before long their cities rivaled even Wisdom in size and grandeur.

" 'Words are more important than wisdom,' said one privately.

" 'Numbers are more important than wisdom,' thought the other to himself.

"And they grew to dislike each other more and more.

"The old king, however, who knew nothing of his sons' animosity, was very happy in the twilight of his reign and spent his days quietly walking and contemplating in the royal gardens. His only regret was that he'd never had a daughter, for he loved little girls as much as he loved little boys. One day as he was strolling peacefully about the grounds, he discovered two tiny babies that had been abandoned in a basket under the grape arbor. They were beautiful golden-haired girls.

"The king was overjoyed. 'They have been sent to crown my old age,' he cried, and called the queen, his ministers, the palace staff, and, indeed, the entire population to see them.

" 'We'll call this one Rhyme and this one Reason,' he said, and so they became the Princess of Sweet Rhyme and the Princess of Pure Reason and were brought up in the palace.

"When the old king finally died, the kingdom was divided between his two sons, with the provision that they would be equally responsible for the welfare of the young princesses. One son went south and became Azaz, the unabridged king of Dictionopolis, and the other went north and became the Mathemagician, ruler of Digitopolis; and, true to their words, they both provided well for the little girls, who continued to live in Wisdom.

"Everyone loved the princesses because of their great beauty, their gentle ways, and their ability to settle all controversies fairly and reasonably. People with problems or grievances or arguments came from all over the land to seek advice, and even the two brothers, who by this time were fighting continuously, often called upon them to help decide matters of state. It was said by everyone that 'Rhyme and Reason answer all problems.'

"As the years passed, the two brothers grew farther and farther apart and their separate kingdoms became richer and grander. Their disputes, however, became more and more difficult to reconcile. But always, with patience and love, the princesses set things right.

"Then one day they had the most terrible quarrel of all. King Azaz insisted that words were far more significant than numbers and hence his kingdom was truly the greater and the Mathemagician claimed that numbers were much more important than words and hence his kingdom was supreme. They discussed and debated and raved and ranted until they were on the verge of blows, when it was decided to submit the question to arbitration by the princesses.

"After days of careful consideration, in which all the evidence was weighed and all the witnesses heard, they made their decision:

" 'Words and numbers are of equal value, for, in the cloak of knowledge, one is warp and the other woof. It is no more important to count the sands than it is to name the stars. Therefore, let both kingdoms live in peace.'

"Everyone was pleased with the verdict. Everyone, that is, but the brothers, who were beside themselves with anger.

" 'What good are these girls if they cannot settle an argument in someone's favor?' they growled, since both were more interested in their own advantage than in the truth. 'We'll banish them from the kingdom forever.'

"And so they were taken from the palace and sent far away to the Castle in the Air, and they have not been seen since. That is why today, in all this land, there is neither Rhyme nor Reason."

"And what happened to the two rulers?" asked Milo.

"Banishing the two princesses was the last thing they ever agreed upon, and they soon fell to warring with each other. Despite this, their own kingdoms have continued to prosper, but the old city of Wisdom has fallen into great disrepair, and there is no one to set things right. So, you see, until the princesses return, I shall have to stay here."

Gerald Holton

Modern Science and the Intellectual Tradition

When future generations look back to our day, they will envy us for having lived at a time of brilliant achievement in many fields, and not least in science nad technology. We are at the threshold of basic knowledge concerning the origins of life, the chemical elements, and the galaxies. We are near an understanding of the fundamental constituents of matter, of the process by which the brain works, and of the factors governing behavior. We have launched the physical exploration of space and have begun to see how to conquer hunger and disease on a large scale. Scientific thought appears to be applicable to an ever wider range of studies. With current technical ingenuity one can at last hope to implement most of the utopian dreams of the past.

Hand in hand with the quality of excitement in scientific work today goes an astonishing quantity. The world-wide output is vast. There are now over 50,000 scientific and technical journals, publishing annually about 1,200,000 articles of significance for some branch of research and engineering in the physical and life sciences. Every year there are about 60,000 new science books and 100,000 research reports.[1] And the amount of scientific work being done is increasing at a rapid rate, dou-

Reprinted with permission of the author and editor from Gerald Holton, "Modern Science and the Intellectual Tradition," in Science, *vol. 131, no. 3408 (April 22, 1960), pp. 1187–93.*

[1] "Improving the Availability of Scientific and Technical Information in the United States," President's Science Advisory Committee Report (1958).

bling approximately every 20 years. Every phase of daily and national life is being penetrated by some aspect of this exponentially growing activity.

It is appropriate, therefore, that searching questions are now being asked about the function and place of this lusty giant. Just as a man's vigorously pink complexion may alert the trained eye to a grave disease of the circulatory system, so too may the spectacular success and growth of science and technology turn out, on more thorough study, to mask a deep affliction of our culture. And indeed, anyone committed to the view that science should be a basic part of our intellectual tradition will soon find grounds for concern.

Some of the major symptoms of the relatively narrow place science, as properly understood, really occupies in the total picture are quantitative. For example, while the total annual expenditure for scientific research and development in this country is now at the high level of over $10 billion, basic research—the main roots of the tree that furnishes scientific knowledge and the fruits of technology—has a share of about 7 percent at best.[2] Correspondingly, a recent manpower study showed that of the 750,000 trained scientists and engineers, only 15,000 are responsible for the major part of the creative work being done in basic research.[3] Another nationwide survey found that in 1958 nearly 40 percent of the men and women who had attended college in the United States confessed that they had taken not a single course in the physical and biological sciences.[4] Similarly, in contrast to the overwhelming amount of, and concern with, science and technology today, the mass media pay only negligible attention to their substance; the newspapers have been found to give less than 5 percent of their (nonadvertising) space to factual presentations of science, technology, and medicine, and television stations, only about 0.3 percent of their time.[4, 5] In short, all our voracious consumption of technological devices, all our talk about the threats or beauties of science, and all our money spent on en-

2 "Reviews of Data on Research and Development," *National Science Foundation Rept. No. 15* (1959); "Federal Funds for Science," *National Science Foundation Rept. No.* 8 (1959).

3 *Naval Research Advisory Committee Report on Basic Research in the Navy* (1 June 1959), vol. 1, p. 29; *ibid.* vol. 2, p. 34.

4 *The Public Impact of Science in the Mass Media* (Univ. of Michigan, Ann Arbor, 1958), p. 150; pp. 1–3.

5 There is evidence that these figures have been increased by a factor of perhaps 1.5 since the survey was conducted. See H. Krieghbaum, *Science* 129, 1095 (1959).

gineering development should not draw attention from the fact that the pursuit of scientific knowledge itself is not a strong component of the operative system of general values.

THE ATOMIZATION OF LOYALTIES

In the qualitative sense, and particularly among intellectuals, the symptoms are no better. One hears talk of the hope that the forces of science may be tamed and harnessed to the general advance of ideas, that the much deplored gap between scientists and humanists may be bridged. But the truth is that both the hopes and the bridges are illusory. The separation—which I shall examine further—between the work of the scientist on the one hand and that of the intellectual outside science on the other is steadily increasing, and the genuine acceptance of science as a valid part of culture is becoming less rather than more likely.

Moreover, there appears at present to be no force in our cultural dynamics strong enough to change this trend. This is due mainly to the atrophy of two mechanisms by which the schism was averted in the past. First, the common core of their early education and the wide range of their interests was apt to bring scholars and scientists together at some level where there could be mutual communication on the subjects of their individual competence; and second, the concepts and attitudes of contemporary science were made a part of the general humanistic concerns of the time. In this way a reasonable equilibrium of compatible interpretations was felt to exist, during the last century, between the concepts and problems of science on the one hand and of intelligent common sense on the other; this was also true with respect to the scientific and the non-scientific aspects of the training of intellectuals. Specialists, of course, have always complained of being inadequately appreciated; what is more, they are usually right. But although there were some large blind spots and some bitter quarrels, the two sides were not, as they are now in danger of coming to be, separated by a gulf of ignorance and indifference.[6]

It is of course not my purpose here to urge better science edu-

[6] Perhaps the most eloquent and influential voice among those who have recently addressed themselves to this problem is that of C. P. Snow in the Rede Lecture, *The Two Cultures and the Scientific Revolution* (Cambridge Univ. Press, Cambridge and New York, 1959). I recommend his book, although with certain reservations. See also E. Ashby, *Technology and the Academics* (Macmillan, London, 1958) and F. Burkhardt, *Science and the Humanities* (Antioch Press, Yellow Springs, Ohio, 1959).

cation at the expense of humanistic and social studies. On the contrary; the latter do not fare much better than science does, and the shabby effort devoted to science is merely the symptom of a more extensive sickness of our educational systems. Nor do I want to place all blame on educators and publicists. Too many scientists have forgotten that especially at a time of rapid expansion of knowledge they have an extra obligation and opportunity with respect to the wider public, that some of the foremost research men, including Newton and Einstein, took great pains to write expositions of the essence of their discoveries in a form intended to be accessible to the nonscientist. And in the humanities, too many contributors and interpreters seem to scoff at Shelley's contention in his *Defence of Poetry* that one of the artist's tasks is to "absorb the new knowledge of the sciences and assimilate it to human needs, color it with human passions, transform it into the blood and bone of human nature."

It is through the accumulation of such neglects just as much as through deterioration in the quantity and quality of instruction given our future intellectual leaders that the acceptance of science as a meaningful component of our culture has come to be questioned. Again, this process is to a large extent merely one aspect of the increasing atomization of loyalties within the intelligentsia. The writer, the scholar, the scientist, the engineer, the teacher, the lawyer, the politician, the physician—each now regards himself first of all as a member of a separate, special group of fellow professionals to which he gives almost all his allegiance and energy; only very rarely does the professional feel a sense of responsibility toward, or of belonging to, a larger intellectual community. This loss of cohesion is perhaps the most revelant symptom of the disease of our culture, for it points directly to one of its specific causes. As in other cases of this sort, this is a failure of image.

PURE THOUGHT AND PRACTICAL POWER

Each person's image of the role of science may differ in detail from that of the next, but all public images are in the main based on one or more of seven positions. The first of these goes back to Plato and portrays science as an activity with double benefits: Science as pure thought helps the mind find truth, and science as power provides tools for effective action. In book 7 of the *Republic*, Socrates tells Glaucon why the young rulers in the Ideal State should study mathematics: "This, then, is knowledge of the kind we are seeking, having a double use, military and philosophical; for the man of war must learn the art of number, or he will not know how to array his troops; and the philosopher also, because he has to rise out of the sea of change and lay hold of true being. . . . This will be the easiest way for the soul to pass from becoming to truth and being."

The main flaw in this image is that it omits a third vital aspect. Science has always had also a mythopoeic function—that is, it generates an important part of our symbolic vocabulary and provides some of the metaphysical bases and philosophical orientations of our ideology. As a consequence the methods of argument of science, its conceptions and its models, have permeated first the intellectual life of the time, then the tenets and usages of everyday life. All philosophies share with science the need to work with concepts such as space, time, quantity, matter, order, law, causality, verification, reality. Our language of ideas, for example, owes a great debt to statics, hydraulics, and the model of the solar system. These have furnished powerful analogies in many fields of study. Guiding ideas—such as conditions of equilibrium, centrifugal and centripetal forces, conservation laws, feedback, invariance, complementarity—enrich the general arsenal of imaginative tools of thought.

A sound image of science must embrace each of the three functions. However, usually only one of the three is recognized. For example, folklore often depicts the life of the scientist either as isolated from life and from beneficent action [7] or, at the other extreme, as dedicated to technological improvements.

ICONOCLASM

A second image of long standing is that of the scientist as iconoclast. Indeed, almost every major scientific advance has been interpreted—either triumphantly or with apprehension—as a blow against religion. To some extent science was pushed into this position by the ancient tendency to prove the existence of God by pointing to problems which science could not solve at the time. Newton thought that the regularities and stability of the solar system proved it "could only proceed from the counsel and dominion of an intelligent and

[7] See, for example, the disturbing findings of M. Mead and R. Metraux, "Image of the scientist among high-school students," *Science* 126, 384 (1957). I have presented the approach in this middle section in the "Adventures of the Mind" series, *Saturday Evening Post*, 9 January 1960.

powerful Being," and the same attitude governed thought concerning the earth's formation before the theory of geological evolution, concerning the descent of man before the theory of biological evolution, and concerning the origin of our galaxy before modern cosmology. The advance of knowledge therefore made inevitable an apparent conflict between science and religion. It is now clear how large a price had to be paid for a misunderstanding of both science and religion: to base religious beliefs on an estimate of what science cannot do is as foolhardy as it is blasphemous.

The iconoclastic image of science has, however, other components not ascribable to a misconception of its functions. For example, Arnold Toynbee charges science and technology with usurping the place of Christianity as the main source of our new symbols. Neo-orthodox theologians call science the "self-estrangement" of man because it carries him with idolatrous zeal along a dimension where no ultimate—that is, religious—concerns prevail. It is evident that these views fail to recognize the multitude of divergent influences that shape a culture, or a person. And on the other hand there is, of course, a group of scientists, though not a large one, which really does regard science as largely an iconoclastic activity. Ideologically they are descendants of Lucretius, who wrote on the first pages of *De rerum natura*, "The terror and darkness of mind must be dispelled not by the rays of the sun and glittering shafts of day, but by the aspect and the law of nature; whose first principle we shall begin by thus stating, nothing is ever gotten out of nothing by divine power." In our day this ancient trend has assumed political significance owing to the fact that in Soviet literature scientific teaching and atheistic propaganda are sometimes equated.

ETHICAL PERVERSION

The third image of science is that of a force which can invade, possess, pervert, and destroy man. The current stereotype of the soulless, evil scientist is the psychopathic investigator of science fiction or the nuclear destroyer—immoral if he develops the weapons he is asked to produce, traitorous if he refuses. According to this view, scientific morality is inherently negative. It causes the arts to languish, it blights culture, and when applied to human affairs, it leads to regimentation and to the impoverishment of life. Science is the serpent seducing us into eating the fruits of the tree of knowledge—thereby dooming us.

The fear behind this attitude is genuine but not confined to science: it is directed against all thinkers and innovators. Society has always found it hard to deal with creativity, innovation, and new knowledge. And since science assures a particularly rapid, and therefore particularly disturbing, turnover of ideas, it remains a prime target of suspicion.

Factors peculiar to our time intensify this suspicion. The discoveries of "pure" science often lend themselves readily to widespread exploitation through technology. The products of technology—whether they are better vaccines or better weapons—have the characteristics of frequently being very effective, easily made in large quantities, easily distributed, and very appealing. Thus we are in an inescapable dilemma—irresistibly tempted to reach for the fruits of science, yet, deep inside, aware that our metabolism may not be able to cope with this ever-increasing appetite.

Probably the dilemma can no longer be resolved, and this increases the anxiety and confusion concerning science. A current symptom is the popular identification of science with the technology of superweapons. The bomb is taking the place of the microscope, Wernher von Braun, the place of Einstein, as symbols for modern science and scientists. The efforts to convince people that science itself can give man only knowledge about himself and his environment, and occasionally a choice of action, have been largely unavailing. The scientist *as scientist* can take little credit or responsibility either for facts he discovers—for he did not create them—or for the uses others make of his discoveries, for he generally is neither permitted nor specially fitted to make these decisions. They are controlled by considerations of ethics, economics, or politics and therefore are shaped by the values and historical circumstances of the whole society.[8]

There are other evidences of the widespread notion that science itself cannot contribute positively to culture. Toynbee, for example, gives a list of "creative individuals," from Xenophon to Hindenburg and from Dante to Lenin, but does not include a single scientist. I cannot forego the remark that there is a significant equivalent on the level of casual conversation. For when the man in the street—or many an intellectual—hears that you are a physicist or mathe-

[8] It is, however, also appropriate to say here that there has been only a moderate success in persuading the average scientist of the proposition that the privilege of freely pursuing a field of knowledge having large-scale secondary effects imposes on him, in his capacity as citizen, a proportionately larger burden of civic responsibility.

matician, he will usually remark with a frank smile, "Oh, I never could understand that subject"; while intending this as a curious compliment, he betrays his intellectual dissociation from scientific fields. It is not fashionable to confess to a lack of acquaintance with the latest ephemera in literature or the arts, but one may even exhibit a touch of pride in professing ignorance of the structure of the universe or one's own body, of the behavior of matter or one's own mind.

THE SORCERER'S APPRENTICE

The last two views held that man is inherently good and science evil. The next image is based on the opposite assumption—that man cannot be trusted with scientific and technical knowledge. He has survived only because he lacked sufficiently destructive weapons; now he can immolate his world. Science, indirectly responsible for this new power, is here considered ethically neutral. But man, like the sorcerer's apprentice, can neither understand this tool nor control it. Unavoidably he will bring upon himself catastrophe, partly through his natural sinfulness, and partly through his lust for power, of which the pursuit of knowledge is a manifestation. It was in this mood that Pliny deplored the development of projectiles of iron for purposes of war: "This last I regard as the most criminal artifice that has been devised by the human mind; for, as if to bring death upon man with still greater rapidity, we have given wings to iron and taught it to fly. Let us, therefore, acquit Nature of a charge that belongs to man himself."

When science is viewed in this plane—as a temptation for the mischievous savage—it becomes easy to suggest a moratorium on science, a period of abstinence during which humanity somehow will develop adequate spiritual or social resources for coping with the possibilities of inhuman uses of modern technical results. Here I need point out only the two main misunderstandings implied in this recurrent call for a moratorium.

First, science of course is not an occupation, such as working in a store or on an assembly line, that one may pursue or abandon at will. For a creative scientist, it is not a matter of free choice what he shall do. Indeed it is erroneous to think of him as advancing toward knowledge; it is, rather, knowledge which advances towards him, grasps him, and overwhelms him. Even the most superficial glance at the life and work of a Kepler, a Dalton, or a Pasteur would clarify this point. It would be well if in his education each person were shown by example that the driving power of creativity is as strong and as sacred for the scientist as for the artist.

The second point can be put equally briefly. In order to survive and to progress, mankind surely cannot ever know too much. Salvation can hardly be thought of as the reward for ignorance. Man has been given his mind in order that he may find out where he is, what he is, who he is, and how he may assume the responsibility for himself which is the only obligation incurred in gaining knowledge.

Indeed, it may well turn out that the technological advances in warfare have brought us to the point where society is at last compelled to curb the aggressions that in the past were condoned and even glorified. Organized warfare and genocide have been practiced throughout recorded history, but never until now have even the war lords openly expressed fear of war. In the search for the causes and prevention of aggression among nations, we shall, I am convinced, find scientific investigations to be a main source of understanding.

ECOLOGICAL DISASTER

A change in the average temperature of a pond or in the salinity of an ocean may shift the ecological balance and cause the death of a large number of plants and animals. The fifth prevalent image of science similarly holds that while neither science nor man may be inherently evil, the rise of science happened, as if by accident, to initiate an ecological change that now corrodes the only conceivable basis for a stable society. In the words of Jacques Maritain, the "deadly disease" science set off in society is "the denial of eternal truth and absolute values."

The main events leading to this state are usually presented as follows. The abandonment of geocentric astronomy implied the abandonment of the conception of the earth as the center of creation and of man as its ultimate purpose. Then purposive creation gave way to blind evolution. Space, time, and certainty were shown to have no absolute meaning. All a priori axioms were discovered to be merely arbitrary conveniences. Modern psychology and anthropology led to cultural relativism. Truth itself has been dissolved into probabilistic and indeterministic statements. Drawing upon analogy with the sciences, liberal philosophers have become increasingly relativistic, denying either the necessity or the possibility of postulating immutable verities, and so have undermined the old foundations of moral and social authority on which a stable society must be built.

It should be noted in passing that many applications of recent scientific concepts outside science merely reveal ignorance about science. For example, relativism in nonscientific fields is generally based on farfetched analogies. Relativity theory, of course, does not find that truth depends on the point of view of the observer but, on the contrary, reformulates the laws of physics so that they hold good for every observer, no matter how he moves or where he stands. Its central meaning is that the most valued truths in science are wholly independent of the point of view. Ignorance of science is also the only excuse for adopting rapid changes within science as models for antitraditional attitudes outside science. In reality, no field of thought is more conservative than science. Each change necessarily encompasses previous knowledge. Science grows like a tree, ring by ring. Einstein did not prove the work of Newton wrong; he provided a larger setting within which some contradictions and asymmetries in the earlier physics disappeared.

But the image of science as an ecological disaster can be subjected to a more severe critique.[9] Regardless of science's part in the corrosion of absolute values, have those values really given us always a safe anchor? A priori absolutes abound all over the globe in completely contradictory varieties. Most of the horrors of history have been carried out under the banner of some absolutistic philosophy, from the Aztec mass sacrifices to the auto-da-fé of the Spanish Inquisition, from the massacre of the Huguenots to the Nazi gas chambers. It is far from clear that any society of the past did provide a meaningful and dignified life for more than a small fraction of its members. If, therefore, some of the new philosophies, inspired rightly or wrongly by science, point out that absolutes have a habit of changing in time and of contradicting one another, if they invite a re-examination of the bases of social authority and reject them when those bases prove false (as did the Colonists in this country), then one must not blame a relativistic philosophy for bringing out these faults. They were there all the time.

In the search for a new and sounder basis on which to build a stable world, science will be indispensable. We can hope to match the resources and structure of society to the needs and potentialities of people only if we know more about man. Already science has much to say that is valuable and important about human relation-

[9] See, for example, C. Frankel, *The Case for Modern Man* (Beacon, Boston, 1959).

ships and problems. From psychiatry to dietetics, from immunology to meteorology, from city planning to agricultural research, by far the largest part of our total scientific and technical effort today is concerned, indirectly or directly, with man—his needs, relationships, health, and comforts. Insofar as absolutes are to help guide mankind safely on the long and dangerous journey ahead, they surely should be at least strong enough to stand scrutiny against the background of developing factual knowledge.

SCIENTISM

While the last four images implied a revulsion from science, scientism may be described as an addiction to science. Among the signs of scientism are the habit of dividing all thought into two categories, up-to-date scientific knowledge and nonsense; the view that the mathematical sciences and the large nuclear laboratory offer the only permissible models for successfully employing the mind or organizing effort; and the identification of science with technology, to which reference was made above.

One main source for this attitude is evidently the persuasive success of recent technical work. Another resides in the fact that we are passing through a period of revolutionary change in the nature of scientific activity—a change triggered by the perfecting and disseminating of the methods of basic research by teams of specialists with widely different training and interests. Twenty years ago the typical scientist worked alone or with a few students and colleagues. Today he usually belongs to a sizable group working under a contract with a substantial annual budget. In the research institute of one university more than 1500 scientists and technicians are grouped around a set of multimillion-dollar machines; the funds come from government agencies whose ultimate aim is national defense.

Everywhere the overlapping interests of basic research, industry, and the military establishment have been merged in a way that satisfies all three. Science has thereby become a large-scale operation with a potential for immediate and world-wide effects. The results are a splendid increase in knowledge, and also side effects that are analogous to those of sudden and rapid urbanization—a strain on communication facilities, the rise of an administrative bureaucracy, the depersonalization of some human relationships.

To a large degree, all this is unavoidable. The new scientific revolution will justify itself by the flow of new knowledge and of material benefits that will no doubt follow. The danger—and this is the point where scientism enters—is that the fascination with the *mechanism* of this successful enterprise may change the scientist himself and society around him. For example, the unorthodox, often withdrawn individual, on whom most great scientific advances have depended in the past, does not fit well into the new system. And society will be increasingly faced with the seductive urging of scientism to adopt generally what is regarded—often erroneously—as the pattern of organization of the new science. The crash program, the breakthrough pursuit, the megaton effect are becoming ruling ideas in complex fields such as education, where they may not be applicable.

MAGIC

Few nonscientists would suspect a hoax if it were suddenly announced that a stable chemical element lighter than hydrogen had been synthesized, or that a manned observation platform had been established at the surface of the sun. To most people it appears that science knows no inherent limitations. Thus, the seventh image depicts science as magic, and the scientist as wizard, *deus ex machina*, or oracle. The attitude toward the scientist on this plane ranges from terror to sentimental subservience, depending on what motives one ascribes to him.

IMPOTENCE OF THE MODERN INTELLECTUAL

The prevalance of these false images is a main source of the alienation between the scientific and nonscientific elements in our culture, and therefore the failure of image is important business for all of us. Now to pin much of the blame on the insufficient instruction in science which the general student receives at all levels is quite justifiable. I have implied the need, and most people nowadays seem to come to this conclusion anyway. But this is not enough. We must consider the full implications of the discovery that not only the man in the street but almost all of our intellectual leaders today know at most very little about science. And here we come to the central point underlying the analysis made above: the chilling realization that our intellectuals, for the first time in history, are losing their hold of understanding upon the world.

The wrong images would be impossible were they not anchored in two kinds of ignorance. One kind is ignorance on the basic level, that of *facts*—what biology says about life, what chemistry and physics say about matter, what astronomy says about the development and structure of our galaxy, and so forth. The nonscientist realizes that the old common-sense foundations of thought about the world of nature have become obsolete during the last two generations. The ground is trembling under his feet; the simple interpretations of solidity, permanence, and reality have been washed away, and he is plunged into the nightmarish ocean of four-dimensional continua, probability amplitudes, indeterminacies, and so forth. He knows only two things about the basic conceptions of modern science: that he does not understand them, and that he is now so far separated from them that he will never find out what they mean.

On the second level of ignorance, the contemporary intellectual knows just as little of the way in which the main facts from the different sciences fit together in the picture of the world taken as a whole. He has had to leave behind him, one by one, those great syntheses which used to represent our intellectual and moral home—the world view of the book of Genesis, of Homer, of Dante, of Milton, of Goethe. In the mid-20th century he finds himself abandoned in a universe which is to him an unsolvable puzzle on either the factual or the philosophical level. Of all the bad effects of the separation of culture and scientific knowledge, this feeling of bewilderment and basic homelessness is the most terrifying. Here is the reason, it seems to me, for the ineffectiveness and self-denigration of our contemporary intellectuals. Nor are the scientists themselves protected from this fate, for it has always been and must always be, the job of the humanist to construct and disseminate the meaningful total picture of the world.

To illustrate this point concretely we may examine a widely and properly respected work by a scholar who warmly understands both the science and the philosophy of the 16th and 17th centuries. The reader is carried along by his authority and enthusiasm. And then, suddenly, one encounters a passage unlike any other book, an anguished cry from the heart: [10] "It was of the greatest consequence for succeeding thought that now the great Newton's authority was squarely behind that view of the cosmos which saw in man a puny, irrelevant spectator (so far as a being, wholly imprisoned in a dark room, can be called such) of the vast mathematical system whose regular motions according to mechanical principles constituted the world of nature. The gloriously romantic universe of Dante and

[10] E. A. Burtt, *The Metaphysical Foundations of Modern Science* (Doubleday, New York, ed. 2, 1932), pp. 238–9.

Milton, that set no bounds to the imagination of man as it played over space and time, had now been swept away. Space was identified with the realm of geometry, time with the continuity of number. The world that people had thought themselves living in—a world rich with colour and sound, redolent with fragrance, filled with gladness, love and beauty, speaking everywhere of purposive harmony and creative ideals—was crowded now into minute corners in the brains of scattered organic beings. The really important world outside was a world hard, cold, colorless, silent, and dead; a world of quantity, a world of mathematically computable motions in mechanical regularity. The world of qualities as immediately perceived by man became just a curious and quite minor effect of that infinitive machine beyond. In Newton, the Cartesian metaphysics, ambiguously interpreted and stripped of its distinctive claim for serious philosophical consideration, finally overthrew Aristotelianism and became the predominant world-view of modern times."

For once, the curtain usually covering the dark fears modern science engenders is pulled away. This view of modern man as a puny, irrelevant spectator lost in a vast mathematical system—how far it is from the exaltation of man that Kepler found through scientific discovery: "Now man will at last measure the power of his mind on a true scale, and will realize that God, who founded everything in the world on the norm of quantity, also has endowed man with a mind which can comprehend these norms!" Was not the universe of Dante and Milton so powerful and "gloriously romantic" precisely because it incorporated, and thereby rendered meaningful, the contemporary scientific cosmology alongside the current moral and esthetic conceptions? Leaving aside the question of whether Dante's and Milton's contemporaries, by and large, were really living in a rich and fragrant world of gladness, love, and beauty, it is fair to speculate that if our new cosmos is felt to be cold, inglorious, and unromantic, it is not the new cosmology which is at fault but the absence of new Dantes and Miltons.

And yet, Burtt correctly reflects the present dilemma. What his outburst tells us, in starkest and simplest form, is this: By having let the intellectual remain in terrified ignorance of modern science, we have forced him into a position of tragic impotence; he is blindfold in a maze which he cannot traverse.

Once this is understood, the consequence also becomes plain. I find it remarkable that the intellectual today does not have even more distorted images and hostile responses with regard to science, that he has so far not turned much more fiercely against the source of apparent threats to his personal position and sanity[11]—in short, that the dissociation has not resulted in an even more severe cultural psychosis.

But this, I am convinced, is likely to be the result, for there is at present no countercyclical mechanism at work. Some other emergencies of a similar or related nature have been recognized and are being dealt with: We need more good scientists, and they are now being produced in greater numbers; we need more support for studies in humanities and social science, and the base of support is growing gratifyingly. We sorely need to give our young scientists more broad humanistic studies—and if I have not dwelled on this it is because, in principle, this can be done with existing programs and facilities; for the existing tools of study in the humanities, unlike the tools in science, are still in touch with our ordinary sensibilities. But hardly anything being done or planned now is adequate to deal with the far more serious problem, the cultural psychosis engendered by the separation of science and culture.

One may of course speculate as to how one could make science again a part of every intelligent man's educational equipment—not because science is more important than other fields, but because it is an important part of the whole jigsaw puzzle of knowledge. A plausible program would include sound and thorough work at every level of education—imaginative new programs and curricula; strengthened standards of achievement; extension of college work in science to comprise perhaps one-third of the total number of courses taken by the nonscience student, as used to be the rule in good colleges some 50 years ago; greater recognition of excellence; expansion of opportunity for adult education, including the presentation of factual and cultural aspects of science through the mass media. But while some efforts are being made here and there, few people have faced the real magnitude of the problem, or are even aware of the large range and amount of scientific knowledge that is needed before one can "know science" in any sense at all. Moreover, while some time lag between new discoveries and their wider dissemination has always existed, the increase in degree of abstraction, and in tempo, of present-day science, coming precisely at a time of inadequate

[11] For a striking recent example see the virulent attack on modern science in the final chapter of Arthur Koestler's *The Sleepwalkers* (Macmillan, New York, 1959).

educational effort even by old standards, has begun to change the lag into a discontinuity.

This lapse, it must be repeated, is not the fault of the ordinary citizen; necessarily, he can only take his cue from the intellectuals —the scholars, writers, and teachers who deal professionally in ideas. It is among the latter that the crucial need lies. Every great age has been shaped by intellectuals of the stamp of Hobbes, Locke, Berkeley, Leibnitz, Voltaire, Montesquieu, Rousseau, Kant, Jefferson, and Franklin—all of whom would have been horrified by the proposition that cultivated men and women could dispense with a good grasp of the scientific aspect of the contemporary world picture. This tradition is broken; very few intellectuals are now able to act as informed mediators. Meanwhile, as science moves every day faster and further from the bases of ordinary understanding, the gulf grows, and any remedial action becomes more difficult and more unlikely.

To restore science to reciprocal contact with the concerns of most men—to bring science into an orbit about us instead of letting it escape from our intellectual tradition—that is the great challenge that intellectuals face today.

Marjorie Nicolson

Milton and the Telescope

When Milton was born, in 1608, Tycho Brahe's "new star" of 1572, the appearance of which may well have startled his grandfather, and Kepler's "new star" of 1604, the excitement over which his father must have remembered, had already become history. Milton was only an infant when, in 1610, Galileo gave the world the first intimation of the greatest astronomical discoveries of the century, and revealed to man the existence of countless new stars, a new conception of the moon and the Milky Way, and the knowledge of four new "planets" of Jupiter. Milton had therefore no such opportunity as John Donne to realize at first hand the excitement caused by these discoveries or to experience the immediate transformation of imagination produced by the first "optic tube." He grew up in a period that gradually came to take the telescope for granted; he lived into an age which became familiar also with the wonders of the microscope, and began to ponder a world of life too minute for the human eye, as Galileo's contemporaries had considered anew the possibility of life in other inhabited worlds beyond sight. Although in youth Milton undoubtedly knew of the telescope, and may even have read the *Sidereus Nuncius*, he was trained under a system of education which paid no attention to contemporary scientific theories and discoveries, and his own tastes and interests were for letters. The astronomical background of his early works was a

Reprinted with the permission of the author and The Johns Hopkins Press from Marjorie Nicolson, "Milton and the Telescope," in ELH A Journal of English, *vol. 2 (1955), pp. 1–32.*

heritage from the classics, not from science. As a young man, he never knew the excitement of his older contemporaries who, in youth, had read of a new cosmos which almost overnight disrupted the immutable heavens of Aristotle.

Yet every reader of *Paradise Lost* is aware of the fact that Milton's imagination had been stimulated by astronomy, and more than one modern critic has pointed out the extent to which that astronomy was Copernican or Galilean. The problem of his astronomical references has been so frequently discussed that it needs little repetition here, nor am I concerned with what we usually call "the astronomy" of Milton or any other poet—with his acceptance, that is, of the Ptolemaic, the Copernican, the Tychonic, or the Cartesian hypothesis. I am concerned rather with the stimulus of imagination which the telescope produced in the seventeenth century, and the transformation of imagination which resulted from that instrument. In such a study, Milton affords the most remarkable example of the century. Unlike Donne, whose mind also was clearly stirred by implications of the "perspective glass," Milton's imagination, I am persuaded, was stimulated less by books about the new astronomy than by the actual sense experience of celestial observation. As almost in one night Galileo saw a new universe, so Milton on some occasion "viewed all things at one view" through a telescope. Like his own Satan

> Before [his] eyes in sudden view appear
> The secrets of the hoary Deep—a dark
> Illimitable ocean, without bound,
> Without dimension. . . .

That experience he never forgot; it is reflected again and again in his mature work; it stimulated him to reading and to thought; and it made *Paradise Lost* the first modern cosmic poem in which a drama is played against a background of interstellar space.

I

The early poetry of Milton is the best evidence that before his journey to Italy there had occurred no stimulation of the imagination in astronomical matters such as may be found in Donne in 1611. Although astronomical references are common enough in the *Minor Poems,* there is no significant sentence, no awareness of the ideas of Galileo, Kepler, Bruno. Most of the early figures of speech are merely descriptive: the *sun* appears frequently, but in such lines as these:

> Now while the heaven, by the Sun's team untrod,
> Hath took no print of the approaching light.

The moon shines for him as for any poet of antiquity:

> the wandering moon
> Riding near her highest noon,
> Like one that had been led astray
> Through the heaven's wide pathless way.

The stars that shine upon his youthful poetry are still the stars of Aristotle, undisturbed by the inruption of Tycho's or Kepler's *novae*. They are "bright morning star, Day's harbinger"; "the star that rose at evening bright"; or the day star that sinks in the ocean bed. Other references are to conventional astrology. His stars are "bending one way their precious influence," such stars as in their malign aspect have influenced that "starred Ethiop Queen." His planets are not the Medicean, but the mediaeval planets which affected men's lives:

> Whose power hath a true consent
> With planet or with element.

The cosmos of the youthful Milton he inherited from the past and apparently did not question. The "starry threshold of Jove's court" is still the boundary of man's world; "bright Spirits" hover "above that high first-moving sphere"; the "celestial Sirens" of Plato "sit upon the nine infolded spheres." There is nothing, in short, in the early poems of Milton to suggest that his mind had been stirred by pondering upon the new astronomy. Indeed, there is one piece of evidence that it had not. The long passage in *Comus*, in which the Lady and Comus, like academic disputants, consider whether Nature is an evidence of superabundance, bidding man pour himself forth with lavish and unrestraining hand, or whether she is a "good Cateress," who teaches frugality, restraint, proportion, anticipates the dialogue of Adam and the Angel in *Paradise Lost* on the same subject. But while argument in the later poem is drawn from various astronomical hypotheses, no such proof occurred to Milton as he pondered the same problem in youth. His illustrations in *Comus* are from Nature as she shows herself in this little world, Comus suggesting that wherever man looks, whether at the vegetation, the sea, or the earth, he sees Nature pouring herself forth, the Lady replying with what is at best a mild form of ethical socialism, concerned only with the difference between "lewedly-pampered Luxury" and the "holy dictate of spare Temperance." In *Paradise Lost*, after astronomical conceptions have entered into Milton's imagination, and Adam finds himself confused between theories which, on the one hand, argue for disproportion and superfluity, on the other, for moderation and restraint, the arguments are drawn entirely from current theories of astronomy. It is seldom that a poet has given us, in the work of his youth and his maturity, two passages which so clearly suggest the difference which years and experience brought in the seventeenth century.

While the poems offer no evidence that Milton had pondered the new astronomy, his early prose indicates that the soil was being prepared for new ideas on such matters.[1] Milton's college exercises, suggest that he was inclined toward at least a mild academic radicalism. He was among that group at Cambridge who opposed the traditional philosophy. His *Third Academic Exercise* is an attack on the scholastic philosophy and a defense of the sort of studies Bacon had advocated. Since the adherents of the new astronomy were on the whole anti-Aristotelian rather than anti-Ptolemaic,[2] it is significant that Milton shows himself one with the anti-Aristotelians on various other aspects of the quarrel. But it is even more important to notice whom Milton defended than whom he

[1] In Milton's *Sixth Academic Exercise* (*Private Correspondence and Academic Exercises*, translated by Phyllis B. Tillyard, Cambridge, 1932, p. 103) occurs what is evidently a reference to the telescope, in which Milton puns upon the popular title, "perspective-glass":

> And in times long and dark Prospective Glass,
> Fore-saw what future dayes should bring to pass.

So far as I can see, there is no other reference in the early works to the telescope, and none to Galilean astronomy.

[2] This is a point which, in my opinion, has not been sufficiently stressed by those who have seen in the adherents of the "new astronomy" disciples of Copernicus ranged against disciples of Ptolemy. The student who reads the early work of Kepler, for instance, will observe that his arguments are against Aristotelian rather than Ptolemaic astronomy. The explanation is to be found in the fact that *philosophically* it was Aristotle, not Ptolemy—who was considered primarily as astronomer and mathematician, rather than as philosopher—who had established the conception of the heavens which dominated thought.

attacked. The *De Idea Platonica* shows him not only cleverly satirizing the literal-minded Aristotelians of the day, but defending the Platonic philosophy. Even more important is his frequently expressed love of the Pythagorean philosophy, for it must be remembered that to many seventeenth-century minds, the discoveries of such men as Copernicus and Galileo were considered important less for novelty than because they brought back the beliefs of Pythagoras; even a cursory reading of Kepler will suggest the extent to which his mysticism was influenced by the supposed "mystick Mathematick" of the Pythagoreans. To Milton in youth Pythagoras seemed "a very god among philosophers" and his *Second Academic Exercise*, "On the Harmony of the Spheres," is filled with a defense of the philosopher against Aristotle, "the rival and constant detractor of Pythagoras and Plato."

There are other passages in the early exercises even more important as showing the direction of Milton's interests. His *Oration in Defense of Learning* contains many sentences showing his interest in the new arts and sciences which were attracting the thoughtful men of his day; the "Ignorance" he attacks is in part the "ignorance of gownsmen," the "sluggish and languid" complacency of the past, which so satisfied men that they felt there was nothing new to learn, the complete dependence upon mediaeval logic and scholastic metaphysics which, declares Milton, is "not an Art at all, but a sinister rock, a quagmire of fallacies, devised to cause shipwreck and pestilence." Here, as in his later *Tractate on Education*, Milton urges the sort of learning which is not barren, which produces, as Bacon would have said, both "Fruit" and "Light." In one passage in these early works, Milton suggests the so-called "Copernican" point of view.[3] There is still another attitude of mind in these academic exercises which, while not specifically concerned with astronomical ideas, was to prove significant in Milton's thinking, and to make his mind receptive to certain implications in the new astronomy. "Let not your mind," he says, "rest content to be bounded and cabined by the limits which encompass the earth, but let it wander beyond the confines of the world."[4] In spite of the checks which he consciously put upon it, Milton's was one of those minds of which he speaks in the *Areopagitica*, "minds that can wander beyond limit

[3] *Seventh Academic Exercise*, p. 108.
[4] *Third Academic Exercise*, p. 72.

and satiety," can play with concepts of time and space, can deal in "those thoughts that wander through eternity." Such minds were peculiarly sensitive to the implications of the new philosophy.[5]

II

Until the last few years, there has been no question that during his Italian journey Milton visited Galileo, and consequently no reason to doubt that it was Galileo's telescope which disclosed to him the new conception of the heavens and space reflected in *Paradise Lost.* His own statement in the *Areopagitica* that he "found and visited the famous Galileo, grown old a prisoner to the Inquisition," has always been considered sufficient to establish the fact of the visit. In 1918, however, that statement was challenged by S. B. Liljegren [6] as a part of his general attack on Milton's veracity, and his attempt to build up a conception of Milton's character in which the chief characteristics of the poet were egocentricity and an unscrupulous desire for self-aggrandisement. While Liljegren has not succeeded in persuading most critics,[7] his argument cannot be passed over without consideration. Liljegren's most important point is his evidence —based upon documents which he quotes from the great national edition of Galileo, edited by Antonio Favaro—that during the period 1638–39 Galileo was so inaccessible, both because of the sentence of the Inquisition and because of his own health, that approach to him was difficult, almost impossible.[8] Perhaps the best single answer

[5] Psychologically it is evident that the most important adherents of the "new astronomy," particularly those, who, like Campanella and Kepler, attempted to read important philosophical implications into it, possessed this type of imagination. The opposite type of imagination is seen in Bacon, who, as is well known, showed little interest in any of the conceptions of the new astronomy, and who indeed saw in this tendency of human minds which Milton praises, one of the *Idols of the Tribe.* Cf. the passage in the *Novum Organum,* Aphorism 48, beginning "The human understanding is unquiet; it cannot stop or rest, and still presses onward, but in vain. . . .

[6] S. B. Liljegren, *Studies in Milton,* Lund, 1908.

[7] See the article by Walter Fischer, *Englische Studien* 52. 390–6, with the reply, *ibid.* 54. 358–66; G. Hübener, *Deutsche Literaturzeitung* 40. 150–1; A. Brandl, *Archiv* 138. 246–7; H. Mutschmann, *Beiblatt* 29. 228–35; F. A. Pompen, *Neophilologus* 5. 88–96, with a continuation of the argument, *ibid.* 354–5. Most of these critics are concerned primarily with Liljegren's contention in regard to "Milton and the Pamela Prayer." His argument about Milton and Galileo, a secondary point, has not occasioned much comment.

[8] Liljegren, pp. 25–34. It should be noticed that while Liljegren acknowledges

that can be made to this argument is that Signor Favaro himself, who has more intimate knowledge of this evidence than any other scholar, has found no reason to doubt Milton's statement.[9] Nor have other Italian critics who have considered the matter.[10] There is nothing

the visit of D. Benedetto Castelli in the autumn of 1638, he lays stress rather upon the difficulties Castelli met than upon the fact that he succeeded in his request; he passes too easily over the visit of Padre Clement in January, 1639; see Favaro, *Le Opere* 18, p. 42. He omits entirely the visits of Vincenzo Viviani and Torricelli in 1639 and 1641; see *Le Opere* 18, pp. 126, 164. In his over-emphasis upon the difficulties of Castelli, he neglects to point out sufficiently that the Inquisition may have had reasons for suspicion of Castelli which did not exist in Milton's case, particularly if Milton's visit occurred during his first stay in Florence. At that time Milton was completely unknown to the Inquisition; he was merely a young English traveller, who carried acceptable letters of introduction. Some of the Italian critics mentioned below agree that Milton might have found more difficulty in obtaining access to Galileo after his visit to Rome.

9 Favaro takes the meeting for granted in *Le Opere*, and evidently has found no reason since to doubt it, since in an article in *Il Giornale d'Italia*, 18 Giugno, 1922, "Galileo e Milton in Arcetri," he surveys some of the recent important work on Milton, and discusses the visits of Hobbes and Milton to Galileo.

10 The chief Italian treatments of Milton in Italy are the following: Alfredo Reumont in *Archivo storico italiano* 26 (1902). 427 seqq.; Teresa Guazzaroni, "Giovanni Milton in Italia," Roma, 1902 (Estratto dal *Giornale Arcardio*, serie 3); Ettore Allodali, *Giovanni Milton e l'Italia*, 1907 (Chap. 2, "Questione della visita di Milton a Galileo"; cf. also J. G. Robertson, *Modern Language Review* 2, 1907, 376) Antoni Serao, *Giovanni Milton*, Salerno, 1907 (this work is not biographical, and does not discuss the matter); G. Ferrando, "Milton in Toscana," *Illustrazione Italiana*, October, 1925; Anon., "Milton a Firenza," *Marzocco*, November 9, 1925; G. N. Giordano-Orsini, *Milton e il suo poema*, 1928; D. Angeli, *Giovanni Milton*, 1928. The most recent Italian work on the subject is *Galileo Galilei* by Giovanni Lattanzi, which I have not seen, but Lattanzi's position on the subject is clear from a short article "Gli Ultimi anni di Galileo Galilei" in *Gli Astri*, Giugno-Luglio, 1924, pp. 210–4, for copy of which I am indebted to Signor Abetti of Arcetri. Signor Abetti, who is in charge of the Galileo collections at Arcetri, has found no reason to doubt Milton's statement in regard to his visit, as I am informed by my colleague Miss Emma Detti, who was good enough to discuss the matter with him at my request. The only problem these Italian critics raise is whether Milton's visit occurred in the autumn or the spring. Reumont is inclined to believe that Milton would have found more difficulties after his visit to Rome, when his own political and religious views were known, but considers it certain that the visit took place (cf. p. 19). Signor Lattanzi in his article, p. 214, quotes a letter which he supposes to have been written by Milton to Grotius after his visit, in which he speaks of Galileo "tormentato com' è dalle sue malattie." The letter, however, was not written by Milton, but by Grotius to Vossius (*Epistola* 964). It is quoted, with correct attribution, by Teresa Guazzaroni, in her article, pp. 8–9. In this connection should be mentioned the series of letters published by R. Owen, "Milton and

in the other arguments of Liljegren which deserves or needs consideration—nothing which does not arise merely from his own conception of Milton's character. Against his purely hypothetical position, then, we still have the evidence of Milton's own statement—evidence which must remain conclusive until better proof is produced, and we may continue to believe in Milton's visit to Galileo, as have the poets and artists whose imagination has reconstructed the event.[11] Whether it was Galileo's telescope or not is of no consequence, however, to the main contention of this paper. Telescopes were common both in Italy and in England, and Milton must have had many

Galileo," *Fraser's Magazine* 79 (1869), 678–84, which, were they genuine, would afford conclusive evidence of Milton's visit. The letters, supposed to have been written by Milton, Galileo, and Louis XIV, were from the collection of M. Chasles, and were by him presented to the Académie des Sciences, and published in *Comptes rendus,* 28 Mars, 1869, with comments by Elie de Beaumont, *ibid.,* 5 Avril, 1869. Evidently their authenticity was not doubted at that time; Mr. Owen discusses them seriously, but there seems no reason to believe that they do not belong with other "Miltonic Myths" discussed by J. Churton Collins, *National Review* 43 (1904).

[11] For the benefit of other students who, like myself, may have had difficulty in tracing the effect of the Milton-Galileo meeting upon Italian imagination, I may refer to the valuable section on this subject by J. J. Fahie, *Memorials of Galileo Galilei,* 1929, and add the following information. In 1868 Giacomo Zanella wrote a poem on the subject, "Milton e Galileo," *Poesie di Giacomo Zanella,* Firenze, 1933, pp. 99–124, in which he reconstructed imaginatively the meeting. This poem served as inspiration to Annibale Gatti, who *circa* 1877 painted a picture representing the meeting. The scene of the painting is laid in the Torre del Gallo, instead of Galileo's house in Arcetri where the meeting probably took place. Various copies are extant, some showing variations from the original (Fahie, pp. 97–100). For an edition of the original picture, see Giuseppe Palagi, "Milton e Galileo alla Torre del Gallo, quadretto a olio del Cav. Prof. Annibale Gatti: descritto e illustrato da Giuseppe Palagi," Firenze, 1877. In 1893 Tito Lessi produced a smaller picture, which, while less ambitious, is more nearly true to reality, "Milton e Galileo in Arcetri." A reproduction may be found in the issue of *Gli Astri* referred to above, p. 211; see also the note of Antonio Favaro in the same issue, p. 217. In 1880 the sculptor Cesare Aureli produced a marble composition, again following Zanella (Fahie, pp. 77–80). In his article in *Il Giornale d'Italia,* Professor Favaro describes this group and devotes a section of his paper to a plea that the statue may be moved to Arcetri, "la città scientifica fiorentina per sfolgorare al sole di Arcetri dove la storica visita ebbe luogo" as a consecration of friendship between England and Italy. See also "Galileo with Milton at Torre del Gallo," translated by Paul Selver from *The Apostles* of J. S. Machar, *Sewanee Review* 32 (1924). 30–1. I may also mention Solomon Alexander Hart's picture "Milton visiting Galileo in Prison," 1826, and in addition to the English works already well known on the subject, the imaginative picture given by Alfred Noyes in his *Watchers of the Sky,* 1922.

opportunities to survey the heavens at night, before his blindness made vision impossible. Since all his specific references in *Paradise Lost* are to the Florentine, not to the English instrument, one may still insist that, whether Galileo's or another, an Italian "optic glass" first made him conscious of realms of vision and of thought which his youth had never imagined.

Three of Milton's allusions to the telescope in *Paradise Lost* have been so frequently noted that they need little comment here: a specific reference to the "glass of Galileo"; his comparison of Satan's shield to the "optic glass" of the "Tuscan artist" at evening "from the top of Fesole Or in Valdarno"; and his suggestion that the Garden of Eden was

> a spot like which perhaps
> Astronomer in the Sun's lucent orb
> Through his glazed optic tube yet never saw.[12]

There are, in addition, two references to the telescope in *Paradise Regained* less frequently noticed, both of them in scenes in which Satan displays to Christ the kingdoms of the world and the glory thereof. The means Satan employed for that vision did not trouble the writer of the Gospels; but Milton, product of a scientific age, paused to wonder, and concluded:

> By what strange parallax or optic skill
> Of vision, multiplied through air, or glass
> Of telescope, were curious to inquire.[13]

Satan returns to the same idea when, in the passage which follows, he suggests that Christ may see many things at one view because "so well I have disposed My aery microscope." [14]

[12] 5. 261–3; 1. 287–91; 3. 588–90. Since Milton seems to be referring here to such "sunspots" as those Galileo discovered, this reference also may be said to be associated in his mind with the Italian rather than the English instrument.

[13] *Paradise Regained* 4. 40–2.

[14] *Ibid.*, 56–7. The use of the word *microscope* here is curious. The term *microscopium* or *microscopio* was used in Italy at least as early as 1625. While microscopes were known in England between 1625 and 1660, they did not come into common use until after 1660. The first microscopical observations reported to the Royal Society were those of Robert Hooke on March 25, 1663. Clearly, from the *Transactions* of the society, microscopes were still a novelty at that time. Since Milton was then totally blind, there is no possibility that he had seen a microscope, and I am inclined to believe that either he was using the

In *Paradise Lost* are to be found the discoveries which, from the time of the publication of the *Sidereus Nuncius* in 1610 enthralled poetic as well as scientific minds. Here are the "thousand thousand stars," the sun-spots, and the Milky Way.[15] The moon appears in *Paradise Lost* as it had in Italy. This is no longer the moon of conventional poetry—the moon of *Il Penseroso.* It is vastly larger—the largest circular body Milton could think of when he sought an apt comparison with the shield of Satan.[16] The moon is to Milton as to Galileo a world much like this earth in its appearance. There are "new lands, Rivers or mountains in her spotty globe";[17] "imagined lands and regions in the moon." The Angel ponders the same problem when he questions "if land be there, Fields or inhabitants." There are spots in the moon, the Angel declares:

> Whence in her visage round those spots, unpurged
> Vapours not yet into her substance turned.[18]

Again the Angel suggests the significance of those spots as the seventeenth century understood them:

word loosely or that from vague accounts of the new instrument, he misunderstood its function. In the passage in question, he seems to be suggesting a combination of a telescope and some supposed instrument which would show *interiors* as well as exteriors, since Satan says that by this means Christ may behold "Outside and inside both." This is an entirely possible interpretation, since the invention of the microscope and telescope precipitated a number of fantastic experiments with other instruments which were supposed to have strange powers.

15 *Paradise Lost* 7. 383, 577–81.

16 I do not mean to say that the conventional moon of poetry does not appear in *Paradise Lost.* Cf. for example 4. 606–9. The moon seen by Adam and Eve is the traditional moon of poetry, except in the scene in which Adam discusses astronomy with the Angel; but the majority of Milton's references are Galilean.

17 *Paradise Lost* 1. 287–91. In discussing this passage, Allan Gilbert says ("Milton and Galileo," p. 159): "In mentioning 'rivers' Milton is not following Galileo, who held that there was no water on the moon." He bases this statement upon the *Dialogo intorno ai due massimi sistemi del mondo, Le Opere di Galilei,* 1842, 1. 112. But in the *Sidereus Nuncius,* Galileo said (*Sidereal Messenger,* translated by E. S. Carlos, 1880, pp. 19–20): "If any one wishes to revive the old opinion of the Pythagoreans, that the Moon is another Earth, so to say, the brighter portion may very fitly represent the surface of the land, and the darker the expanse of water. Indeed, I have never doubted that if the sphere of the Earth were seen from a distance, when flooded with the Sun's rays, that part of the surface which is land would present itself to view as brighter, and that which is water as darker in comparison."

18 *Paradise Lost* 5. 419–20.

Her spots thou seest
As clouds, and clouds may rain, and rain produce
Fruit in her softened soil, for some to eat.[19]

Like the disciples of Galileo, also, Milton was impressed with the discovery of the planets of Jupiter, and by the possibility which Kepler had immediately suggested that other planets might also be found to have their unknown attendants:

and other Suns, perhaps
With their attendant Moons, thou wilt descry,
Communicating male and female light,
Which two great sexes animate the World.[20]

In common with Galileo and many others of the century, too, Milton had been impressed by contemporary theories of meteors and comets and shooting stars. A nineteenth-century commentator has drawn attention to his observation that meteors are most common in autumn,[21] as Milton suggests in his picture of Uriel's descent:

Swift as a shooting star
In autumn thwarts the night.

Comets, too, had interested Milton, perhaps because of the various controversies to which Galileo's theories on comets gave rise, perhaps because he remembered in his childhood the comet of 1618, and had heard from others of the appearance in the year before his birth of "Halley's comet," which startled the early seventeenth century, and was the cause of many pamphlets, ranging from direful prophecy to scientific theory. At least two fine figures of speech in *Paradise Lost* reflect this interest. Satan as he opposes the unknown Death

like a comet burned,
That fires the length of Ophiuchus huge
In the arctic sky, and from his horrid hair
Shakes pestilence and war.[22]

19 *Ibid.* 8. 145–7.

20 *Ibid.* 8. 148–51.

21 This observation was made by Professor Mitchell, the astronomer, and is reported in a paper by his sister, Maria Mitchell, published in *Poet-Lore* 6 (1894). 313–323. Professor Mitchell comments, p. 319, "We of this age suppose this was first known since our recollections." Cf. also Milton's figure, 1. 745–6.

22 *Paradise Lost* 2. 708–11. W. T. Lynn, "Comet Referred to by Milton." *Notes and Queries*, series 7, no. 2 (1886), p. 66, suggests that this refers to the appearance of the comet of November, 1664.

The last of Milton's majestic figures in the poem is drawn from the same source. To the sad eyes of Adam and Eve

> The brandished sword of God before them blazed,
> Fierce as a comet.[23]

Yet it may be objected that these passages, though they show that Milton had known and pondered the discoveries of Galileo—as what thoughtful man of his age had not?—might have been written by anyone who knew of them from books, that they do not exhibit actual personal experience with the telescope. There are, however, two characteristics which make *Paradise Lost* (and in the first instance *Paradise Regained*) unique, characteristics that critics and poets have always felt peculiarly "Miltonic," yet which have never, it seems to me, been satisfactorily explained. Even a casual reader of Milton is aware of the vast canvas with which Milton worked, and on which he displayed his cosmic pictures. I propose to analyze again some of those familiar passages, seeking to determine in how far Milton's imagination had been stirred by the extent of space of the universe which the telescope had discovered.

III

One of the peculiarities of Milton's technique is his sense of *perspective.* I shall here only raise, because I cannot pretend to answer, the question: in how far was the new sense of perspective in seventeenth-century art, both pictorial and literary, the result of the telescope? Certainly during the period in which the telescope was first impressing the popular mind, we feel the expansion of space on canvas and in poetry, as in the century that followed we can detect in descriptive technique a new feeling for distance. But this is intended for the present merely as a suggestion. So far as Milton is concerned, the case is clear. No preceding poet had been able to take us in imagination to such heights, such vantage points from which, like Satan or like God, we behold in one glance Heaven, Earth, Hell, and Space surrounding all. Even when he is not dealing with cosmic space, Milton in his mature poems loves far views. *Paradise Regained* contains a succession of them, all limited to this world alone, even though the scope of some of them is such as to stagger comprehension. The "high mountain" to which Satan led Christ offers at one view a perspective which includes "a spacious

[23] *Ibid.* 12. 633–4.

plain," two rivers, with their junction with the sea, cities; and, adds Milton,

> so large
> The prospect was that here and there was room
> For barren desert fountainless and dry.[24]

The topography of the scene is enough to give the needed impression of extensiveness; but, not content with that, Milton goes further, suggesting that "turning with easy eye, thou may'st behold" Assyria, Araxes and the Caspian Lake, Indus, Euphrates, the Persian Bay, the Arabian Desert, Nineveh, Babylon, Persepolis, and half a dozen other real and fabulous places. This is the vastest prospect in *Paradise Regained*, yet the same general technique is evident, on a lesser scale, in the vision of Rome, and of Athens. That Milton himself associated such views with the sense of distance and perspective given by the telescope is evident from his references in these passages to the "telescope" and the "aery microscope."

The use of perspective in *Paradise Lost* is at once more difficult and more subtle. Geography has become cosmography. But because the scene of *Paradise Lost* is the cosmos, Milton has all the more reason to use the technique of the telescope in order to describe the universe which the telescope had opened to the eyes of his century. Again and again we have a sensation of the sudden view of far distance, as with Satan we look "down with wonder at the sudden view Of all this World at once." Uriel, explaining the scene to the Satan he does not recognize, sounds to our ears curiously like a seventeenth-century schoolmaster who combines, with a lesson in theory, practical demonstration through the telescope:

> Look downward on that globe, whose hither side
> With light from hence, though but reflected, shines:
> That place is Earth the seat of Man: that light
> His day, which else, as the other hemisphere,
> Night would invade; but there the neighbouring Moon
> (So call that opposite fair star) her aid
> Timely interposes, and, her monthly round
> Still ending, still renewing, through mid-heaven,
> With borrowed light her countenance triform
> Hence fills and empties, to enlighten the Earth,
> And in her pale dominion checks the night.[25]

[24] *Paradise Regained* 3. 262–4. Cf. *Paradise Lost* 11. 377–411 for a similar prospect from a hill.

[25] *Paradise Lost* 3. 722–32.

In other scenes of cosmic perspective, however, Milton, for all the strangeness and novelty of the material with which he is dealing, forgets the teacher in the artist. Sometimes it is God himself whom we observe in far-off prospect of the universe:

> Now had the Almighty Father from above,
> From the pure Empyrean where he sits
> High-throned above all highth, bent down his eye,
> His own works and their works at once to view.[26]

More often it is Satan:

> upon the firm opacous globe
> Of this round World, whose first convex divides
> The luminous inferior Orbs, enclosed
> From Chaos, and the inroad of Darkness old,
> Satan alighted walks. A globe far off
> It seemed; now seems a boundless continent
> Dark, waste, and wild, under the frown of Night
> Starless expos'd.[27]

It is Satan again who, in prospect of Eden, looks sadly from the earth:

> Sometimes towards Eden, which now in his view
> Lay pleasant, his grieved look he fixes sad;
> Sometimes towards Heaven and the full-blazing Sun,
> Which now sat high in his meridian Tower.[28]

Through Satan's eyes we view the most telescopic of all the scenes in *Paradise Lost:* as Satan

> Looks down with wonder at the sudden view
> Of all this World at once . . .
> Round he surveys, (and well might, where he stood
> So high above the circling canopy
> Of Night's extended shade) from eastern point
> Of Libra to the fleecy star that bears
> Andromeda far off Atlantic seas
> Beyond the horizon; then from pole to pole
> He views his breadth,—and, without longer pause,
> Down right into the World's first region throws

[26] *Ibid.* 3. 56–9.
[27] *Ibid.* 3. 418–25.
[28] *Ibid.* 4. 27–30.

His flight precipitant, and winds with ease
Through the pure marble air his oblique way
Amongst innumerable stars that shone,
Stars distant, but nigh-hand seemed other worlds.[29]

It is, too, through Satan's eyes that we first see far off this tiny world of ours, which has become like the other planets which Galileo had discovered—

This pendent World, in bigness as a star
Of smallest magnitude close by the moon.[30]

Such a sense of cosmic perspective is as characteristic of Milton as is the so-called "Miltonic style"—for which, indeed, it is in part responsible; yet it is also characteristic of his generation. We do not find it a century before; and though we may find it frequently enough in the century which follows, in the cosmic poems of the eighteenth century familiarity has lost something of the amazement and fascination with which this first generation of men surveyed the new cosmos. Yet even this magnificent sense of perspective was not Milton's greatest heritage from Galileo and his telescope.

IV

"Shakespeare," Professor David Masson used to say in his lectures at Edinburgh, "lived in a world of time, Milton in a universe of space." [31] The distinction Professor Masson felt is the distinction between two worlds—the old and the new; and the profound difference arises from the seventeenth-century awareness of the immensity of space. How valid the distinction is will be clear to any student of Shakespeare and Milton, who, considering them merely as reflectors of the thought of their respective periods, observes their obsession with certain dominant conceptions. Of Milton's fascination with *space,* to which *Paradise Lost* bears witness in nearly every book, there is no indication in Shakespeare. And yet that was not because Shakespeare's imagination was not influenced by abstract conceptions. *Time* with Shakespeare is equally an obsession. The use of

[29] *Ibid.* 3. 542–66.
[30] *Ibid.* 2. 1052–3.
[31] This sentence was quoted to me by President William Allan Neilson, who had been one of Masson's students. Masson only suggests the idea in his *Life of Milton.* See the 1875 edition, 6. 532 and note.

actual words is perhaps misleading; yet it is at least interesting to observe that the word *space*—according to concordances—occurs in Shakespeare only thirty-two times, always with an obviously limited meaning; *space* to him was little more than "the distance between two objects." The same concordances list more than eight columns of the use of *time*. An *Index to Shakespeare's Thought*[32] makes no reference to his thoughts about space; yet the same index devotes page after page to his thoughts about time, from Rosalind and Orlando's light dialogues on the relativity of time, through familiar references to the "whirligig of time" which brings in its revenges, to the constant reflections on time on the part of more serious characters. Time is to Shakespeare, "the king of men, He's both their parent, and he is their grave." There are the fine lines in the *Rape of Lucrece* beginning: "Time's glory is to calm contending kings," and, as everyone knows, many of Shakespeare's most familiar sonnets deal with the poet's insistent awareness of time. But with the exception of a few dubious lines, there are no passages in Shakespeare that show his mind playing with concepts of space. His world is still bounded by the sphere of the fixed stars, and, indeed, the orb of the moon is the limit of space in his plays. Though travellers' tales could hold Desdemona spellbound, and the geographical world had grown immensely, Puck could "put a girdle round about the earth in forty minutes." Shakespeare's astronomy is still largely astrology; his conception of the order and relation of the heavenly bodies, when suggested at all, still conventional mediaevalism. There is no interest in "other worlds." Certainly no vision through a telescope had disturbed his placid cosmos; nor had he heard, as had Milton's generation

> A shout that tore Hell's concave, and beyond
> Frighted the reign of Chaos and old Night.

No reader of *Paradise Lost*, on the other hand, can fail to be aware of the tremendous scale on which it is conceived, or the part which the concept of space plays in its structure.[33] One explanation of the way in which Milton produces this effect is to be found in his

[32] Cecil Arnold, *An Index to Shakespeare's Thought*, 1880.

[33] This was pointed out by Masson, and by Nadal, in his "Cosmogony of *Paradise Lost*," and has been reiterated by Gilbert in "The Outside Shell of Milton's World." Nevertheless many critics, since Addison, interpret such a line as, "This little world in bigness as a star" as referring merely to the terrestrial globe.

conception of the *world*, which, when compared with earlier cosmic poems, indicates the effect of the new astronomy. When Milton uses the term *world* he customarily means not the "little world of man" but the universe. Milton makes much of the difference between this earth as it seems to those who dwell upon it and to those who survey it from afar, to whom it shows its relative unimportance in the cosmic scheme. To Adam and Eve, as to man at all times, earth seems fixed and secure, the center of the universe. At night they survey from their peaceful bower "this fair Moon, And these the gems of Heaven, her starry train." In the morning, they praise in conventional Biblical language "this universal frame, Thus wondrous fair." Satan perceives the difference between the earth as it appears to the angels and to its inhabitants, for, when he finally reaches it, after his first vision from a distance, he finds

> A globe far off
> It seemed; now seems a boundless continent.

But to those who view it from far off—whether God or Satan—and see it in its relation to the vast expanse of space, "this world that seemed Firm land imbosom'd" is but a "punctual spot," a tiny body, merely one of many stars "not unconform to other shining globes." It has shrunk to minute proportions, "a spot, a grain, An atom, with the Firmament compared." It is, "in comparison of Heaven, so small, nor glistering." The Angel, who knows both the world of man and the great cosmos of which it is a tiny part, explains to Adam the vastness of the universe beyond:

> regions to which
> All thy dominion, Adam, is no more
> Than what this garden is to all the earth,
> And all the sea, from one entire globose
> Stretched into longitude.[34]

Beyond the universe of man—even the vastly expanded universe of the telescope which Milton himself had beheld—there stretched in his imagination space. *Space* dominates *Paradise Lost.* We begin to perceive it first through the eyes of Satan as, astounded and momentarily appalled, he gazes into the Chaos that opens beyond the gates of Hell. This is not Satan's first awareness of the extent of

[34] *Paradise Lost* 5. 750–4.

the universe. When earlier he warned his followers in Hell of the herculean task which awaited them, he remembered "the dark, unbottomed, infinite Abyss," the "uncouth way," the "vast Abrupt," the "dreadful voyage," as Belial remembered "the wide womb of uncreated Night" in which the fallen angels had so nearly been "swallowed up and lost." There is no exaggeration in Satan's warning of the "void profound Of unessential Night . . . Widegaping" which threatens even angelic natures "with utter loss of being. . . plunged in that abortive gulf." He sets out

> with lonely steps to tread
> The unfounded Deep, and through the void immense
> To search, with wandering quest.

The passage in which Milton describes Chaos reflects the *new space* of telescopic astronomy. There was as yet no vocabulary to express it, and Milton, in common with the astronomers of his day, was driven to a succession of negatives as

> Before their eyes in sudden view appear
> The secrets of the hoary Deep—a dark
> Illimitable ocean, without bound,
> Without dimension; where length, breadth, and highth,
> And time, and place, are lost.[35]

The "wild Abyss" before him, "the womb of Nature and perhaps her grave," is "neither Sea, nor Shore, nor Air, nor Fire." Again and again Milton searches for terms as Satan "with head, hands, wings, or feet, pursues his way." He meets "a vast vacuity"; he springs upward into the "wild expanse"; he forces his way over the "boiling gulf" of the "dark Abyss," until after immense labor he finally approaches the "sacred influence Of Light" where "Nature first begins Her farthest verge." Milton's description of Chaos, both in its vocabulary and its conception, is the first great attempt of English poetry to picture the indefinite the telescope had shown. Many of its details are classical, some are mediaeval, but fundamentally it is a modern Chaos which no mind had conceived before Galileo.

But the description of Chaos is only the beginning of Milton's attempt to depict the new space. We see it through the eyes of

[35] *Ibid.* 2. 890 ff. Cf. also the passages which describe Satan's return, 10. 282–8; 300; 366–71; 397; 470–7.

God as he "bent down his eye His own works and their works at once to view," and saw in one glance the sanctities of Heaven close about Him, the "Happy Garden" upon earth, "Hell and the gulf between." We realize it again in the further voyages of Satan—voyages which were inherited from and which were to influence the "voyages to the moon" in which the seventeenth century delighted. At one time Satan beholds "Far off the empyreal Heaven"; at another he wanders in the Paradise of Fools in which strong cross winds blow fools "ten thousand leagues awry." Finding at last an entrance to earth, Satan upon the lower stair of Heaven's steps "Looks down with wonder at the sudden view Of all this World at once," and "from pole to pole He views his breadth," before he "throws His flight precipitant" downward. Milton's idea of other worlds adds greatly to the expanse of the universe in such passages as these, for we watch Satan at one time winding his "oblique way Amongst innumerable stars" which to men below seemed distant "but nigh hand seemed other worlds." At another time "through the vast ethereal sky" he "sails between worlds and worlds."

It is not alone Satan's voyages which give the reader the sense of space that pervades the whole poem. One need only compare Milton's story of the creation with its original in *Genesis* to realize the expansion of imagination astronomy has produced. The passages to which he has added non-Scriptural details are particularly those that show the creation of the universe rather than those dealing with earth and man. As Christ and his attendant angels survey the Chaos upon which Deity is to impose order, they see it as had Satan at the gates of Hell:

> On Heavenly ground they stood, and from the shore
> They viewed the vast immeasurable Abyss,
> Outrageous as a sea, dark, wasteful, wild,
> Up from the bottom turned by furious winds
> And surging waves.[36]

The first Creation produces the earth: "And Earth, self-balanced, on her centre hung." The firmament that follows the creation of light is diffused

> In circuit to the uttermost convex
> Of this great round.

[36] *Ibid.* 7. 210–4.

The Sun and Moon follow, together with the "thousand lesser lights," many of them, even to the phases of Venus and the Milky Way, in accordance with the new astronomy.[37] The greatness of the descriptive technique in the passage becomes apparent when we realize the subtlety with which Milton suggests the vastness of Space by stressing the *limitation* which Deity imposed "to circumscribe the universe." As the mystic compasses turn "through the vast profundity obscure," the mystic words are spoken:

> 'Thus far extend, thus far thy bounds;
> This be thy just circumference, O World!' [38]

Vast as seems the world, with its light, its firmament, its "thousand, thousand stars," it is yet only a small portion of space. Earlier God had circumscribed for the rebel angels a portion of space that seemed to those still angelic beings to confine them, in spite of the fact that their "adventurous bands" were to discover vast continents of ice and snow, dark and dreary vales, "a gulf profound as that Serbonian bog." The "new-made World," to the angels who beheld its emergence, might seem "of amplitude almost immense," but beyond the world, beyond Hell, even beyond Heaven, in Milton's imagination stretched the "vast unbounded Deep" of Space.

Important as are the scenes of Creation, Milton is still too bound by reverence for the Scriptures to read into them some of the profound ideas which the new concept of space was bringing to men's minds. It remained for the inquiring mind of Adam to raise—if the Angel could not answer—other problems. The long astronomical conversation between Adam and the Angel is concerned with Copernicanism, to be sure, but it also shows the awareness of a vast universe which is post-Copernican. Even to Adam, it is now clear that this Earth is minute in comparison with heaven, an atom when compared with the Firmament:

> And all her numbered stars, that seem to roll
> Spaces incomprehensible, (for such
> Their distance argues, and their swift return).[39]

[37] There is no more charming example of the conjunction of old and new in this age than Milton's introduction into his expansion of *Genesis* of his passage on the phases of Venus, discovered by Galileo (7. 364–9), followed not long afterwards by a Galilean description of the Milky Way (7. 577–81).

[38] *Paradise Lost* 7. 230–1.

[39] *Ibid.* 8. 19–21.

He ponders, as had the century, the incredible speed at which these vast bodies must move in incredible space, "incorporeal speed . . . Speed, to describe whose swiftness number fails." The Angel speaks of this also:

> The swiftness of those Circles attribute,
> Though numberless, to his omnipotence,
> That to corporeal substances could add
> Speed almost spiritual.[40]

The vastness of the universe which both the Angel and Adam feel is increased by an idea which the Angel introduces in this particular scene, but which has been recurrent in Milton's mind throughout the poem, as we have already seen—the idea of other inhabited worlds. In this particular passage, it is the Moon which may conceivably be inhabited—"if land be there, Fields and inhabitants." But in other lines in *Paradise Lost*, Milton shows that his mind, as earlier Campenella's, had lingered on the possible existence of other worlds in other stars and planets. Satan considers the possibility as he wends his way

> Amongst innumerable stars, that shone
> Stars distant, but nigh-hand seemed other worlds,
> Or other worlds they seemed, or happy isles,
> Like those Hesperian Gardens famed of old,
> Fortunate fields, and groves, and flowering vales;
> Thrice happy isles! But who dwelt happy there
> He staid not to inquire.[41]

Some such idea is in Satan's mind when, close to Heaven, he pauses to inquire of Uriel, as both of them survey the myriad worlds before them:

> In which of all these shining orbs hath Man
> His fixed seat—or fixed seat hath none,
> But all these shining orbs his choice to dwell . . .
> On whom the great Creator hath bestowed
> Worlds. . . .[42]

Such a universe of habitable worlds is hymned, too, by the chorus of angels on the seventh day when, creation accomplished, they sing not of one world but of many:

40 *Ibid.* 8. 107–10.
41 *Ibid.* 3. 565–71.
42 *Ibid.* 3. 668–74.

> stars
> Numerous, and every star perhaps a world
> Of destined habitation.[43]

True, the Angel, at the end of his astronomical discussion, adds to his suggestions to Adam:

> Dream not of other worlds, what creatures there
> Live, in what state, condition, or degree,[44]

in the same mood in which he assures him that the knowledge of the true astronomical hypothesis is not essential to man. As if in obedience to the command of the Angel, the theme of "other worlds" disappears from *Paradise Lost,* nor does it enter again into any of Milton's works. Yet Milton's mind being what it was—like Adam's, curious in regard to the world about him—we may justly conclude that the apparent coincidence is due less to angelic behest than to the fact that from this time on, he dealt almost exclusively with matters of this world, in the remaining books of *Paradise Lost* and in his last two poems.

Not only are there other existing worlds in Milton's cosmic scheme, but he suggests a still more far-reaching conception which in the age which followed was to develop implications more profound than Milton himself read into it. "Space may produce new worlds," declared Satan to his despondent host upon the lake of Hell. Though Milton did not further develop the suggestion in Satan's speech—for Satan, after all, was little concerned with metaphysics and much with expediency—the idea lies behind several passages in *Paradise Lost.* The "wild Abyss" is "The womb of Nature, and perhaps her grave." The Angel, who, unlike Satan, is concerned with metaphysical ponderings, goes a step farther, after having suggested to Adam the possibility of life upon the moon. As the telescope of Galileo had discovered satellites around Jupiter, so the Angel suggests there may well be "other Suns with their attendant Moons

> Communicating male and female light,
> Which two great sexes animate the World,
> Stores in each Orb perhaps with some that live.[45]

[43] *Ibid.* 7. 620–2.
[44] *Ibid.* 8. 175–6.
[45] *Ibid.* 8. 148–52.

Thus having prodigally filled the expanded firmament with suns and stars, having filled the moon with life, and surrounded the suns with attendant moons, the Angel suggests the possibility of future creation, in order that there may not be

> such vast room in Nature unpossessed
> By living soul, desert and desolate.[46]

This is the superabundance and the fertility of Nature which the century was coming to realize, as their conception of life expanded with the expansion of the universe. The development of imagination that has occurred between *Comus* and *Paradise Lost* is obvious. In the youthful poem "Nature" was confined to this earth. Though she might "pour her bounties forth with such a full and unwithdrawing hand," she was still only the productive force which governs the "odours, fruits, and flocks," the "spawn innumerable," the "millions of spinning worms." Her possible "waste fertility" would be shown in an "earth cumbered and the winged air darked with plumes." The last possibility which Comus can conceive is that, unrestrained, she should "bestud with stars" the firmament. The older Milton perceives not only without dismay but even with exultation the vast expansion of a world into a bewildering universe, the possible existence of other inhabited worlds, even the possibility of production of worlds to come.

Yet these are exceptional passages, and no one of them is developed to its full implications. Milton did not in *Paradise Lost* reach such a conception of the infinity of space as Bruno, nearly a century earlier, nor such an idea of infinite fullness as evidence of Deity as did Leibniz, not much later. Though we may justly say that in comparison with Dante's, Milton's universe has become indefinite, there is here no conception of infinity. Indeed, one of the most remarkable characteristics of Milton's conception of space is his combination of definiteness and indefiniteness. Like his Christ, in the scene of creation, he seems on the one hand enthralled by the "vast immeasurable Abyss," on the other, laboring "to circumscribe This universe." If his "rising World" is "won from the void and formless Infinite," it is nevertheless a measurable world, in which Hell is

[46] *Ibid.* 8. 153–4.

As far removed from God and light of Heaven
As from the centre thrice to the utmost pole.[47]

True, Milton's angel warns us that in speaking of things infinite, he must speak, as it were, Platonically, and must describe "what surmounts the reach Of human sense" in such terms "as may express them best." Nevertheless, even in his conception of that immeasurable Space which continues beyond the world already created and the worlds to come, Milton does not approach the problem of absolute space as did his Cambridge contemporary Henry More, for example, who at almost the same time was introducing into English thought new concepts of space which were to influence Barrow, Newton, and others. Only at one point in *Paradise Lost* does Milton suggest the problem of Infinite Space and Infinite Deity, the problem which motivates so much of the philosophy of Henry More and of Malebranche. It is tempting to read the words of Milton's Deity

Boundless the Deep, because I am who fill
Infinitude; nor vacuous the space. . . .[48]

in the light of contemporary spatial conceptions; and, indeed, considered with More and Malebranche, they may seem to take on new meaning. But so much has already been made of this passage that any Milton student must be aware of the dangers of seeking in any one source the origin of what was probably in Milton's mind a conventional, though complex, theological idea. There is no question that to Milton, God, not Space, was infinite; and no one was more conscious than he of the logical and theological fallacy of making

Strange contradiction; which to God himself
Impossible is held, as argument
Of weakness, not of power.[49]

In the *Treatise of Christian Doctrine*, in which Milton, as theologian, might well have discussed further implications of the *idea of infinity* which were being reflected in contemporary philosophical works, he avoids the whole problem of the nature of space in his

[47] *Ibid.* 1. 73–4.
[48] *Ibid.* 7. 168–9.
[49] *Ibid.* 10. 799–801. Cf. *Treatise of Christian Doctrine*, Chapter 2, section 9.

discussion both of the creation and of the nature of God. Milton's theology, on the whole, as has been pointed out, draws from a tradition which is antithetic to that which was at least temporarily to triumph in establishing in the seventeenth century a theory of infinite universe as the inevitable expression of infinite Deity, the essence of whose Nature is the overflowing goodness that must show itself in the creation of all possible forms of existence in the created universe. Had he expressed himself on the subject in the *Treatise of Christian Doctrine*, there is little doubt that he would have denied the possibility of infinite space. Yet Milton was first of all a poet; as poet he shows in *Paradise Lost* a momentary imaginative response to certain impressions of the "new astronomy," which, carried to their ultimate conclusion, were inconsistent with his own theological premises. But Milton in *Paradise Lost* was concerned much more deeply with ethics than with metaphysics. Like his Angel, he turns from astronomical implications and from metaphysical considerations of space, to bid Adam, "Think only what concerns thee and thy being." It is enough for him that the expanded universe suggests an expansion of Deity; vast though the universe has become, "Heaven's wide circuit" bespeaks for Milton, as for the Psalmist and the Prophets,

> The Maker's high magnificence, who built
> So spacious, and his line stretched out so far,
> That Man may know he dwells not in his own—
> An edifice too large for him to fill.[50]

Although Milton's mature prose and poetry, then, offers little to the philosopher seeking new concepts of absolute or infinite space stimulated by the new astronomy, *Paradise Lost* still affords a remarkable example of the extent to which telescopic astronomy effected in an imaginative mind a vast expansion of the idea of space. Sensitive men of the seventeenth century, who by actual physical experience of the night sky seen through an "optic glass" had become aware of "stars that seem to roll Spaces incomprehensible," did not return to the limited conception of the universe which they had once taken for granted. As *Paradise Lost* was affected by the new astronomy, so in its turn it affected other poets. The impression of space which Milton achieved is imitated with more or less success by many poets of the later and the next century. The "sub-

[50] *Ibid.* 8. 100–4.

limity" of Milton to them was not a matter only of his language, and his lofty conception of God and Satan, Heaven and Hell, but even more of his sense of space, the vast reaches of his cosmic imagination—

> Et sine fine Chaos, et sine fine Deus,
> Et sine fine magis, si quid magis est sine fine. . . .[51]

The eighteenth-century growing "delight in wide views" of which critics have spoken, has usually been associated with growing interest in mountains and in mountainous scenery; but in the sense of perspective and the awareness of space that enters English writing after *Paradise Lost,* there is in part a direct heritage from Galileo's telescope and in part a heritage from Milton, whose patron goddess was "Urania," and who, even more truly than we have realized, succeeded in portraying in *Paradise Lost* "things unattempted yet in prose or rhyme."

[51] Barrow's commendatory verses, prefixed to the second edition. While I have purposely read into the second line—by omitting the next—an implication which the poet did not intend, the whole poem indicates the impression which Barrow had received of Milton's boundless conceptions.

James B. Conant

Science and Human Conduct

In the two previous lectures of this series, I have reviewed some aspects of the history of science and technology in this century. In this lecture I propose to explore certain consequences of the revolution in physics in terms of their effect on human conduct. Let me make it quite plain at the outset, however, that I do not intend to focus attention on the science of human conduct (if there be such a science) or on the science of human behavior. This is not to be in any sense a review of recent advances in either psychology or sociology. Not only would such an undertaking be entirely beyond both my capacity and my ambitions, but also it would not serve to direct attention to the problems with which I have dealt in my two previous lectures.

In my first lecture I spoke of the striking social phenomenon of our times—the scientist turned inventor. In my second, I briefly examined the so-called revolution in physics which for many people has cast doubt on the nature of what scientists said they were doing. Fifty or seventy-five years ago the scientist was supposed to be discovering nature's laws; the inventor was taking advantage of these discoveries for practical ends. The old-fashioned inventor has now disappeared; the basic assumptions of those who once popularized science have been challenged. I propose in this lecture and the next to see what, if any, significance the new interpretation of science has for the philosophy of life

Reprinted with permission of Columbia University Press from James B. Conant, Modern Science and Modern Man *(New York: Columbia University Press, 1952), pp. 103–41.*

that guides the daily decisions of thoughtful men and women.

There are two current fallacies about the nature of science; one tends to equate the scientist with a magician, the other confuses him with a mathematician. It is from the second of these popular misconceptions that the notion arises of a sharp dichotomy between the world of science and the realm of values. One's school experience with the theorems of Euclid and the Q.E.D. comes to mind when the words "science" and "truth" are used in the same sentence. According to the general philosophic outlook that I am presenting in these lectures, the truths of the propositions of geometry are inherent in their premises; mathematical or abstract reasoning as such is, in one sense, a vast tautology. But, I hasten to add, this tautology is of enormous value to the scientists because the theorems and operations in this abstract universe of discourse can be related to the world of the experiences of the physical scientist by certain approximations.

The demonstration of mathematical theorems, the repetition of those experiments whose interpretation has become a matter of common acceptance, the calculations carried out in those areas where the degree of empiricism is low—these activities, we feel, are somehow different from the activities involved in negotiating a treaty between two nations or a contract between two firms or from comforting a friend in sorrow. The first group, it is commonly said, is science; the second, human conduct involving ethics, morals, ideals, and matters of the spirit. But such statements, I believe, are essentially erroneous. The activities I have listed are not science; they are either exercises in logic, or the repetition of activities once significant in the advance of science, or essentially trivial and tiresome mental operations for some practical end, entirely equivalent to making change. Science is a dynamic undertaking directed to lowering the degree of the empiricism involved in solving problems; or, if you prefer, science is a process of fabricating a web of interconnected concepts and conceptual schemes arising from experiments and observations and fruitful of further experiments and observations.

As I have attempted to show in the preceding lectures, science is an activity; many of the results of this activity have become intermeshed with common-sense ideas. Scientific concepts are so much a part of the equipment of men and women in our culture that they are used both consciously and unconsciously in making decisions that we call ethical or moral. The activities of scientists in their laboratories are shot through with value judgments. Such at least is the twofold thesis I am defending now.

The concepts of scientists and their conceptual schemes (such as the atomic theory) can be regarded as serving the same purpose for research workers as do "common-sense ideas" for most people in the routine of living. The intermingling of precepts and concepts involved in the simplest acts of everyday life became a habit with us so early as to defy analysis of their origin. These habitual responses alone enable us to survive. By the time we are able to think at all and handle ourselves in the world, we have a mass of concepts (common-sense ideas) ready at hand. These have come to us in large part as a result of trial and error, in part by experiences that cluster together and which we designate as other persons. In an immediate situation, many of these concepts come into play, as a matter of course, as guides to action. Only philosophers attempt to analyze their origin and question their validity or verifiability. The uniformity of nature is one of these common-sense ideas. Skepticism about such ideas has no place in everyday life. The butcher, the baker, and the candlestick maker may have no valid reasons for believing that the world in which they operate has a uniformity, but they are certain they can slaughter and bake and fabricate by the same rules tomorrow as they have employed all their lives.

The common-sense world is one of partial uniformity only. There are areas of experience where we know that uncertainty is the certainty—the weather is an obvious example and to be contrasted with the regularity of day and night. To operate in a world of partial uniformity, we clearly need rules of experience. And the invention of such rules and of abstract ideas related to such rules has been of the utmost importance in the advance of civilization. Long before the idea of number had emerged, primitive people had evolved the conceptual scheme of a three-dimensional world. There were solid objects which could be seen, felt, and kicked; there were shadows that could be seen but neither felt nor kicked. To tie together all the empirical rules about nature, speculative thinking developed such concepts as those involved in animism and mythology. From the point of view I am here presenting, these ideas must be considered as early prototypes of the far more sophisticated Aristotelian principles and of such scientific theories as the caloric fluid and the luminiferous ether.

As guides to human conduct, common-sense ideas and scientific concepts interpenetrate to such an extent today that no one can say where one begins and the other ends. This is so obvious in regard to all the machinery that surrounds a civilized man that it requires no comment. But it is equally true with respect to habits which are far more primitive than the use of conveniences unknown to the ancient world. Consider our dietary and sanitary habits. Examine your own conduct for a day or two and try to list how many decisions, made at least half consciously, are determined by the findings of scientists in the last one hundred years. There would be many borderline cases which illustrate the point I am trying to make. And the certainty of the decisions would by no means be determined by their relation to modern science.

This last point I should like to dwell on for a moment as it illustrates a matter I believe to be of great importance. Our conduct in regard to eating is tied to deep-seated emotional complexes far more than to scientific theories. Robust individuals have been stimulated to active nausea by being told they had just eaten an article of food outside their dietary code. The Indian guide of a friend of mine was so afflicted when he saw his sophisticated companion start to dine on frogs' legs. This is primitive behavior, you may say, but a long process of education is required to overcome such unconscious responses on the part of even the most highly civilized among us. To what degree long experience with the conceptual schemes of modern science brings about the same deep-seated attachment to these schemes as that expressed by the Indian guide for his beliefs, I do not know. Perhaps a bacteriologist would automatically vomit if convinced that he had swallowed a mass of deadly bacteria; I doubt it. I think he would call for a stomach pump. All this may seem trivial to some of you, but I believe the recognition that there is a distinction between different degrees of attachment to conceptual frameworks is a matter of some importance. Further exploration of this field by psychologists and psychiatrists may yield a rich harvest. Roughly speaking, this is the area in which fall the phenomena investigated by those who study psychosomatic medicine. I shall return to the question of degrees of attachment or conviction as applied to ethical decisions and religious beliefs in my next and concluding lecture.

Tonight I want to confine my attention to decisions affecting human conduct that seem to be fairly evenly balanced, where no deep-seated emotional reactions are involved—rational decisions, we may say. These may range from a determination to buy high-test gasoline rather than a cheaper grade, to the making up of one's mind to sign a petition to outlaw the atomic bomb. Or, if you are in a responsible position in the affairs of this highly industrialized world, you may have to vote yes or no on a proposed loan for the purpose of building a pilot plant to make a new product or a new machine.

There is a fairly common fallacy that if you are dealing with scientific and technical matters, judgment of values rarely, if ever, enters in. Facts speak for themselves in science, we are often told. Anyone who is familiar with the course of scientific research and development knows this is nonsense. What is true is that the area of debate is fairly definitely circumscribed. The proponent of a process for making a new fabric, for example, is unlikely to quote either Plato or Aristotle on behalf of his proposal. Nor is he likely to appeal to the doctrines set forth in the Declaration of Independence or to the decisions of the Supreme Court. But that does not mean that what is proposed is not controversial. It means simply that the number of people qualified to take part in the controversy is highly limited. And this fact is one pregnant with trouble for our free society. Indeed, among the highly significant but dangerous results of the development of modern science is the fact that scientific experts now occupy a peculiarly exalted and isolated position. Of course, this is an age of experts of all types; one of the vital problems of education is to start a trend of mind among our young people that will lead to a better understanding by one group of experts of what other groups of experts are doing. But I cannot take the time tonight to digress into this topic of general education.

The notion that a scientist is a cool, impartial, detached individual is, of course, absurd. The vehemence of conviction, the pride of authorship burn as fiercely among scientists as among any creative workers. Indeed, if they did not, there would be no advance in science. But this emotional attachment to one's own point of view is particularly insidious in science because it is so easy for the proponent of a project to clothe his convictions in technical language. Therefore it is necessary to explore ways and means of balancing the biases of experts whenever their opinions are of prime importance in the making of decisions.

First of all, a healthy skepticism is in order in listening to an expert, particularly an enthusiastic one. The next step is to try to find a person of equal technical competence but with an opposite emotional bias. If such a one is not at hand, some competent individual hitherto unconcerned with whatever project is in question should be asked to undertake the job of being "devil's advocate," as it were. He should be asked to devote hmself to preparing the case for a reasoned opposition to what has been proposed. Such procedures for balancing the bias of technical men, particularly scientists turned inventors, have been worked out almost without plan in the successful industries of this nation. But similar methods of operating have not yet been evolved in other areas; they are absent in the United States Government. Yet here they are particularly needed, for, as I pointed out in my first lecture, the government has entered research and development on a very large scale indeed. It is inevitable that in any technological undertaking, conservatism must continually face enthusiasm. In so doing, emotions are aroused and personal fortunes become entangled with technological considerations.

In 1940, those of us who were in Washington as civilians were concerned mostly with the technological conservatism of the men in uniform. I will relate no stories to prove the point. The conflict between the professors and the "brass" is too well known. Most of the versions do less than justice to the military man and give too much credit to the professor. Be that as it may, what I am concerned with is not the technological conservatism of the men in uniform in 1940 but the almost fanatic enthuisasm for research and development of their successors in 1952. It is a phenomenon not unlike that of an old-fashioned religious conversion. The Defense Department, in regard to research, is not unlike the man who sprang onto his horse and rode madly off in all directions.

This is not the time nor place for me to outline in detail my remedy for what many feel to be a bad situation. I will content myself by saying that I believe that if the Department of Defense would gradually introduce a quasi-judicial system of review which provided forced opposition to new projects, the taxpayers' money would be more wisely spent. When a question came up to be settled, even if three or four echelons from the top, one or two referees or judges might hear the arguments pro and con. The important point is that there should be arguments *against* the proposal: they should be vigorous but candid; a technical expert should speak on behalf of the taxpayer against each large proposal. Then adequate briefs for the two sides could be prepared (not compromise committee reports). With opposing briefs, arguments, and cross-questioning, many facets of the problem, many prejudices of the witnesses would be brought out into the open. The forced opposition is the important point.

There may be some who feel that my attitude towards science is defeatist, that instead of suggesting how the emotional reactions of scientists should be balanced when they are giving advice about future action, I should demand that scientists act like scientists and eliminate their prejudices. For example, a social scientist in answering affirmatively the question, "Can science save us?" has written as follows:

"Science, as a method, is a form of human behavior. It consists of asking clear, answerable questions in order to direct one's observations, which are made in a calm and unprejudiced manner and which are then reported as accurately as possible and in such a way as to answer the questions that were asked to begin with, after which any pertinent beliefs or assumptions that were held before the observations were made are revised in the light of observations made and answers obtained." All of which is a typical description of what is often called scientific behavior, but I venture to suggest it is not a description of the characteristic way the natural sciences have advanced; it is rather an account of the use of very limited working hypotheses not dissimilar to those employed in everyday life.

To illustrate what I mean by a limited working hypothesis, I shall have to revert for a moment to what I said in my first lecture about the development of modern science. I suggested that the activity we designate as scientific research is compounded of the empirical procedures by which man has improved the practical arts ever since the dawn of civilization, general speculative ideas, and mathematical or abstract reasoning. Science began to progress rapidly in the sixteenth and seventeenth centuries when people saw how to relate these three activities. When employed, the speculative ideas became working hypotheses on a grand scale; such conceptual schemes as "the earth is surrounded by a sea of air" could be tested by experiment only by being connected with actual manipulations by a series of limited working hypotheses. These are of the type "if I turn this stopcock, then such and such will happen." Only by a long chain of reasoning is the specific "if, then" proposition, which can be tested, related to the validity of the working hypothesis on a grand scale.

To illustrate the relation of limited working hypotheses to those conceptual schemes which have been essential for the advance of science, let me analyze a common-sense inquiry directed to an immediate practical end. Assume that you are confronted with a locked door and a bunch of keys; the hypothesis readily comes to mind that one of these keys will unlock the door. This is a working hypothesis. From it, one can deduce several consequences which can be tested by appropriate action. The most obvious is to try each key in turn in the lock and see if any one will, in fact, unlock the door. This involves a set of experiments which requires a certain degree of order as care must be taken to test *each* key; also, the keys tested must be in fact those originally under consideration (leaving the keys about for a while and then trying them would necessitate the assumption that no one had made a substitution!). A series of limited working hypothesis thus seems involved somewhat as follows: (1) one of this bunch of keys will unlock the door; (2) this particular key will unlock the door; (3) if this particular key will unlock the door when I insert it in the lock and turn it, then the lock will spring. This last "if, then" proposition can be put to the test and yields a yes or no answer. Depending on the outcome, the next key is tried. Such "if, then" propositions are highly limited working hypotheses of exactly the type used throughout experimental science.

To illustrate what I have in mind, let me give one simple example drawn from the history of science. Pascal in the seventeenth century set out to test the idea that the earth was surrounded by a sea of air which exerted pressure. This he proposed to do by observing the height of a column of mercury in a barometer (to use modern terms). His brother-in-law ascended the Puy de Dôme for this purpose and set up a Torricellian tube (a barometer) on the summit and measured the height of the column of mercury. The experiment confirmed Pascal's prediction, based on the new theory, that the column would be appreciably lower than that observed in a barometer at the base of the mountain. Notice that the grand hypothesis that the earth was surrounded by a sea of air was not and could not be tested directly. The limited working hypothesis that was tested was, essentially, "If I set up this barometer here on the summit and measure the height of the mercury column, it will be less than that observed at the base." The connection between the verification or negation of this limited hypothesis and the broad working hypothesis, namely, that the earth is surrounded by a sea of air, involves many steps and many assumptions.

To illustrate further the long chains of reasoning involved in science, let me return to the trivial case mentioned earlier. Here the restricted working hypothesis was connected with a broader, yet limited, working hypothesis, namely, "one of these keys will unlock the door." The latter is the working hypothesis which a quick glance at the problem indicates is being tested. Yet the connection between the observation, turning the hand, observing the lock, and the working hypothesis that is being tested involves a chain of reasoning as well as common-sense concepts and assumptions. To name but a few of the latter, one need only mention that the word "key," "lock," "turning," and "springing the lock" would be meaningless in many cultures. But even more important are common-sense assumptions such as that the ability of the key to spring a lock will remain unchanged over the period of inquiry, and that each key is the "same" key and the lock is the "same." (The latter assumption might easily be false and the former might be invalidated by a sleight-of-hand performer.) The equivalent of these assumptions and concepts in the case of a scientific experiment is by no means trivial. A vast number of errors have resulted from a failure to examine critically such assumptions. Or, more often, the "errors," as we now call them, came from the fact that assumptions which *had to be made to get ahead* turned out to be only first approximations.

The last point is of significance in view of the attention that is being paid today to the analysis of the methods used in physics. Emphasis is being placed on the need to define, in terms of actual manipulations where possible, the concepts used in physics, such as "length" and "simultaneity." Failure to carry out such rigorous thinking in the past, some authors have implied, has delayed the advance of physics. This may be the case. But if one examines the history of chemistry or biology, it becomes plain that clear-cut operational definitions are never possible in the infancy of science. Rather, early investigators in these fields usually must start with common-sense notions which are bound to be hazy and uncertain. Only by being willing to work with these "fuzzy ideas" and relate them to limited working hypotheses and thus to experiment and observations have the pioneers succeeded.

Take as an example Pasteur's study of fermentation. Here was a word, "fermentation," used to describe a group of everyday processes which over the ages men had learned by empirical procedures to control. No clear-cut definition of "fermentation" was possible in Pasteur's time and one would be difficult today. The change from sugar to alcohol fell within this category and had been shown to be associated with the presence of a microorganism, yeast. Another change, from starch to sugar, was associated with something found in sprouting barley that could be extracted with warm water. Pasteur put forward as a working hypothesis on a grand scale the concept that all fermentations were the result of the growth of living organisms. To rule out the starch-sugar case, where clearly no living organism was present, he hedged his statement by the phrase, "fermentations properly so called." He then found he could demonstrate the necessary growth of organisms in many changes hitherto classed as fermentations and these became, of course, for him "fermentations properly so called."

Pasteur comes very close to arguing in a circle. This is particularly clear today when we know that both his "fermentations properly so called" and the other similar changes where no organism is present are all brought about by enzymes. Yet one might better call Pasteur's procedure a spiral argumentation, for it certainly was fruitful. It was highly illogical for him to define fermentation so as to exclude the known cases where living organisms were *not* involved and then turn around and point with pride to the instances where fermentation and life were correlative. But his concept as a policy, a guide to action, was successful; indeed, if Pasteur had been more rigorous in his logic, his results might have been less revolutionary.

Unless I am much mistaken, the successful use of hazy concepts in biology, biochemistry, and, above all, in medicine has deep significance for those concerned with human behavior. John Tyndall, reviewing the application of Pasteur's discoveries to the brewer's art, contrasted "the scientific account of the agencies which come into play in the manufacture of beer" with the hitherto "empirical observations" of the brewers. Pasteur's working hypothesis on a grand scale (namely, that fermentation and life were correlative) was the first major step in lowering the degree of empiricism in the fermentation industries. But we must not forget to what extent pure empiricism over the ages has improved the making of beer and wine, nor the vast amount of empirical knowledge thus accumulated.

Substitute for "fermentation" the words "typhoid fever" or "syphilis" or "pneumonia," and you would be able to trace a somewhat similar path of progress in lowering the degree of empiricism. You would meet the same difficulties in defining the basic concepts (what is a disease in operational terms?), but you would record far less success over the ages in solving the problem by pure empiricism. Indeed, since human lives, not spoiled casks of fermenting juice, are here involved, the errors of pure empiricism loom large in the history of medical sciences. We can laugh at any superstitions of the wine makers of earlier times, but we shudder when we think of the needless deaths due to "bleeding" and similar medical practices now discarded. The trial-and-error procedures of pure empiricism are slow and wasteful, even when they are well ordered; through them the arts have gradually progressed, but the art of medicine in the process of development undoubtedly shortened the lives of a considerable percentage of those who could afford to consult physicians. Indeed, it is probable that only within this century have medical men and surgeons helped more people than they have injured—one might almost say, cured more persons than they have killed.

The parallel with the social sciences, I suggest, is worth considering. All the sciences concerned with human beings that range from the abstractions of economics through sociology to anthropology and psychology are, in part, efforts to lower the degree of empiricism in certain areas; in part they are efforts to organize and systematize empirical procedures. Whether or not in each of the divisions or subdivisions a Pasteur has yet arisen is not for me to say. But if he has, his contribution has been the introduction of some new broad concepts, some working hypotheses on a grand scale that have been fruitful of further investigations. It would seem important to distinguish, if possible, the advances connected with such broad working hypotheses, which are the essense of a science, and the continued efforts to improve human society by empirical procedures. As to the latter, at least, we may be certain there has been a vast amount of labor expended within recent years.

Many social scientists, I imagine, would not dissent too strongly from the proposition that their whole area of investigation is in a state comparable with that of the biological sciences (including medicine) a hundred or a hundred and fifty years ago. If that be the case, the balance of this century should witness great strides forward; but by the very nature of science (as compared to empiricism), it is impossible to foretell in what precise direction the advance will be made. Which one of the common-sense fuzzy ideas about consciousness, love, or the zest for power will be picked up by a rare genius and be the basis for a vast expansion of fruitful scientific work? Perhaps some of you will say I am being unduly cautious; that already the pioneers have done their work; that in one direction Pavlov has opened new vistas about human behavior, in another, Freud has been at least as successful as was Pasteur.

In attempting to appraise the advance of social sciences as sciences, we are always in the same difficulty as with medicine. It is hard to separate the purely empirical from the scientific; it is impossible to be unconcerned with immediate results and difficult to evaluate practical success or failure. To those who tend to belittle the practical consequences of the work of psychiatrists, psychologists, and sociologists, I offer for consideration the interesting case of Dr. Thomas Beddoes of Bristol, England. An eminent physician of the early nineteenth century, abreast of the advances in science, he founded a pneumatic institute for the treatment of disease by means of the new gases discovered not long before. James Watt designed effective machinery for administering the gases to the patients, and a brilliant youth by the name of Humphrey Davy received his start in science by serving as the chemist. It is fortunate no one was killed; it is certain no one was cured. But Dr. Beddoes was no charlatan. In a charitable mood one may even claim he was a chemotherapist a hundred and fifty years ahead of his time and employing the wrong chemicals!

Neither medicine nor the medical sciences were advanced in Dr. Beddoes' Pneumatic Institute. But the same spirit that prompted him has been at work in countless other members of his profession; gradually at first, and with amazing speed in this century, the medical sciences as sciences have advanced. In retrospect we do not count the honest follies of men like Dr. Beddoes nor the innumerable charlatans who follow in such men's wake. So, too, in the whole field of the social sciences; it seems to me probable that a hundred years hence the historians will be able to separate out the science from the empiricism and both from the charlatanism of the 1950's. We are too much immersed in the pioneer stage to be able to make this appraisal ourselves. But surely those who demand progress, with capital letters, in the social sciences and believe it can be achieved by planned attack and exhortation might well profit by reading the history of medicine in the nineteenth century.

If there be any lessons to be drawn from history, they are surely that while advances in sciences are never divorced from empirical processes, they arise from the most unexpected quarters. Success in lowering the degree of empiricism comes suddenly from one knows not where. Not long after Dr. Beddoes was making his frontal attack on disease by means of the new chemistry, a French physicist, Baron Charles Gagniard de la Tour, demonstrated that yeast globules essential for beer-making were organized bodies belonging to the vegetable kingdom. Who could have guessed that the French physicist rather than the English doctor was starting down the track that was to lead to the control of infectious diseases? The hits in science are usually made with a crooked ball.

The implication of what I have just been saying for those who wish to assist the social sciences is obvious: support the uncommitted investigator who has ideas, irrelevant as these ideas may seem to practical problems. The practical arts, including the art of human relations, are bound to progress, even if slowly, by trial-and-error methods; society is always ready to assist such undertakings. The successes here are not to be despised, even if they are empirical; just as today in metallurgy, as I pointed out in my first lecture, there is a vast amount of empiricism mixed with some science, so, too, the same situation exists in many of the social sciences. In this century we have refined the process of trial-and-error experimentation; we have learned wisdom about empirical procedures. The record of industry demonstrates this beyond question, as far as the natural sciences are concerned. A candid review of what has been accomplished in pedagogy, in handling some types of abnormal psychology, in a few restricted areas of economics, perhaps in certain kinds of human relations, would show progress and would demonstrate that we can solve certain types of problems involving human beings better than our ancestors.

The demand for practitioners in these fields continues high; but one need not be a cynic to remember that the services of physicians were eagerly sought by the sick even when the members of this profession were on the whole doing more harm than good. There is no need for one to be a Pollyana optimist to remember that if by edict the practice of medicine had been stopped throughout the Western world, mankind never would have learned to control infectious diseases. Errors in practice as well as in theory appear to be the inescapable price we pay for progress in learning to solve problems.

Now, a final word as to science and human conduct. Literally every step we take in life is determined by a series of interlocking concepts and conceptual schemes. Every goal we formulate for our actions, every decision we make, be it trivial or momentous, involves assumptions about the universe and about human beings. To my mind, any attempt to draw a sharp line between common-sense ideas and scientific concepts is not only impossible but unwise. Belief in the whole apparatus of a three-dimensional world and in the existence of other people is a policy essential for an individual's survival; for a physicist or chemist in his laboratory, a new working hypothesis is a policy guiding his conduct as an experimenter. Where is one to draw the line? The common-sense ideas of our ancestors before the dawn of modern science were the foundation of all their value judgments. If scientific concepts are now part of our common-sense assumptions, and who can doubt they are, then to this degree, at least, the consequences of the actions of previous scientists now affect our value judgments. This much connection between science and human conduct seems to me quite certain.

In his laboratory, every scientist is forever deciding that this is a better way to proceed than that. Every experiment he plans was, in its inception, cradled by judgments of what would be worth while, what would warrant the effort, including an over-all value judgment that the investigator should stay in his laboratory rather than go fishing.

At this point some of you may be inclined to say with impatience, if not with heat, "For a whole hour the main guide to human conduct has been ignored! Not a word about ethics, not a mention of morals, no reference to religion." To which I would reply that an analysis of the relation of values to science and of both to relatively trivial examples of human decisions appears to me to be a necessary prelude to a consideration of the Big Questions of the nature and destiny of man and the problem of good and evil. To what extent modern science has anything to say to the individual who ponders on the meaning of life, on definitions of moral standards, and on the whole realm of spiritual values depends on certain basic philosophic presuppositions. These presuppositions, in turn, reflect one's attitude toward science.

Reverting to my previous lecture, I will remind you that a scientific concept can be regarded either as a policy or as a creed. If the latter, then this creed is equivalent to a map of the material universe (even if only a first approximation) and must be congruous with an account of human beings and their destiny. A consistent, unitary World Hypothesis with appropriate subcategories for man, for life, for matter, for energy, has been the goal of theologians and philosophers for centuries. In the eighteenth and nineteenth centuries, scientists joined hands with such endeavors. Before the revolution in physics, this looked like a simpler undertaking than it has in fact turned out to be. It is interesting that among those who formulated a scientific creed in the opening years of this century there were both optimists and pessimists. The same assumptions (or very nearly the same assumptions) could lead to quite different moods. As to the optimists I shall have something to say in my next lecture. This lecture I conclude by quoting what Bertrand Russell wrote in his *A Free Man's Worship* fifty years ago. Speaking of "the world which science presents for our belief," he wrote. "That man is the product of causes which had no prevision of the end they were achieving; that his origin, his growth, his hopes and fears, his loves and his beliefs, are but the outcome of accidental collocations of atoms; that no fire, no heroism, no intensity of thought and feeling, can preserve an individual life beyond the grave; that all the labors of the ages, all the devotion, all the inspiration, all the noonday brightness of human genius, are destined to extinction in the vast death of the solar system, and that the whole temple of Man's achievement must inevitably be buried beneath the debris of a universe in ruins—all these things, if not quite beyond dispute, are, yet so nearly certain, that no philosophy which rejects them can hope to stand. Only within the scaffolding of these truths, only on the firm foundation of unyielding despair, can the soul's habitation henceforth be safely built." [1]

In using this quotation, I think it only fair to say that I doubt if the distinguished philosopher would express these views today in the same language. But the difficulty of assuming that science is a creed or part of a creed, a map of the universe, however imperfect, is illustrated by this quotation. The modern cosmology is based on experimental results unimagined fifty years ago and this cosmology is subject to a somewhat different interpretation from that of Russell in 1903. Whether or not any of these interpretations bear on the problem of good and evil is a question I shall consider in my concluding lecture.

[1] First published in *Independent Review*, December, 1903; included in *Mysticism and Logic and Other Essays* (Longmans, Green, and Co., London and New York, 1918); separately published as *A Free Man's Worship* (Mosher, Portland, Maine, 1923).

Robert K. Merton

Puritanism, Pietism, and Science

In his prolegomena to a culutral sociology Alfred Weber has discriminated between the processes of society, culture, and civilization.[1] Since his primary interest lay in differentiating these categories of sociological phenomena, Weber in large measure ignored their specific interrelationships, a field of study which is fundamental for the sociologist. It is precisely this interaction between certain elements of culture and civilization, with especial reference to seventeenth-century England, which constitutes the object–matter of the present essay.

THE PURITAN ETHOS

The first section of this paper outlines the Puritan value-complex in so far as it was related to the notable increase of interest in science during the latter part of the seventeenth century, while the second presents the relevant empirical materials concerning the differential cultivation of natural science by Protestants and other religious affiliates.

It is the thesis of this study that the Puritan ethic,

Reprinted with permission of the author and the Sociological Review. *This article appeared originally in* Sociological Review *(old series) vol. 28, part 1 (January 1936). It is reprinted here from Robert K. Merton,* Social Theory and Social Structure *(New York: Free Press of Glencoe, 1957, revised edition), pp. 574–606.*

1 Alfred Weber, "Prinzipielles zur Kultursoziologie: Gesellschaftsprozess, Zivilisationsprozess und Kulturbewegung," *Archiv für Sozialwissenschaft und Sozialpolitik*, xlvii, 1920, 47, 1–49. See the similar classification by R. M. MacIver, *Society: Its Structure and Changes*, chap. xii; and the discussion of these studies by Morris Ginsberg, *Sociology* (London, 1934), 45–52.

as an ideal-typical expression of the value-attitudes basic to ascetic Protestantism generally, so canalized the interests of seventeenth-century Englishmen as to constitute one important *element* in the enhanced cultivation of science. The deep-rooted religious *interests* [2] of the day demanded in their forceful implications the systematic, rational, and empirical study of Nature for the glorification of God in His works and for the control of the corrupt world.

It is possible to determine the extent to which the values of the Puritan ethic stimulated interest in science by surveying the attitudes of the contemporary scientists. Of course, there is a marked possibility that in studying the avowed motives of scientists we are dealing with rationalizations, with derivations, rather than with accurate statements of the actual motives. In such instances, although they may refer to isolated specific cases, the value of our study is by no means vitiated, for these conceivable rationalizations themselves are evidence (Weber's *Erkenntnismitteln*) of the motives which were regarded as socially acceptable, since, as Kenneth Burke puts it, "a terminology of motives is moulded to fit our general orientation as to purposes, instrumentalities, the good life, etc."

Robert Boyle was one of the scientists who attempted explicitly to link the place of science in social life with other cultural values, particularly in his *Usefulness of Experimental Natural Philosophy*. Such attempts were likewise made by John Ray, whose work in natural history was path-breaking and who was characterized by Haller as the greatest botanist in the history of man; Francis Willughby, who was perhaps as eminent in zoology as was Ray in botany; John Wilkins, one of the leading spirits in the "invisible College" which developed into the Royal Society; Oughtred, Wallis, and others. For additional evidence we can turn to the scientific body which, arising about the middle of the century, provoked and stimulated scientific advance more than any other immediate agency:

[2] "Nicht die ethische Theorie theologischer Kompendien, die nur als ein (unter Umständen allerdings wichtiges) Erkenntnismittel dient, sondern die in den psychologischen und pragmatischen Zusammenhängen der Religionen gegründeten praktischen Antriebe zum Handeln sind das, was in Beracht kommt [unter 'Wirtschaftsethik' einer Religion]." Max Weber, *Gesammelte Aufsätze zur Religionssoziologie* (Tübingen, 1920), 1, 238. As Weber justly indicates, one freely recognizes the fact that religion is but *one* element in the determination of the religious ethic, but none the less it is at present an superable, and for our purposes, unnecessary task to determine *all* the component elements of this ethic. That problem awaits further analysis and falls outside the scope of this study.

the Royal Society. In this instance we are particularly fortunate in possessing a contemporary account written under the constant supervision of the members of the Society so that it might be representative of their views of the motives and aims of that association. This is Thomas Sprat's widely read *History of the Royal-Society of London*, published in 1667, after it had been examined by Wilkins and other representatives of the Society.[3]

Even a cursory examination of these writings suffices to disclose one outstanding fact: certain elements of the Protestant ethic had pervaded the realm of scientific endeavour and had left their indelible stamp upon the attitudes of scientists toward their work. Discussions of the why and wherefore of science bore a point-to-point correlation with the Puritan teachings on the same subject. Such a dominant force as was religion in those days was not and perhaps could not be compartmentalized and delimited. Thus, in Boyle's highly commended apologia for science it is maintained that the study of Nature is to the greater glory of God and the Good of Man.[4] This is the motif which recurs in constant measure. The juxtaposition of the spiritual and the material is characteristic. This culture rested securely on a substratum of utilitarian norms which constituted the measuring-rod of the desirability of various activities. The definition of action designed for the greater glory of God was tenuous and vague, but utilitarian standards could easily be applied.

Earlier in the century, this keynote had been sounded in the resonant eloquence of that "veritable apostle of the learned societies," Francis Bacon. Himself the initiator of no scientific discoveries, unable to appreciate the importance of his great contemporaries, Gilbert, Kepler, and Galileo, naïvely believing in the possibility of a

[3] *Cf.* C. L. Sonnichsen, *The Life and Works of Thomas Sprat* (Harvard University, unpublished doctoral dissertation, 1931), 131 ff., where substantial evidence of the fact that the *Historian's* representative of the views of the Society is presented. It is of further interest that the statements in Sprat's book concerning the aims of the Society bear a distinct similarity on every score to Boyle's characterizations of the motives and aims of scientists in general. This similarity is evidence of the dominance of the ethos which included these attitudes.

[4] Robert Boyle, *Some Considerations Touching the Usefulness of Experimental Natural Philosophy* (Oxford, 1664), 22 ff. See, also, the letters of William Oughtred in *Correspondence of Scientific Men of the Seventeenth Century*, edited by S. J. Rigaud (Oxford, 1841), xxxiv, *et passim;* or the letters of John Ray in the *Correspondence of John Ray*, edited by Edwin Lankester (London, 1848), 389, 395, 402, *et passim.*

scientific method which "places all wits and understandings nearly on a level," a radical empiricist holding mathematics to be of no use in science, he was, nevertheless, highly successful as one of the principal protagonists of a positive social evaluation of science and of the disclaim of a sterile scholasticism. As one would expect from the son of a "learned, eloquent, and religious woman, full of puritanic fervour" who was admittedly influenced by his mother's attitudes, he speaks in the *Advancement of Learning* of the true end of scientific activity as the "glory of the Creator and the relief of man's estate." Since, as is quite clear from many official and private documents, the Baconian teachings constituted the basic principles on which the Royal Society was patterned, it is not strange that the same sentiment is expressed in the charter of the Society.

In his last will and testament, Boyle echoes the same attitude, petitioning the Fellows of the Society in this wise: "Wishing them also a happy success in their laudable attempts, to discover the true Nature of the Works of God; and praying that they and all other Searchers into Physical Truths, may cordially refer their Attainments to the Glory of the Great Author of Nature, and to the Comfort of Mankind."[5] John Wilkins proclaimed the experimental study of Nature to be a most effective means of begetting in men a veneration for God.[6] Francis Willughby was prevailed upon to publish his works—which he had deemed unworthy of publication—only when Ray insisted that it was a means of glorifying God.[7] Ray's *Wisdom of God*, which was so well received that five large editions were issued in some twenty years, is a panegyric of those who glorify Him by studying His works.[8]

To a modern, comparatively untouched by religious forces, and noting the almost complete separation, if not opposition, between science and religion today, the recurrence of these pious phrases is apt to signify merely customary usage, and nothing of deep-rooted motivating convictions. To him these excerpts would seem to be a case of *qui nimium probat nihil probat*. But such an interpretation is possible only if one neglects to translate oneself within the framework of seventeenth-century values. Surely such a man as Boyle, who

[5] Quoted by Gilbert, Lord Bishop of Sarum, *A Sermon Preached at the Funeral of the Hon. Robert Boyle* (London, 1692), 25.

[6] *Principles and Duties of Natural Religion* (London, 1710—sixth edition), 236 *et passim*.

[7] *Memorials of John Ray*, 14 f.

[8] *Wisdom of God* (London, 1691), 126–129, *et passim*.

spent considerable sums to have the Bible translated into foreign tongues, was not simply rendering lip service. As G. N. Clark very properly notes in this connection:

> There is . . . always a difficulty in estimating the degree to which what we call religion enters into anything which was said in the seventeenth century in religious language. It is not solved by discounting all theological terms and treating them merely as common form. On the contrary, it is more often necessary to remind ourselves that these words were then seldom used without their accompaniment of meaning, and that their use did generally imply a heightened intensity of feeling.[9]

The second dominant tenet in the Puritan ethos designated social welfare, the good of the many, as a goal ever to be held in mind. Here again the contemporary scientists adopted an objective prescribed by the current values. Science was to be fostered and nurtured as leading to the domination of Nature by technological invention. The Royal Society, we are told by its worthy historian, "does not intend to stop at some particular benefit, but goes to the root of all noble inventions."[10] But those experiments which do not bring with them immediate gain are not to be condemned, for as the noble Bacon has declared, experiments of Light ultimately conduce to a whole troop of inventions useful to the life and state of man. This power of science to better the material condition of man, he continues, is, apart from its purely mundane value, a good in the light of the Evangelical Doctrine of Salvation by Jesus Christ.

And so on through the principles of Puritanism there was the same point-to-point correlation between them and the attributes, goals, and results of science. Such was the contention of the protagonists of science at that time. Puritanism simply made articulate the basic values of the period. If Puritanism demands systematic, methodic labour, constant diligence in one's calling, what, asks Sprat, more active and industrious and systematic than the Art of Experiment, which "can never be finish'd by the perptual labours of any one man, nay, scarce by the successive forces of the greatest Assembly?"[11] Here is employment enough for the most indefatigable industry, since even those hidden treasures of Nature which

[9] G. N. Clark, *The Seventeenth Century* (Oxford, 1929), 323.
[10] Thomas Sprat, *History of the Royal Society*, 78–79.
[11] *Ibid.*, 341–2.

are farthest from view may be uncovered by pains and patience.[12]

Does the Puritan eschew idleness because it conduces to sinful thoughts (or interferes with the pursuit of one's vocation)? "What room can there be for low, and little things in a mind so usefully and successfully employ'd [as in natural philosophy]?" [13] Are plays and playbooks pernicious and flesh-pleasing (and subversive of more serious pursuits)? [14] Then it is the "fittest season for experiments to arise, to teach us a Wisdome, which springs from the depths of Knowledge, to shake off the shadows, and to scatter the mists [of the spiritual distractions brought on by the Theatre]." [15] And finally, is a life of earnest activity within the world to be preferred to monastic asceticism? Then recognize the fact that the study of natural philosophy "fits us not so well for the secrecy of a Closet: It makes us serviceable to the World." [16] In short, science embodies two highly prized values: utilitarianism and empiricism.

In a sense this explicit coincidence between Puritan tenets and the qualities of science as a calling is casuistry. It is an express attempt to fit the scientist *qua* pious layman into the framework of the prevailing social values. It is a bid for religious and social sanction, since both the constitutional position and the personal authority of the clergy were much more important then than now. But this is not the entire explanation. The justificatory efforts of Sprat, Wilkins, Boyle, or Ray do not simply present opportunistic obsequiousness, but rather an earnest attempt to justify the ways of science to God. The Reformation had transferred the burden of individual salvation from the Church to the individual, and it is this "overwhelming and crushing sense of the responsibility for his own

[12] Ray, *Wisdom of God*, 125.

[13] Sprat, *op. cit.*, 344–5.

[14] Richard Baxter, *Christian Directory* (London, 1825—first published in 1664), I, 152; II, 167. *Cf.* Robert Barclay, the Quaker apologist, who specifically suggests "geometrical and mathematical experiments" as innocent divertissements to be sought instead of pernicious plays. *An Apology for the True Christian Divinity* (Phila., 1805—first written in 1675), 554–5.

[15] Sprat, *op. cit.*, 362.

[16] *Ibid.*, 365–6. Sprat perspicaciously suggests that monastic asceticism induced by religious scruples was partially responsible for the lack of empiricism of the Schoolmen. "But what sorry kinds of Philosophy must the Schoolmen needs produce, when it was part of their Religion, to separate themselves, as much as they could, from the converse of mankind? When they were so far from being able to discover the secrets of Nature, that they scarce had opportunity to behold enough of its common works." *Ibid.*, 19.

soul" which explains the acute religious interest. If science were not demonstrably a lawful and desirable calling, it dare not claim the attention of those who felt themselves "ever in the Great Task-master's eye." It is to this intensity of feeling that such apologias were due.

The exaltation of the faculty of reason in the Puritan ethos—based partly on the conception of rationality as a curbing device of the passions—inevitably led to a sympathetic attitude toward those activities which demand the constant application of rigorous reasoning. But again, in contrast to medieval rationalism, reason is deemed subservient and auxiliary to empiricism. Sprat is quick to indicate the pre-eminent adequacy of science in this respect.[17] It is on this point probably that Puritanism and the scientific temper are in most salient agreement, for the combination of *rationalism and empiricism* which is so pronounced in the Puritan ethic forms the essence of the spirit of modern science. Puritanism was suffused with the rationalism of neo-Platonism, derived largely through an appropriate modification of Augustine's teachings. But it did not stop there. Associated with the designated necessity of dealing successfully with the practical affairs of life within this world—a derivation from the peculiar twist afforded largely by the Calvinist doctrine of predestination and *certitudo salutis* through successful worldly activity—was an emphasis upon empiricism. These two currents brought to convergence through the logic of an inherently consistent system of values were so associated with the other values of the time as to prepare the way for the acceptance of a similar coalescence in natural science.

Empiricism and rationalism were canonized, beatified, so to speak. It may very well be that the Puritan ethos did not directly influence the method of science and that this was simply a parallel development in the internal history of science, but it is evident that through the psychological compulsion toward certain modes of thought and conduct this value-complex made an empirically-founded science commendable rather than, as in the medieval period, reprehensible or at best acceptable on sufferance. This could not but have

[17] Sprat, *op. cit.*, 361. Baxter in a fashion representative of the Purians decried the invasion of "enthusiasm" into religion. Reason must "maintain its authority in the command and government of your thoughts." *CD.*, ii, 199. In like spirit, those who at Wilkins' lodgings laid the foundation of the Royal Society "were invincibly arm'd against all the inchantments of Enthusiasm." Sprat, *op. cit.*, 53.

directed some talents into scientific fields which otherwise would have engaged in more highly esteemed professions. The fact that science to-day is largely if not completely divorced from religious sanctions is itself of interest as an example of the process of secularization.

The beginnings of such secularization, faintly perceptible in the latter Middle Ages, are manifest in the Puritan ethos. It was in this system of values that reason and experience were first markedly considered as independent means of ascertaining even religious truths. Faith which is unquestioning and not "rationally weighed," says Baxter, is not faith, but a dream or fancy or opinion. In effect, this grants to science a power which may ultimately limit that of theology.

Thus, once these processes are clearly understood, it is not surprising or inconsistent that Luther particularly, and Melanchthon less strongly, execrated the cosmology of Copernicus and that Calvin frowned upon the acceptance of many scientific discoveries of his day, while the religious ethic which stemmed from these leaders invited the pursuit of natural science.[18] In so far as the attitudes of the theologians dominate over the, in effect, subversive religious ethic—as did Calvin's authority in Geneva until the early eighteenth century—science may be greatly impeded. But with the relaxation of this hostile influence and with the development of an ethic, stemming from it and yet differing significantly, science takes on a new life, as was indeed the case in Geneva.

Perhaps the most directly effective element of the Protestant ethic for the sanction of natural science was that which held that the study of nature enables a fuller appreciation of His works and thus leads us to admire the Power, Wisdom, and Goodness of God

[18] On the basis of this analysis, it is surprising to note the statement *accredited* to Max Weber that the opposition of the Reformers is sufficient reason for not coupling Protestantism with scientific interests. See *Wirtschaftsgeschichte* (München, 1924), 314. This remark is especially unanticipated since it does not at all accord with Weber's discussion of the same point in his other works. *Cf. Religionssoziologie*, I, 141, 564; *Wissenschaft als Beruf* (München, 1921), 19–20. The probable explanation is that the first is not Weber's statement, since the *Wirtschaftsgechichte* was compiled from classroom notes by two of his students who may have neglected to make the requisite distinctions. It is unlikely that Weber would have made the elementary error of confusing the Reformers' opposition to certain scientific discoveries with the unforeseen consequences of the Protestant ethic, particularly since he expressly warns against the failure to make such discriminations in his *Religionssoziologie.* For perceptive but vague adumbrations of Weber's hypothesis, see Auguste Comte, *Cours de philosophie positive* (Paris, 1864), IV, 127–130.

manifested in His creation. Though this conception was not unknown to medieval thought, the consequences deduced from it were entirely different. Thus Arnaldus of Villanova, in studying the products of the Divine Workshop, adheres strictly to the medieval ideal of determining properties of phenomena from *tables* (in which all combinations are set forth according to the canons of logic). But in the seventeenth century, the contemporary emphasis upon empiricism led to investigating nature primarily through observation.[19] This difference in interpretation of substantially the same doctrine can only be understood in the light of the different values permeating the two cultures.

For a Barrow, Boyle, or Wilkins, a Ray or Grew, science found its rationale in the end of all existence: glorification of God. Thus, from Boyle: [20]

> . . . God loving, as He deserves, to be honour'd in all our Faculties, and consequently to be glorified and acknowledg'd by the acts of Reason, as well as by those of Faith, there must be sure a great Disparity betwixt that general, confus'd and lazy Idea we commonly have of His Power and Wisdom, and the Distinct, rational and affecting notions of those Attributes which are form'd by an attentive Inspection of those Creatures in which they are most legible, and which were made chiefly for that very end.

Ray carries this conception to its logical conclusion, for if Nature is the manifestation of His power, then nothing in Nature is too mean for scientific study.[21] The universe and the insect, the macrocosm and microcosm alike, are indications of "divine Reason, running like a Golden Vein, through the whole leaden Mine of Brutal Nature."

Up to this point we have been concerned in the main with the directly felt sanction of science through Puritan values. While this was of great influence, there was another type of relationship which,

19 Walter Pagel, "Religious motives in the medical biology of the seventeenth century," *Bulletin of the Institute of the History of Medicine,* 1935, 3, 214–15.

20 *Usefulness of Experimental Natural Philosophy,* 53; *cf.* Ray, *Wisdom of God,* 132; Wilkins, *Natural Religion,* 236 ff.; Isaac Barrow, *Opuscula,* iv, 88 ff.; Nehemiah Grew, *Cosmologia sacra* (London, 1701), who points out that "God is the original End," and that "we are *bound* to study His works."

21 Ray, *Wisdom of God,* 130 ff. Max Weber quotes Swammerdam as saying: "ich bringe Ihnen hier den Nachweis der Vorsehung Gottes in der Anatomie einer Laus." *Wissenschaft als Beruf,* 19.

subtle and difficult of apprehension though it be, was perhaps of paramount significance. It has to do with the preparation of a set of largely implicit assumptions which made for the ready acceptance of the scientific temper characteristic of the seventeenth and subsequent centuries. It is not simply that Protestanism implicitly involved free inquiry, *libre examen*, or decried monastic ascetism. These are important but not exhaustive.

It has become manifest that in each age there is a system of science which rests upon a set of assumptions, usually implicit and seldom questioned by the scientists of the time.[22] The *basic* assumption in modern science "is a widespread, instinctive conviction in the existence of an *Order of Things*, and, in particular, of an Order of Nature." [23] This belief, this faith, for at least since Hume it must be recognized as such, is simply "impervious to the demand for a consistent rationality." In the systems of scientific thought of Galileo, Newton, and of their successors, the testimony of experiment is the ultimate criterion of truth, but the very notion of experiment is ruled out without the prior assumption that Nature constitutes an intelligible order, so that when appropriate questions are asked, she will answer, so to speak. Hence this assumption is final and absolute.[24] As Professor Whitehead indicated, this "faith in the possibility of science, generated antecedently to the development of modern scientific theory, is an unconscious derivative from medieval theology." But this conviction, prerequisite of modern science though it be, was not sufficient to induce its development. What was needed was a constant interest in searching for this order in nature in an empirico-rational fashion, that is, an active interest in this world and its occurrences plus a specific frame of mind. With Protestantism, religion provided this interest: it actually imposed obligations of intense concentration upon secular activity with an emphasis upon experience and reason as bases for action and belief.

Even the Bible as final and complete authority was subject to the interpretation of the individual upon these bases. The similarity in approach and intellectual attitude of this system to that of the

[22] A. E. Heath, in *Isaac Newton: A Memorial Volume*, ed. by W. J. Greenstreet (London, 1927), 133 ff.; E. A. Burtt, *The Metaphysical Foundations of Modern Physical Science* (London, 1925).

[23] A. N. Whitehead, *Science and the Modern World* (New York, 1931), 5 ff.

[24] Cf. E. A. Burtt in *Isaac Newton: A Memorial Volume*, 139. For the classic exposition of this scientific faith, see Newton's "Rules of Reasoning in Philosophy," in his *Principia* (London, 1729 ed.), II, 160 ff.

contemporary science is of more than passing interest. It could not but mould an attitude of looking at the world of sensuous phenomena which was highly conducive to the willing acceptance, and indeed, preparation for, the same attitude in science. That the similarity is deep-rooted and not superficial may be gathered from the following comment upon Calvin's theology: [25]

> Die Gedanken werden objektiviert und zu einem objektiven Lehrsystem aufgebaut und abgerundet. Es bekommt geradezu ein naturwissenschaftliches Gepräge; es ist klar, leicht fassbar und formulierbar, wie alles, was deräusseren Welt angehört, klarer zu gestalten ist als das, was im Tiefsten sich abspielt.

The conviction in immutable law is as pronounced in the theory of predestination as in scientific investigation: "the immutable law is there and must be acknowledged." [26] The similarity between this conception and the scientific assumption is clearly drawn by Hermann Weber: [27]

> . . . die Lehre von der Prädestination in ihrem tiefsten Kerne getroffen zu sein, wenn mann sie als Faktum im Sinne eines naturwissenschaftlichen Faktums begreift, nur dass das oberste Prinzip, das auch jedem naturwissenschaftlichen Erscheinungskomplex zugrunde liegt, die im tiefsten erlebte gloria dei ist.

The cultural environment was permeated with this attitude toward natural phenomena which was derived from both science and religion and which enhanced the continued prevalence of conceptions characteristic of the new science.

There remains a supremely important part of this study to be completed. It is not sufficient verification of our hypothesis that the cultural attitudes induced by the Protestant ethic were favourable to science. Nor, yet again, that the consciously expressed motivation of many eminent scientists was provided by this ethic. Nor, still further, that the cast of thought which is characteristic of modern science, namely, the combination of empiricism and rationalism and the faith in the validity of one basic postulate, an apprehensible order in Nature, bears any other than fortuitious congruency with

[25] Hermann Weber, *Die Theologie Calvins* (Berlin, 1930), 23.

[26] *Ibid.*, 31. The significance of the doctrine of God's foreknowledge for the re-enforcement of the belief in natural law is remarked by H. T. Buckle, *History of Civilization in England* (New York, 1925), 482.

[27] *Op. cit.*, 31.

the values involved in Protestantism. All this can but provide some evidence of a certain probability of the connection we are arguing. The most significant test of the hypothesis is to be found in the confrontation of the results *deduced* from the hypothesis with relevant empirical data. If the Protestant ethic involved an attitudinal set favourable to science and technology in so many ways, then we should find amongst Protestants a greater propensity for these fields of endeavour than one would expect simply on the basis of their representation in the total population. Moreover, if, as has been frequently suggested,[28] the impression made by this ethic has lasted long after much of its theological basis has been largely disavowed, then even in periods subsequent to the seventeenth century, this connection of Protestantism and science should persist to some degree. The following section, then, will be devoted to this further test of the hypothesis.

THE PURITAN IMPETUS TO SCIENCE

In the beginnings of the Royal Society there is found a closely wrought nexus between science and society. The Society itself arose from an antecedent interest in science and the subsequent activities of its members provided an appreciable impetus to further scientific advance. The inception of this group is found in the occasional meetings of devotees of science in 1645 and following. Among the leading spirits were John Wilkins, John Wallis, and soon afterwards Robert Boyle and Sir William Petty, upon all of whom religious forces seem to have had a singularly strong influence.

Wilkins, later an Anglican bishop, was raised at the home of his maternal grandfather, John Dod, an outstanding Non-conformist theologian, and "his early education had given him a strong bias toward Puritanical principles." [29] Wilkins' influence as Warden of Wadham College was profound; under it came Ward, Rooke, Wren, Sprat, and Walter Pope (his half-brother), all of whom were origi-

[28] As Troeltsch puts it: "The present-day world does not live by logical consistency, any more than any other; spiritual forces can exercise a dominant influence even where they are avowedly repudiated." *Die Bedeutung des Protestantismus für die Entstehung der modernen Welt* (München, 1911), 22: *cf.* Georgia Harkness, *John Calvin: The Man and his Ethics* (New York, 1931), 7 ff.

[29] Memorials of John Ray, 18–19; P. A. W. Henderson, *The Life and Times of John Wilkins* (London, 1910), 36. Moreover, after Wilkins took holy orders, he became chaplain to Lord Viscount Say and Seale, a resolute and effective Puritan.

nal members of the Royal Society.[30] John Wallis, to whose *Arithmetica Infinitorum* Newton was avowedly indebted for many of his leading mathematical conceptions, was a clergyman with strong leanings toward Puritan principles. The piety of Boyle has alreday been remarked; the only reason he did not take holy orders, as he said, was because of the "absence of an inner call." [31]

Theodore Haak, the German virtuoso who played so prominent a part in the formation of the Royal Society, was a pronounced Calvinist. Denis Papin, who during his prolonged stay in England contributed notably to science and technology, was a French Calvinist compelled to leave his country to avoid religious persecution. Thomas Sydenham, sometimes called "the English Hippocrates," was an ardent Puritan who fought as one of Cromwell's men. Sir William Petty was a latitudinarian; he had been a follower of Cromwell, and in his writings he evinced clearly the influences of Puritanism. Of Sir Robert Moray, described by Huyghens as the "Soul of the Royal Society," it could be said that "religion was the mainspring of his life, and amidst courts and camps he spent many hours a day in devotion." [32]

It is hardly a fortuitous circumstance that the leading figures of this nuclear group of the Royal Society were divines or eminently religious men, though it is not quite accurate to maintain, as did Dr. Richardson, that the beginnings of the Society occurred in a small group of learned men among whom Puritan *divines* predominated.[33] But it is quite clearly true that the originative spirits of the Society were markedly influenced by Puritan conceptions.

Dean Dorothy Stimson, in a recently published paper, has independently arrived at this same conclusion.[34] She points out that of the ten men who constituted the "invisible college," in 1645, only

30 Henderson, *op. cit.*, 72–3.

31 *Dictionary of National Biography*, II, 1028. This reason, effective also for Sir Samuel Morland's turning to mathematics rather than to the ministry, is an example of the direct working of the Protestant ethic which, as exposited by Baxter for example, held that only those who felt an "inner call" should enter the clergy, and that others could better serve society by adopting other accredited secular activities. On Morland, see the "Autobiography of Sir Samuel Morland," in J. O. Halliwell-Phillipps' *Letters Illustrative of the Progress of Science in England* (London, 1841), 116 ff.

32 *Dictionary of National Biography*, xiii, 1299.

33 C. F. Richardson, *English Preachers and Preaching* (New York, 1928), 177.

34 Dorothy Stimson, "Puritanism and the new philosophy in seventeenth-century England," *Bulletin of the Institute of the History of Medicine*, 1935, 3, 321–34.

one, Scarbrough, was clearly non-Puritan. About two of the others there is some uncertainty, though Merret had a Puritan training. The others were all definitely Puritan. Moreover, among the original list of members of the Society of 1663, forty-two of the sixty-eight concerning whom information about their religious orientation is available were clearly Puritan. Considering that the Puritans constituted a relatively small minority in the English population, the fact that they constituted sixty-two per cent of the initial membership of the Society becomes even more striking. Dean Stimson concludes: "that experimental science spread as rapidly as it did in seventeenth-century England seems to me to be in part at least because the moderate Puritans encouraged it."

THE PURITAN INFLUENCE ON SCIENTIFIC EDUCATION

Nor was this relationship only evidenced among the members of the Royal Society. The emphasis of the Puritans upon utilitarianism and empiricism was likewise manifested in the type of education which they introduced and fostered. The "formal grammar grind" of the schools was criticized by them as much as the formalism of the Church.

Prominent among the Puritans who so consistently sought to introduce the new realistic, utilitarian, and empirical education into England was Samuel Hartlib. He formed the connecting link between the various Protestant educators in England and in Europe who were earnestly seeking to spread the academic study of science. It was to Hartlib that Milton addressed his tractate on education and Sir William Petty dedicated his "Advice ... for the Advancement of some particular Parts of Learning," namely, science, technology, and handicraft. Moreover, it was Hartlib who was instrumental in broadcasting the educational ideas of Comenius and in bringing him to England.

The Bohemian Reformist, John Amos Comenius, was one of the most influential educators of this period. Basic to the system of education which he promulgated were the norms of utilitarianism and empiricism: values which could only lead to an emphasis upon the study of science and technology, of *Realia*.[35] In his most influential work, *Didactica Magna*, he summarizes his views: [36]

[35] Wilhelm Dilthey, "Pädagogik: Geschichte und Grundlinien des Systems," *Gesammelte Schriften* (Leipzig & Berline, 1934), 163 ff.

[36] J. A. Comenius, *The Great Didactic*, translated by M. W. Keatinge (London 1896), 292, 337; see also 195, 302, 329, 341.

> The task of the pupil will be made easier, if the master, when he teaches him everything, shows him at the same time its practical application in everyday life. This rule must be carefully observed in teaching languages, dialectic, arithmetic, geometry, physics, etc.
>
> . . . the truth and certainty of science depend more on the witness of the senses than on anything else. For things impress themselves directly on the senses, but on the understanding only mediately and through the senses. . . . Science, then, increases in certainty in proportion as it depends on sensuous perception.

Comenius found welcome among Protestant educators in England who subscribed to the same values; individuals such as Hartlib, John Dury, Wilkins, and Haak.[37] At the request of Hartlib, he came to England for the express purpose of making Bacon's Solomon's House a reality. As Comenius himself remarked: "nothing seemed more certain than that the scheme of the great Verulam, of opening in some part of the world a universal college, whose one object should be the advancement of the sciences, would be carried into effect." [38] But this aim was frustrated by the social disorder attendant upon the rebellion in Ireland. However, the Puritan design of advancing science was not entirely without fruit. Cromwell founded the only new English university instituted between the Middle Ages and the nineteenth century, Durham University, "for all the sciences." [39] And in Cambridge, during the height of the Puritan influence there, the study of science was considerably augmented.[40]

In the same vein, the Puritan Hezekiah Woodward, a friend of Hartlib, emphasized realism (things, not words) and the teachings of science.[41] In order to initiate the study of the new science on a much more widespread scale than had hitherto obtained, the Puritans instituted a number of Dissenting Academies. These were schools of university standing opened in various parts of the kingdom. One of the earliest of these was Morton's Academy wherein there was pronounced stress laid upon scientific studies. Charles Morton later went to New England, where he was chosen vice-president of Harvard College, in which "he introduced the system of science that he used in England." [42] At the influential Northamp-

[37] Robert F. Young, *Comenius in England* (Oxford, 1932), 5–9.

[38] *Opera Didactica Omnia* (Amsterdam, 1657), Book II, preface.

[39] F. H. Hayward, *The Unknown Cromwell* (London, 1934), 206–30, 315.

[40] James B. Mullinger, *Cambridge Characteristics in the Seventeenth Century* (London, 1867), 180–81 *et passim*.

[41] Irene Parker, *Dissenting Academies in England* (Cambridge, 1914), 24.

[42] *Ibid.*, 62.

ton Academy, another of the Puritan educational centres, mechanics, hydrostatics, physics, anatomy, and astronomy had an important place in the time-table. These studies were pursued largely with the aid of actual experiments and observations.

But the marked emphasis placed by the Puritans upon science and technology may perhaps best be appreciated by a comparison between the Puritan academies and the universities. The latter, even after they had introduced scientific subjects, continued to give an essentially classical education; the truly cultural studies were those which, if not entirely useless, were at least definitely nonutilitarian in purpose. The academies, in contrast, held that a truly liberal education was one which was "in touch with life" and which should therefore include as many utilitarian subjects as possible. As Dr. Parker puts it: [43]

> . . . the difference between the two educational systems is seen not so much in the introduction into the academies of "modern" subjects and methods as in the fact that among the Nonconformists there was a totally different system at work from that found in the universities. The spirit animating the Dissenters was that which had moved Ramus and Comenius in France and Germany and which in England had actuated Bacon and later Hartlib and his circle.

This comparison of the Puritan academies in England and Protestant educational developments on the Continent is well warranted. The Protestant academies in France devoted much more attention to scientific and utilitarian subjects than did the Catholic institutions.[44] When the Catholics took over many of the Protestant academies, the study of science was considerably diminished.[45] Moreover, as we shall see, even in the predominantly Catholic France, much of the scientific work was being done by Protestants. Protestant exiles from France included a large number of important scientists and inventors.[46]

VALUE-INTEGRATION OF PURITANISM AND SCIENCE

Of course, the mere fact that an individual is *nominally* a Catholic or a Protestant has no bearing upon his attitudes toward science.

[43] *Ibid.*, 133–4.

[44] P. D. Bourchenin, *Étude sur les académies protestantes en France au XVIième et au XVIIième siècle* (Paris, 1882), 445 ff.

[45] M. Nicholas, "Les académies protestantes de Montauban et de Nimes," *Bulletin de la société de l'histoire du protestantisme française*, 1858, 4, 35–48.

[46] D. C. A. Agnew, *Protestant Exiles from France* (Edinburgh, 1866), 210 ff.

It is only as he adopts the tenets and implications of the teachings that his religious affiliation becomes significant. For example, it was only when Pascal became thoroughly converted to the teachings of Jansenius that he perceived the "vanity of science." For Jansenius characteristically maintained that above all we must beware of that vain love of science, which though seemingly innocent, is actually a snare "leading men away from the contemplation of eternal truths to rest in the satisfaction of the finite intelligence."[47] Once Pascal was converted to such beliefs, he resolved "to make an end of all those scientific researches to which he had hitherto applied himself."[48] It is the firm acceptance of the values basic to the two creeds which accounts for the difference in the respective scientific contributions of Catholics and Protestants.

The same association of Protestantism and science was marked in the New World. The correspondents and members of the Royal Society who lived in New England were "all trained in Calvinistic thinking."[49] The founders of Harvard sprang from this Calvinistic culture, not from the literary era of the Renaissance or from the scientific movement of the seventeenth century, and their minds were more easily led into the latter than the former channel of thought.[50] This predilection of the Puritans for science is also noted by Professor Morison, who states: "the Puritan clergy, instead of opposing the acceptance of the Copernican theory, were the chief patrons and promoters of the new astronomy, and of other scientific discoveries, in New England."[51] It is significant that the younger John Winthrop, of Massachusetts, later a member of the Royal Society, came to London in 1641 and probably spent some time with Hartlib, Drury, and Comenius in London. Apparently, he suggested to Comenius that he come to New England and found a scientific college there.[52] Some years later, Increase Mather (Presi-

[47] Émile Boutroux, *Pascal*, trans. by E. M. Creak (Manchester, 1902), 16.

[48] *Ibid.*, 17; *cf.* Jacques Chevalier, *Pascal* (New York, 1930), 143; Pascal's *Pensées*, trans. by O. W. Wright (Boston, 1884), 224, No. xxvii. "*Vanity of the Sciences.* The science of external things will not console me for ignorance of ethics in times of affliction; but the science of morals will always console me for ignorance of external sciences."

[49] Stimson, *op. cit.*, 332.

[50] Porter G. Perrin, "Possible sources of *Technologia* at early Harvard," *New England Quarterly*, 1934, 7, 724.

[51] Samuel E. Morison, "Astronomy at colonial Harvard," *New England Quarterly*, 1934, 7, 3–24; also Clifford K. Shipton, "A plea for Puritanism," *The American Historical Review*, 1935, 40, 463–4.

[52] R. F. Young, *Comenius in England*, 7–8.

dent of Harvard College from 1684–1701) did found a "Philosophical Society" at Boston.[53]

The scientific content of Harvard's educational programme derived greatly from the Protestant Peter Ramus.[54] Ramus had formulated an educational curriculum which in contrast to that of the Catholic universities laid great stress on the study of the sciences.[55] His ideas were welcomed in the Protestant universities on the Continent, at Cambridge (which had a greater Puritan and scientific element than Oxford),[56] and later at Harvard, but were firmly denounced in the various Catholic institutions.[57] The Reformation spirit of utilitarianism and "realism" probably accounts largely for the favorable reception of Ramus' views.

VALUE-INTEGRATION OF PIETISM AND SCIENCE

Dr. Parker notes that the Puritan academies in England "may be compared with the schools of the Pietists in Germany, which under Francke and his followers prepared the way for the *Realschulen,* for there can be no doubt that just as the Pietists carried on the work of Comenius in Germany, so the Dissenters put into practice the theories of Comenius' English followers, Hartlib, Milton, and Petty." [58] The significance of this comparison is profound for, as has been frequently observed, the values and principles of Puritanism and Pietism are almost identical. Cotton Mather had recognized the close resemblance of these two Protestant movements, saying that "ye American puritanism is so much of a piece with ye Frederician pietism" that they may be considered as virtually iden-

[53] *Ibid.,* 95.

[54] Perrin, *op. cit.,* 723–4.

[55] Theobald Ziegler, *Geschichte der Pädagogik* (München, 1895), I, 108. Ziegler indicates that while the contemporary French Catholic institutions only devoted one-sixth of the curriculum to science, Ramus dedicated fully one-half to scientific studies.

[56] David Masson properly calls Cambridge the alma mater of the Puritans. In listing twenty leading Puritan clergymen in New England, Masson found that seventeen of them were alumni of Cambridge, while only three came from Oxford. See his *Life of Milton* (London, 1875), II, 563; cited by Stimson, *op. cit.,* 332. See also *A History of the University of Oxford,* by Charles E. Mallet (London, 1924), II, 147.

[57] Heinrich Schreiber, *Geschichte der Albert-Ludwigs-Universität zu Freiburg* (Freiburg, 1857–68), II, 135. For example, at the Jesuit university of Freiburg, Ramus could only be referred to if he were refuted, and "no copies of his books are to be found in the hands of a student."

[58] Parker, *op. cit.,* 135.

tical.[59] Pietism, except for its greater "enthusiasm," might almost be termed the Continental counterpart of Puritanism. Hence, if our hypothesis of the association between Puritanism and interest in science and technology is warranted, one would expect to find the same correlation among the Pietists. And such was markedly the case.

The Pietists in Germany and elsewhere entered into a close alliance with the "new education": the study of science and technology, of *Realia*.[60] The two movements had in common the realistic and practical point of view, combined with an intense aversion to the speculation of Aristotelian philosophers. Fundamental to the educational views of the Pietists were the same deep-rooted utilitarian and empirical values which actuated the Puritans.[61] It was on the basis of these values that the Pietist leaders, August Hermann Francke, Comenius, and their followers emphasized the new science.

Francke repeatedly noted the desirability of acquainting students with practical scientific knowledge.[62] Both Francke and his colleague, Christian Thomasius, set themselves in opposition to the strong educational movement developed by Christian Weise, which advocated primarily training in oratory and classics, and sought rather "to introduce the neglected modern disciplines, which served their purposes more adequately; such studies as biology, physics, astronomy, and the like." [63]

Wherever Pietism spread its influence upon the educational system there followed the large-scale introduction of scientific and

[59] Kuno Francke, "Cotton Mather and August Hermann Francke," *Harvard Studies and Notes*, 1896, 5, 63. See also the cogent discussion of this point by Max Weber, *Protestant Ethic*, 132–5.

[60] Friedrich Paulsen, *German Education: Past and Present*, trans. by T. Lorenz (London, 1908), 104 ff.

[61] Alfred Heubaum, *Geschichte des deutschen Bildungswesens seit der Mitte des siebzehnten Jahrunderts* (Berlin, 1905), 1, 90. "Ziel der Erziehung [among Pietists] ist praktische Verwendbarkeit des Zöglings im Gemeinwohl. Der starke Einfluss des utilitaristichen Moments . . . vermindert die Gefaher der Uebertreibung des religiösen Moments und sichert der Bewegung für die nächste Zukunft ihre Bedeutung."

[62] During walks in the field, says Francke, the instructor should "nützliche und erbauliche Geschichten erzählen oder etwas aus der Physik von den Geschöpfen und Werken Gottes vorsagen." ". . . im Naturalienkabinet diente dazu, die Zöglinge in ihren Freistunden durch den Anstaltarzt mit naturwissenschaftlichen Erscheinungen, mit Mineralien, Bergarten, hier und da mit Experimenten bekannt zu machen." Quoted by Heubaum, *op. cit.*, I, 89, 94.

[63] *Ibid.*, I, 136.

technical subjects.[64] Thus, Francke and Thomasius built the foundations of the University of Halle, which was the first German university to introduce a thorough training in the sciences.[65] The leading professors, such as Friedrich Hoffman, Ernst Stahl (professor of chemistry and famous for his influential phlogiston theory), Samuel Stryk, and, of course, Francke, all stood in the closest relations with the Pietistic movement. All of them characteristically sought to develop the teaching of science and to ally science with practical applications.

Not only Halle, but other Pietistic universities manifested the same emphases. Königsberg, having come under the Pietistic influence of the University of Halle through the activities of Francke's disciple, Gehr, early adopted the natural and physical sciences in the modern sense of the seventeenth century.[66] The University of Göttingen, an offshoot of Halle, was famous essentially for the great progress which it effected in the cultivation of the sciences.[67] The Calvinistic university of Heidelberg was likewise prominent for instituting a large measure of scientific study.[68] Finally, the University of Altdorf, which was at that time the most conspicuous for its interest in science, was a Protestant University subject to Pietistic influence.[69] Heubaum summarizes these developments by asserting that the essential progress in the teaching of science and technology occurred in Protestant, and more precisely, in Pietistic universities.[70]

RELIGIOUS AFFILIATION OF RECRUITS TO SCIENCE

This association of Pietism and science, which we have been led to anticipate from our hypothesis, did not confine itself to the universities. The same Pietist predilection for science and technology

[64] *Ibid.*, I, 176 ff.

[65] Koppel S. Pinson, *Pietism as a Factor in the Rise of German Nationalism* (New York, 1934), 18; Heubaum, *op. cit.*, I, 118. "Halle war die erste deutsche Universität von ganz eigenartigem wissenschaftlichen und nationalen Gepräge . . ."

[66] Heubaum, *op. cit.*, I, 153.

[67] Paulsen, *op. cit.*, 120–1.

[68] Heubaum, *op. cit.*, I, 60.

[69] S. Günther, "Die mathematischen Studien und Naturwissenschaften an der nürnbergischen Universität Altdorf," *Mitteilungen des Vereins für Geschichte der Stadt Nürnberg*, Heft. III, 9.

[70] Heubaum, *op. cit.*, I, 241; see also Paulsen, *op. cit.*, 122; J. D. Michaelis, *Raisonnement über die protestantischen Universitäten in Deutschland* (Frankfurt, 1768), I, section 36.

was evidenced in secondary school education. The *Pädagogium* of Halle introduced the subjects of mathematics and natural science; stress being laid, in all cases, on the use of object lessons and on practical applications.[71] Johann Georg Lieb, Johann Bernhard von Rohr, and Johann Peter Ludwig (Chancellor of Halle University), all of whom had come under the direct influence of Francke and Pietism, advocated schools of manufacture, physics, mathematics, and economics, in order to study how "manufacture might be ever more and more improved and excelled." [72] They hoped that the outcome of these suggestions might be a so-called *Collegium physicum-mechanicum* and *Werkschulen.*

It is a significant fact, and one which lends additional weight to our hypothesis, that the *ökonomisch-mathematische Realschule* was completely a Pietist product. This school, which centered on the study of mathematics, the natural sciences, and economics, and which was avowedly utilitarian and realistic in temper, was planned by Francke.[73] Moreover, it was a Pietist and a former student of Francke, Johann Julius Hecker, who first actually organized a *Realschule.*[74] Semler, Silberschlag, and Hähn, the directors and co-organizers of this first school, were all Pietists and former students of Francke.[75]

All available evidence points in the same direction. Protestants, without exception, form a progressively larger proportion of the student body in those schools which emphasize scientific and technologic training,[76] while Catholics concentrate their interests on

71 Paulsen, *op. cit.*, 127.

72 Heubaum, *op. cit.*, I, 184.

73 Alfred Heubaum, "Christoph Semlers Realschule und seine Beziehung zu A. H. Francke," *Neue Jahrbücher für Philologie und Pädagogik*, 1893, 2, 65–77; see also Ziegler, *Geschichte der Pädagogik*, I, 197, who observes: ". . . einem inneren Zusammenhang zwischen der auf das Praktische gerichteten Realschule und der aufdas Praktische gerichteten Frömmigkeit der Pietisten fehlte es ja auch nicht, nur éine ganz einseitig religiöse und theologische Auffassung des Pietismus kann das verkennen: im Geist der praktischen Nützlichkeit und Gemeinnützigkeit ist dieser dem Rationalismus vorangegangen und mit ihm eins gewesen, und aus diesem Geist heraus ist zu Franckes Zeiten in Halle die Realschule entstanden."

74 Paulsen, *op. cit.*, 133.

75 Upon the basis of this and other facts, Ziegler proceeds to trace a close "Kausalzusammenhang" between Pietism and the study of science. See his *Geschichte*, I, 1960 ff.

76 The characteristic feature of the *gymnasien* is the classical basis of their curricula. Demarcated from these schools are the *Realschulen*, where the sciences predominate and where modern languages are substituted for the classical tongues.

classical and theological training. For example, in Prussia, the distribution shown in Table 1 was found.[77]

TABLE I. ATTENDANCE AT SECONDARY SCHOOLS DIFFERENTIATED BY RELIGIOUS AFFILIATIONS OF THE STUDENTS, PRUSSIA, 1875–6

Religious Affiliation	*Pro-gym nasium*	*Gymnasium*	*Real-schule*	*Ober-realsch*	*Höheren Bürger*	*Total*	*General Population*
Protestants	49.1	69.7	79.8	75.8	80.7	73.1	64.9
Catholics	39.1	20.2	11.4	6.7	14.2	17.3	33.6
Jews	11.2	10.1	8.8	17.5	5.1	9.6	1.3

This greater propensity of Protestants for scientific and technical studies accords with the implications of our hypothesis. That this distribution is typical may be gathered from the fact that other investigators have noted the same tendency in other instances.[78] Furthermore, these distributions do not represent a spurious correlation resulting from differences in rural-urban distribution of the two religions, as may be seen from the pertinent data for the Swiss canton, Basel-Stadt. As is well known, the urban population tends to contribute more in the fields of science and technology than the rural. Yet for 1910 and following—the period to which Edouard Borel's study, with results similar to those just presented for Prussia, refers—Protestants constituted 63.4 per cent of the total population of the canton, but only 57.1 per cent of the population of Basel (the city proper) and 84.7 per cent of the rural population.[79]

The *Real-gymnasium* is a compromise between these two types, having less classical instruction than the *gymnasium* with more attention paid to science and mathematics. The *Ober-realschulen und höheren Bürgerschulen* are both *Realschulen;* the first with a nine-year course, the second with a six-year course. *Cf.* Paulsen, *German Education*, 46 *et passim*.

[77] Alwin Petersilie, "Zur Statistik der höheren Lehranstalten in Preussen," *Zeitschrift des königlich Preussischen Statistischen Bureaus*, 1877, 17, 109.

[78] Edouard Borel, *Religion und Beruf* (Basel, 1930), 93 ff., who remarks the unusually high proportion of Protestants in the technical professions in Basel; Julius Wolf, "Die deutschen Katholiken in Staat und Wirtschaft," *Zeitschrift fur Sozialwissenschaft*, 1913, 4, 199, notes that "die Protestanten ihren 'naturgemässen' Anteil überschreiten gilt für die wissenschaftliche und sonstige intellektuelle Betätigung (mit Ausnahme des geistlichen Berufs) . . ." In 1860, Ad. Frantz had already noted the same fact. See his "Bedeutung der Religionunterschiede für das physische Leben der Bevölkerungen," *Jahrbücher für Nationalökonomie und Statistik*, 1868, 11, 51. *Cf.* also similar results for Berlin in *Statistisches Jahrbuch der Stadt Berlin*, 1897, 22, 468–72. Buckle, *op. cit.*, 482, notes that "Calvinism is favourable to science." *Cf.* also Weber, *Protestant Ethic*, 38, 189; and Troeltsch, *Social Teachings* . . ., II, 894.

[79] See "Die Bevölkerung des Kantons Basel-Stadt," *Mitteilungen des Statis-*

Martin Offenbacher's careful study includes an analysis of the association between religious affiliation and the allocation of educational interests in Baden, Bavaria, Württemberg, Prussia, Alsace-Lorraine, and Hungary. The statistical results in these various places are of the same nature: Protestants, proportionately to their representation in the population at large, have a much higher attendance at the various secondary schools, with the difference becoming especially marked in the schools primarily devoted to the sciences and technology. In Baden,[80] for example, taking an average of the figures for the years 1885–95, we have Table 2.

However, it must be noted that although the *Realschulen* cur-

TABLE 2

	Protestants, per cent	*Catholics, per cent*	*Jews, per cent*
Gymnasien	43	46	9.5
Realgymnasien	69	31	9
Oberrealschulen	52	41	7
Realschulen	49	40	11
Höheren Bürgerschulen	51	37	12
Average for the five types of schools	48	42	10
Distribution in the general population, 1895	37	61.5	1.5

ricula are primarily characterized by their stress on the sciences and mathematics as contrasted with the relatively little attention paid these studies in the *gymnasien*, yet the latter type of school also prepares for scientific and scholarly careers. But, in general, the attendance of Protestants and Catholics at the *gymnasien* represents different interests. The relatively large number of Catholics at the *gymnasien* is due to the fact that these schools prepare for theology as well, while the Protestants generally use the *gymnasien* as a preparation for the other learned professions. Thus, in the three academic years 1891–4, 226, or over 42 per cent of the 533 Catholic graduates of the Baden *gymnasien* subsequently studied theology, while of the 375 Protestant graduates, only 53 (14 per cent) turned to theology, while 86 per cent went into the other learned professions.[81]

tischen Amtes des Kantons Basel-Stadt, 1932, 48–49; and the same publication for the years 1910 and 1921.

80 Martin Offenbacher, *Konfession und soziale Schichtung* (Tübingen, 1900), 16. The slight errors of the original are here unavoidably reproduced.

81 H. Gemss, *Statistik der Gymnasialabiturienten im deutschen Reich* (Berlin, 1895), 14–20.

Similarly, the Catholic apologist, Hans Rost, though he wishes to establish the thesis that "the Catholic Church has been at all times a warm friend of science," is forced to admit, on the basis of his data, that the Catholics avoid the *Realschulen,* that they show "eine gewisse Gleichgültigkeit und Abneigung gegen diese Anstalten." The reason for this, he goes on to say, is "das die Oberrealschule und das Realgymnasium nicht zum Studium der Theologie berechtigen: denn diese ist häufig die Tribfeder bei den Katholiken zum höheren Studium überhaupt." [82]

Thus, statistical data point to a marked tendency for Protestants, as contrasted with Catholics, to pursue scientific and technical studies. This can also be seen in the statistics for Württemberg, where an average of the years 1872–9 and 1883–98 gives the figures [83] in Table 3.

TABLE 3

	Protestants, per cent	*Catholics, per cent*	*Jews, per cent*
Gymnasien	68.2	28.2	3.4
Lateinschulen	73.2	22.3	3.9
Realschulen	79.7	14.8	4.2
Total population, 1880	69.1	30.0	0.7

Nor do the Protestants evidence these foci of interest only in education. Various studies have found an unduly large representation of Protestants among outstanding scientists.[84] If the foregoing data simply provide slight probabilities that the connection we have traced does in fact obtain, Candolle's well known *Histoire des*

[82] Hans Rost, *Die wirtschaftliche und kulturelle Lage der deutschen Katholiken* (Köln, 1911), 167 ff.

[83] Offenbacher, *op. cit.*, 18. These data are corroborated by the study of Ludwig Cron pertaining to Germany for the years 1869–93; *Glaubenbekenntnis und höheres Studium* (Heidelberg, 1900). Ernst Engel also found that in Prussia, Posen, Brandenburg, Pomerania, Saxony, Westphalia, and the Rhine Provinces, there is a higher incidence of Evangelical students in these schools which provide a maximum of natural science and technical subjects. See his "Beiträge zur Geschichte und Statistik des Unterrichts," *Zeitschrift des königlich Preussischen statistichen Bureaus*, 1869, 9, 99–116, 153–212.

[84] For example, Havelock Ellis' *Study of British Genius*, 66 ff., finds that Protestant Scotland produced twenty-one of the outstanding scientists on his list as against one for Catholic Ireland. Alfred Odin finds that among the littérateurs on his list, the predominant emphasis of Protestants is on scientific and technical matters, rather than on literature, properly so-called. See his *Genèse des grands hommes* (Paris, 1895), I, 477 ff., II, Tables xx–xxi.

sciences et des savants increases these probabilities considerably. Candolle finds that although in Europe, excluding France, there were 107 million Catholics and 68 million Protestants, yet on the list of scientists named foreign associates by the Academy of Paris from 1666–1883, there were only eighteen Catholics as against eighty Protestants.[85] But as Candolle himself suggests, this comparison is not conclusive since it omits French scientists who may have been Catholic. To correct this error, he takes the list of foreign members of the Royal Society of London at two periods when there were more French scientists included than at any other time: 1829 and 1869. In the former year, the total number of Protestant and Catholic scientists (who are foreign members of the Society) is about equal, while in 1869, the number of Protestants actually exceeds that of Catholics. But, outside the kingdom of Great Britain and Ireland, there were in Europe 139½ million Catholics and only 44 million Protestants.[86] In other words, though in the general population there were more than three times as many Catholics as Protestants, there were actually more Protestant than Catholic scientists.

However, there are yet more significant data than these which are based on different populations, where influence of economy, political regime, and other non-religious factors may be suspected to prevail over the actual influence of religion. A comparison of closely allied populations serves largely to eliminate these "extraneous" factors, but the results are the same. Thus, on the list of foreign associates of the Academy of Paris, there is not a single Irish or English Catholic, although their proportion in the population of the three kingdoms exceeded a fifth. Likewise, Catholic Austria is not at all represented, while in general Catholic Germany is similarly lacking in the production of scientists of note relative to Protestant Germany. Finally, in Switzerland, where the two religions are largely differentiated by cantons, or mixed in some of them, and where the Protestants are to the Catholics as three to two there have been fourteen foreign Associates, of whom not one was Catholic. The same differentiation exists for the Swiss and for the Eng-

85 Alphonse de Candolle, *Histoire des sciences et des savants* (Geneva-Basel, 1885), 329.

86 *Ibid.*, 330. *Cf.* J. Facaoaru, *Soziale Auslese* (Klausenberg, 1933), 138–9. "Die Konfession hat einen grossen Einfluss auf die Entwicklung der Wissenschaft gehabt. Die Protestanten wiesen überall eine grössere Zahl hervorragender Männer auf."

lish and Irish of the two religions in the lists of the Royal Society of London and the Royal Academy of Berlin.[87]

With the presentation of these data we close the empirical testing of our hypothesis. In every instance, the association of Protestantism with scientific and technologic interests and achievements is pronounced, even when extra-religious influences are as far as possible eliminated. The association is largely understandable in terms of the norms embodied in both systems. The positive estimation by Protestants of a hardly disguised utilitarianism, of intra-mundane interests, of a thorough-going empiricism, of the right and even the duty of *libre examen*, and of the explicit individual questioning of authority were congenial to the same values found in modern science. And perhaps above all is the significance of the active ascetic drive which necessitated the study of Nature that it might be controlled. Hence, these two fields were well integrated and, in essentials, mutually supporting, not only in seventeenth-century England but in other times and places.

BIBLIOGRAPHICAL POSTSCRIPT

Max Weber's hypothesis of the role of ascetic Protestantism in the furtherance of modern capitalism has given rise to a substantial library of scholarly and polemical works on the subject. By the mid-thirties, for example, Amintore Fanfani could draw upon several hundred publications in his appraisal of the evidence; *Catholicism, Protestantism and Capitalism* (New York: Sheed & Ward, 1935). Weber did not himself conduct a similar inquiry into the relations between ascetic Protestantism and the development of science but concluded his classic essay by describing one of "the next tasks" as that of searching out "the significance of ascetic rationalism, which has only been touched in the foregoing sketch, . . . [for] the development of philosophical and scientific empiricism, [and for] . . . technical development" (*The Protestant Ethic*, 182–183). First published in 1936, the preceding chapter was conceived as an effort to follow this mandate to extend the line of inquiry which Weber had opened up.

The books and papers cited in this chapter have since been supplemented by others bearing on one or another part of the hypothesis connecting Puritanism, Pietism and science. Numerous works have

[87] Candolle, *op. cit.*, 330 ff.

greatly clarified the varieties and shadings of doctrine and values comprised in Puritanism; among these, I have found the following most useful: John Thomas McNeill, *The History and Character of Calvinism* (New York: Oxford University Press, 1954) which shows Calvinism to have formed the core of English Puritanism and traces its varied consequences for society and thought; William Haller, *The Rise of Puritanism* (New York: Columbia University Press, 1939) which describes in rich and convincing detail how Puritan propaganda in press and pulpit helped prepare the way for the parliamentary rebellion, the radicalism of the Levellers, numerous sectarian fissions, an incipient bourgeois ethic and experimental science; Charles H. George, "A social interpretation of English Puritanism," *The Journal of Modern History*, 1953, 25, 327–342, which tries to identify the major components and the major types of Puritanism; G. R. Cragg, *From Puritanism to the Age of Reason* (Cambridge University Press, 1950), a "study of changes in religious thought within the Church of England, 1660–1700."

These and similar works have shown anew that Puritanism, like most religio-social creeds, was not of a piece. Practically all the scholars who have made intensive studies of the matter are agreed that most of the numerous sects comprising ascetic Protestanism provided a value-orientation encouraging work in science. (See also the note by Jean Pelseneer, "L'origine Protestante de la science moderne," *Lychnos*, 1946–47, 246–248.) But there the near-unanimity ends. Some have concluded that it was the more radical sectarians among the Puritans who did most to develop an enlarged interest in science; see, for example, George Rosen, "Left-wing Puritanism and science," *Bulletin of the Institute of the History of Medicine*, 1944, 15, 375–380. The biochemist and historian of science, Joseph Needham, comments on the close connections between the Diggers, the civilian wing of the Levellers, and the new and growing interest in experimental science, in his collection of essays, *Time: The Refreshing River* (New York: The Macmillan Company, 1943), 84–103. Others hold that the climate of values most conducive to an interest in science was found among the *moderate* Puritans, as exemplified by Robert Boyle. See James B. Conant, "The advancement of learning during the Puritan Commonwealth," *Proceedings of the Massachusetts Historical Society*, 1942, 66, 3–31); and for a more generally accessible though less detailed discussion, the same author's *On Understanding Science* (New Haven: Yale University Press, 1947), 60–62. R. Hooykaas, the distinguished Dutch historian of science, reports that his biography of Boyle's scientific and religious orientations confirms the principal findings set out in the foregoing chapter: R. Hooykaas, *Robert Boyle: een studie over Natuurwetenschap en Christendom* (Loosduinen: Kleijwegt, 1943), Chapters 3–4 which analyze Boyle's convictions that the study of natural philosophy is a religiously-founded moral obligation (especially as these are developed in Boyle's *The Christian Virtuoso, shewing, that by being addicted to experimental philosophy a man is rather assisted than indisposed to be a good Christian*, 1690), that empiricism and not merely rationality is required to comprehend God's works, and that tolerance, not persecution, is the policy appropriately governing relations with even the most fanatic sects.

The evidence in support of both the competing premises—that the chief locus of interest is to be found among the radical or the moderate Puritans—is still insufficient to justify a firm conclusion. Detailed distinctions among the various Puritan sects of course serve to specify the hypothesis more rigorously but the data in hand do not yet allow one to say, with any confidence, which of these were most disposed to advance the science of the day.

A recent group of studies provides substantial documentation of the ways in which the ethos of one of these Puritan sects—the Quakers—helped crystallize a distinct interest in science. In much the same terms set forth in the preceding chapter of this book, Frederick B. Tolles, *Meeting House and Counting House* (Chapel Hill: University of North Carolina Press, 1948), 205–213, derives the marked interest of Quakers in science from their religious ethos. Less analytically and, at times, even tendentiously, Arthur Raistrick, *Quakers in Science and Industry, being an account of the Quaker contributions to science and industry during the 17th and 18th centuries* (London: The Bannisdale Press, 1950) emphasizes the *fact* of the large proportion of Quaker members of the Royal Society and the *fact* of their extensive work in science. But as Professor Hooykaas properly notes, these unanalyzed facts do not themselves indicate that the distinctive participation of Quakers in scientific activity stemmed from their religious ethic; it might well be that it reflected the widespread tendency of well-to-do Englishmen, who included a disproportionately large number of Quakers, to turn their interest to matters of natural philosophy (R. Hooykaas, in *Archives Internationales d'Histoire des Sciences*, January, 1951). In a compact and instructive paper, however, Brooke Hindle goes on to show that the religious ethic did play this role among the Quakers of one colonial area; *cf.* his "Quaker background and science in colonial Philadelphia," *Isis*, 1955, 46, 243–250; and his excellent monograph, *The Pursuit of Science in Revolutionary America, 1735–1789* (Chapel Hill: University of North Carolina Press, 1956).

It may be remembered that one of the principal hypotheses of Chapter XVII * held that it was the *unintended and largely unforeseen consequences* of the religious ethic formulated by the great Reformist leaders which progressively developed into a system of values favorable to the pursuit of science (39, this book; *cf.* F. S. Mason, "The scientific revolution and the Protestant Reformation. I. Calvin and Servetus in relation to the new astronomy and the theory of the circulation of the blood. II. Lutheranism in relation to iatrochemistry and German nature philosophy," *Annals of Science*, 1953, 9, 64–87, 154–175). The historical shaping of this ethic was doubtless partly in response to changing social, cultural and economic contexts but partly also, it was an immanent development of the religious ideas and values themselves (as Wesley, above all other Protestant leaders, clearly perceived). This is only to say again that the rôle of ascetic Protestantism in encouraging the development of science did not remain fixed and unchanging. What was only implicit in the sixteenth and early seventeenth centuries became explicit and visible to many in the later seventeenth and eighteenth centuries. Several recent studies confirm this interpretation.

Based upon a close scrutiny of primary sources and present-day research, Paul H. Kocher's *Science and Religion in Elizabethan England* (San Marino, California: The Huntington Library, 1953) testifies to the long distance scholars have come since the day when they considered only the sources of conflict between science and religion as though conflict were plainly the *only* relation which could, and historically did, subsist between these social institutions. In contrast, this monograph shows that there was ample room for the science of Elizabethan England to develop within the bounds set by the religious doctrine of the time. Nor was this simply a matter of religion *tolerating* science. For the period before 1610, Kocher can find no convincing evidence "for or against" the hypothesis that Puritanism provided a more "fertile soil for natural science than ... its rival religions in England." (17)† The data for this early period are inadequate to reach a sound conclusion. But, he goes on to say,

* See *Social Theory and Social Structure.*

† Numbers in parentheses refer to pages in the work cited.

> We can see from our vantage point in the twentieth century that Puritan worldliness was ultimately to aid science more than Puritan otherworldliness was to inhibit it, in proportion more perhaps (though this is much less certain) than could Anglican doctrine or practice. But the effects of such impetus were to become visible only gradually as Puritanism developed. The Elizabethan age came too early to afford concrete evidence for distinguishing and weighing against each other the contributions of Puritans and Anglicans to science. (19)

Considered in terms of the immanent dynamic of the religious ethos, however, Kocher's contrast between the "worldliness" and "otherworldliness" of successive generations of Puritans is more seeming than real. For, as Weber was able to show in detail, "worldliness" was historically generated by the originally "otherworldly" values of Puritanism, which called for active and sustained effort in this world and so subverted the initial value-orientation (this process being an example of what he called the *Paradoxie der Folgen*). Manifest conformity to these values produced latent consequences which were far removed in character from the values which released them.

By the eighteenth century, this process of change had resulted in what has been described by Basil Willey as "the holy alliance between science and religion." (*The Eighteenth Century Background*, New York: Columbia University Press, 1941). Just as Robert Boyle in the seventeenth century, so Joseph Priestley, the scientist and apostle of Unitarianism, in the eighteenth, symbolized and actualized this alliance.

The later connections between science and religion in England from the late eighteenth to the mid-nineteenth century have been painstakingly examined in the monograph by Charles C. Gillispie, *Genesis and Geology: a study in the relations of scientific thought, natural theology and social opinion in Great Britain, 1790–1850* (Cambridge: Harvard University Press, 1951). Concerned less with the role of religion in the recruitment and motivation of scientists than with the grounds on which the findings of geology were regarded as consistent with religious teachings, Gillispie traces the process through which these tended to become culturally integrated.

When the paper which forms the present chapter was written in 1936, I relied almost entirely on Irene Parker's pioneering study (1914) of the role of the Dissenting Academies in advancing the new scientific education of the eighteenth century.[88] The import of her

[88] Should it be asked why I did not make use of the later and amply-documented book, M. McLachlan's *English Education under the Test Acts* (1931),

study is not basically changed but is substantially developed and somewhat modified in the remarkable study by Nicholas Hans, *New Trends in Education in the Eighteenth Century* (London: Routledge & Kegan Paul, 1951). Hans bases part of his study upon a statistical analysis of the social origins, formal education and subsequent careers of some 3,500 individuals who formed the intellectual élite of that century, the basic data having been systematically assembled from the individual biographies in that almost inexhaustible mine of materials for historical sociology, the *Dictionary of National Biography*.[89] Only a few of his numerous pertinent findings will be summarized here. He finds, for example, that the Dissenting Schools and Academies produced about 10 per cent of the élite which, as Hans observes, "was far above their relative strength in the total population of England in the eighteenth century." (20) Nevertheless, he notes, as we have seen to be the case, that religious "motives" were not alone in making for the emergence of modern education (and specifically, of scientific education) in this period; with reli-

I could only reply, in the words of another "harmless drudge," "Ignorance, Madam, pure ignorance." It should be added, however, that McLachlan is in fundamental agreement with the major conclusions of Irene Parker.

89 Studies in historical sociology have only begun to quarry the rich ore available in comprehensive collections of biography and other historical evidence. Although statistical analyses of such materials cannot stand in place of detailed qualitative analyses of the historical evidence, they afford a *systematic* basis for new findings and, often, for correction of received assumptions. At least, this has been my own experience in undertaking statistical analyses of some 6,000 biographies (in the D.N.B.) of those who comprised the élite of seventeenth-century England; of the lists of important discoveries and inventions listed in Darmstädter's *Handbuch zur Geschichte der Naturwissenschaften und der Technik*, and of 2,000 articles published in the *Philosophical Transactions* during the last third of the seventeenth century. (*Cf.* Merton, *Science, Technology and Society in Seventeenth-Century England*, 1938, Chapters II–III.) The most extensive use of such statistical analyses is found in P. A. Sorokin, *Social and Cultural Dynamics* (New York: American Book Co., 1937). Of course, the preparation of statistical summaries of this kind have their hazards; routinized compilations unrestrained by knowledge of the historical contexts of the data can lead to unfounded conclusions. For a discussion of some of these hazards, see P. A. Sorokin and R. K. Merton, "The course of Arabian intellectual development: a study in method," *Isis*, 1935, 22, 516–524; Merton, *op. cit.*, 367 ff., 398 ff.; and for a more thorough review of the problems of procedure, Bernard Berelson, *Content Analysis* (New York: The Free Press, 1951). Numerous recent studies of the social origins of business élites in the historical past have utilized materials of this sort: see the studies by William Miller, C. W. Mills, and Suzanne Keller instructively summarized by Bernard Barber, *Social Stratification* (New York: Harcourt, Brace & World, 1957).

gion were joined "intellectual" and "utilitarian" motives. Thus, while "the Puritans promoted science as an additional support of Christian faith based on revelation, the deists looked upon science as the foundation of any belief in God." (12) The three types of motivation tended to reinforce one another: "The Dissenters, as well as many Puritans within the Church, represented the religious motive for educational reform. The idea of *propagatio fidei per scientia* found many adherents among the Dissenters. The intellectual and utilitarian reasons were put into full motion by secular bodies and teachers before the Dissenting Academies accepted them wholeheartedly." (54)

It is in this last respect that Hans finds it necessary to dissent from the thesis put forward by Irene Parker (which I adopted in my own paper), holding that she attributes almost exclusive influence to the Academies in advancing modern education in the eighteenth century. His corrective modification appears, on the ample evidence, to be thoroughly justified. Furthermore, it serves to clarify a problem which, at least one student of the matter can report, has long been troublesome and unresolved. This is the well-recognized fact that certain extreme forms of Calvinist dissent were for a long time inimical to the advancement of science, rather than conducive to it. As Hans now points out, "although the Calvinist tradition was essentially progressive it easily degenerated into narrow and intolerant dogmatism." (55) The Baptists, for example, were thoroughly "averse to the new learning from conviction and only late in the century joined other Dissenters [particularly the Presbyterians and Independents] in promoting the reform." (55) One wing of nonconformity, in short, adhered literally to certain restrictive tenets of Calvinism and it was this subgroup that manifested the hostility to science which has for so long been found in certain fundamentalist sects of Protestantism. Figuratively, it can be said that "Calvinism contained a seed of modern liberal education but it required a suitable environment to germinate and grow." (57) And, as we have seen, this social and cultural context was progressively provided in England of the time.

Supplementing these studies of the changing relations between Puritanism and science in England is the remarkable study by Perry Miller of these relations under the special conditions afforded by New England. (*The New England Mind: The Seventeenth Century*. Reissue. *The New England Mind: From Colony to Province*. Cambridge: Harvard University Press, 1954.) This comprehensive work demonstrates the notable receptivity to science among the theocratic leaders of the colony and the ensuing process of secularization, with its emphasis on utilitarianism. For a short but instructive comparison of the interpretation advanced by Perry Miller and that advanced in the preceding chapter, see Leo Marx, *Isis*, 1956, 47, 80–81.

As we have seen from the data assembled by Alphonse de Candolle—see pages 54–55 of this book—the connections of ascetic Protestantism and interest in science evidently persisted to some extent through the nineteenth century. Candolle's data have lately been examined again, with the same conclusion. See Isidor Thorner, "Ascetic Protestantism and the development of science and technology," *American Journal of Sociology*, 1952, 58, 25–33, esp. at 31–32. Thorner has also analyzed the data presented by P. A. Sorokin as a basis for questioning this hypothesis and finds that the data are actually in accord with it; *ibid.*, 28–30. For Sorokin's critique, see his *Social and Cultural Dynamics*, II, 150–152.

In another, searching review of Candolle's materials, Lilley has indicated their limitations as well as their uses. S. Lilley, "Social aspects of the history of science," *Archives Internationales d'Histoire des Sciences*, 1949, 28, 376–443, esp. 333 ff. He observes that the correlations between Protestantism and science may be spurious since "on the average the commercial and industrial classes [who have a greater interest in science] have tended to be Protestant in persuasion and the peasantry and more feudal types of landowners to be Catholic." We have taken note of this limitation (52) and have accordingly compared the interest in scientific subjects of Protestants and Catholics drawn from the same areas (52, 54). Lilley also criticizes Candolle's work for failing to take account of historical change in these relationships by lumping together, "without distinction, the whole period from 1666 to 1868." Presumably, religious affiliations in the latter and more secularized period would represent less by way of doctrinal and value commitments than in the earlier period; purely nominal memberships would tend to become more frequent. This criticism also has force, as we have seen. But as Lilley goes on to observe, further evidence in hand nevertheless confirms the underlying relationship between ascetic Protestantism and science, although this relationship may be masked or accentuated by other interdependent social and economic changes.

That the relationship persists to the present day in the United States is indicated by a recent thorough-going study of the social antecedents of American scientists, from 1880 to 1940. R. H. Knapp and H. B. Goodrich, *Origins of American Scientists* (Chicago: University of Chicago Press, 1952). Their evidence on this point is summarized as follows:

> Our data have shown the marked inferiority of Catholic [academic] institutions in the production of scientists [but not of other professionals; for example, lawyers] and, on the other hand, the fact that some of our most productive smaller institutions are closely connected with Protestant denominations and serve a preponderantly Protestant clientele. Moreover, the data presented by Lehman and Visher on the "starred" scientists [i.e. the scientists listed in *American Men of Science* who are judged to be of outstanding merit], although limited, indicate very clearly that the proportion of Catholics in this group is excessively low—that, indeed, some Protestant denominations are proportionately several hundred times more strongly represented. These statistics, taken together with other evidence, leave little doubt that scientists have been drawn disproportionately from American Protestant stock. (274)

Much the same impression, but without systematic supporting data, has been reported by Catholic scientists. "Father Cooper says he 'would be loath to have to defend the thesis that 5 per cent or even 3 per cent of the leadership in American science and scholarship is Catholic. Yet we Catholics constitute something like 20 per cent of the total population.'" J. M. Cooper, "Catholics and scientific research," *Commonweal*, 1945, 42, 147–149, as quoted by Bernard Barber, *Science and the Social Order*, 136. Barber also cites a similar observation by James A. Reyniers, Director of the Lobund Laboratories of Notre Dame University and by Joseph P. Fitzpatrick, S.J.; *ibid.*, 271.

This review of the more recent literature on the subject rather uniformly confirms the hypothesis of an observable positive relationship between ascetic Protestantism and science. The data provided by any one of these studies is typically far from rigorous. But this is, after all, the condition of most evidence bearing upon historically changing relations between social institutions. Considering not this study or that, but the entire array, based upon materials drawn from varied sources, we would seem to have some reasonable assurance that the empirical relationship, supposed in the foregoing study, does in fact exist.

But, of course, the gross empirical relationship is only the beginning, not the end, of the intellectual problem. As Weber noted, early in his celebrated essay on *The Protestant Ethic*, "a glance at the occupational statistics of any country of mixed religious composition brings to light with remarkable frequency a situation which has several times provoked discussion in the Catholic press and literature, and in Catholic congresses in Germany, namely, the fact that business leaders and owners of capital, as well as the higher grades of skilled labor, and even more the higher technically and commercially trained personnel of modern enterprises, are overwhelmingly Protestant." (35) The fortuity that comparable statistics on the religious composition of scientists are not ready to hand but must be laboriously assembled for the present and partially pieced together for the past does not make the empirical finding any more significant in itself (though it may commend to our respectful attention the arduous labors of those doing the spadework). For, as we have seen in examining the status of empirical generalizations (in Chapter II *), this only sets the problem of analyzing and interpreting the observed uniformity, and it is to this problem that the foregoing essay has addressed itself.

The principal components of the interpretation advanced in this essay presumably do not require repetition. However, a recent critique of the study provides an occasion for reviewing certain empirical and theoretical elements of the interpretation which can, apparently, be lost to sight. In this critique—"Merton's thesis on English science," *American Journal of Economics and Sociology*, 1954, 13, 427–432—James W. Carroll reports what he takes to be several oversights in the formulation. It is suggested that the heterogeneity of the beliefs included in Protestantism generally and in Puritanism specifically has been overlooked or imperfectly recognized. Were the charge true, it would plainly have merit. Yet it should be observed that the hypothesis in question is introduced by a chapter which begins by noting "the diversity of theological doctrines among the Protestant groups of seventeenth-century England" and continues by considering the values, beliefs and interests which are common to the numerous sects deriving from Calvinism (Merton, *Science, Technology and Society in Seventeenth-Century England*, Chapter IV, 415 ff.). And, as may be seen from this bibliographical postscript, historical scholarship has more thoroughly established the similarities, and not only the differences, among the Puritan sects stemming from ascetic Calvinism.

Carroll goes on to say that the evidence for the connection be-

* See *Social Theory and Social Structure.*

tween the norms of Puritanism and of science provides only an empirical similarity between the two (or what is described as a Comtean "correlation of assertions"). But this is to ignore the demonstrated fact that English scientists themselves repeatedly invoked these Puritan values and expressly translated them into practice. (*Cf. ibid.*, Chapter V.)

That the Puritan values were indeed expressed by scientists is in fact implied in Carroll's next suggestion that no basis is provided in the study for discriminating between the "rationalizations" and the "motives" of these scientists. This touches upon a theoretical problem of such general import, and widespread misunderstanding, that it is appropriate to repeat part of what was said about it in the earlier study. "Present-day discussions of 'rationalization' and 'derivations' have been wont to becloud certain fundamental issues. It is true that the 'reasons' adduced to justify one's actions often do not account satisfactorily for this behavior. It is also an acceptable hypothesis that ideologies [alone] seldom *give rise* to action and that both the ideology and the action are rather the product of common sentiments and values upon which they in turn react. But these ideas can not be ignored for two reasons. They provide clues for detecting the basic values which motivate conduct. Such signposts can not be profitably neglected. Of even greater importance is the rôle of ideas in directing action into *particular* channels. *It is the dominating system of ideas which determines the choice between alternative modes of action which are equally compatible with the underlying sentiments.*" (*Ibid.*, 450.)

As for distinguishing between the expression of reasons which are merely accommodative lip-service and those which express basic orientations, the test is here, as elsewhere, to be found in the behavior which accords with these reasons, even when there is little or no prospect of self-interested mundane reward. As the clearest and best-documented case, Robert Boyle can here represent the other Puritans among his scientific colleagues who, in varying degree, expressed their religious sentiments in their private lives as in their lives as scientists. It would seem unlikely that Boyle was "merely rationalizing" in saying "that those who labour to deter men from sedulous Enquiries into Nature do (though I grant, designlessly) take a course which tends to defeat God. . . ." (Robert Boyle, *Some Considerations Touching the Usefulness of Experimental Natural Philosophy*, Oxford, 1664; 2d edition, 27). For this is the same Boyle who had written religious essays by the age of twenty-one; had, despite his distaste for the study of language, expressed his veneration for the Scriptures by learning Hebrew, Greek, Chaldee and Syriac that he might read them in their early versions; had provided a pension for Robert Sanderson to enable him to continue writing books on casuistry; had largely paid for the costs of printing the Indian, Irish and Welsh Bibles and, as if this were not enough, for the Turkish New Testament and the Malayan version of the Gospels and Acts; had become Governor of the Corporation for the Spread of the Gospel in New England and as a director of the East India Company had devoted himself and his resources to the diffusion of Christianity in these areas; had contributed substantially to the fund for printing Burnet's *History of the Reformation;* had published his profession of faith in *The Christian Virtuoso* and, quite finally, had provided in his will for endowment of the "Boyle lectures" for the purpose of defending Christianity against unbelievers. (This is the compact record set forth in A. M. Clerke's biography of Boyle in the *Dictionary of National Biography.*) Although Boyle was foremost in piety among Puritan scientists, he was still only first among equals, as witness Wilkins, Willughby and Ray among many others. So far as any historical record of words and action can permit us to say, it would appear that scientists like Boyle were not simply "rationalizing."

Carroll's final criticism, if intended conscientiously and not frivolously, exhibits a melancholy degree of immunity to commonplace and inconvenient facts of history. He observes that in showing the original membership of the Royal Society to have been preponderantly Protestant, the essay under review does not examine the possibility that the "invisible college," from which the Society stemmed, was part of a widespread Protestant movement of reform and that known Catholics were consequently banned from membership. That *Protestants* comprised the original membership of the Royal Society goes, one would suppose, without saying; in that day and age of the 1660's, in spite of the later political traffic of Charles II with the Catholicism of Louis XIV, Catholics would scarcely have been granted the prerogative of founding an association under the auspices of the Crown. The fact which is of more than passing interest is not, of course, that the Society was preponderantly *Protestant,* but that it was preponderantly *Puritan.* As for the observation that avowed Catholics were banned from academic posts, it evidently needs to be recalled that the Test Act of 1673, though later occasionally nullified in particular instances, excluded Nonconformists and not only Catholics and Jews from the universities. Yet, although this remained in force into the nineteenth century, Nonconformists continued to provide a large fraction of the men of science.

This short review of the most recently accumulated evidence suggests that, however contrary this may have been to the intentions of the Great Reformers, the ascetic Protestant sects developed a distinct predilection for working the field of science. In view of the powerful cross-currents of other historical forces, which might have deflected this early orientation toward science, it is notable that the association between ascetic Protestantism and science has persisted to the present day. Profound commitments to the values of ascetic Protestantism have presumably become less common, yet the orientation, deprived of its theological meanings, evidently remains. As with any hypothesis, particularly in historical sociology, this one must be regarded as provisional, subject to review as more of the evidence comes in. But as the evidence now stands, the fact is reasonably well established and has definite implications for the broader problem of the connections between science and other social institutions.

The first of these implications is that, in this case at least, the emerging connections between science and religion were indirect and unintended. For, as has been repeatedly said, the reformers were not enthusiastic about science. Luther was at best indifferent; at worst, hostile. In his *Institutes* and his *Commentarie upon Genesis*, Calvin was ambivalent, granting some virtue to the practical intellect but far less than that owing to revealed knowledge. Nevertheless, the religious ethic which stemmed from Calvin promoted a state of mind and a value-orientation which invited the pursuit of natural science.

Second, it appears that once a value-orientation of this kind becomes established, it develops some degree of functional autonomy, so that the predilection for science could remain long after it has cut away from its original theological moorings.

Third, this pattern of orientation, which can even now be detected statistically, may be unwitting and below the threshold of awareness of many of those involved in it.

Fourth and finally, the highly visible interaction of the institutions of science and religion—as in the so-called war between the two in the nineteenth century—may obscure the less visible, indirect and perhaps more significant relationship between the two.

Percy W. Bridgman

Quo Vadis

It is fashionable to stress the differences between the "sciences" and the "humanities." There are, of course, obvious differences, and for certain purposes and in certain contexts it may be desirable to emphasize them, as, for example, in drawing up a curriculum of instruction or in organizing a university faculty into departments. I believe, however, that the differences are more or less superficial; what is common to the sciences and the humanities is far more fundamental and important than the differences. In the first place, both are human enterprises; this gives them a unity which they cannot escape. Furthermore, they are both predominantly intellectual enterprises, even, if I may be permitted to use the term, enterprises of the intelligence. This I would maintain even if we choose to make a concern with values the touchstone of differentiation between the sciences and the humanities. It is often said that science can tell us nothing about values, and that here lies the fundamental distinction between science and the humanities. Perhaps one could by some tour de force set up a definition of science which would forbid it values, but surely one cannot forbid a concern with values to intelligence. Values can be described, analyzed, appraised, and modified, and these are all activities of the intelligence. We cannot act in any situation involving values without engaging in at least some of these activities.

Reprinted with permission of Daedalus *(The Journal of the American Academy of Arts and Sciences) from Percy W. Bridgman, "Quo Vadis," in* Daedalus, *vol. 87, no. 1 (Winter, 1958), pp. 85–93.*

Whether we practice a science or a humanity we cannot avoid exercising our intelligences. It is to some of the consequences of this that I would call your attention. It is, I think, beginning to dawn on us that there is more to this problem of using our minds intelligently than at first strikes the eye. There are techniques of being intelligent. It is not easy to acquire the proper use of the mental tools which we have thoughtlessly inherited or which are implicit in the construction of our brains. Severe effort and long practice are required.

It seems that we are coming to an awareness of the existence and importance of our mental tools from the side of the sciences rather than from the side of the humanities. The reason is not any reflection on the humanities, but is a consequence of human frailty and the fact that the humanities are so much more complex and difficult than the sciences. By far the most important consequence of the conceptual revolution brought about in physics by relativity and quantum theory lies not in such details as that meter sticks shorten when they move or that simultaneous position and momentum have no meaning, but in the insight that we had not been using our minds properly and that it is important to find out how to do so. Although it is no reflection on the humanities that this insight is coming through the comparatively simple situations of physics, I think it *would* be a reflection if this experience of the sciences did not give the humanities pause, or suggest that it is almost inevitable that some modification is necessary in their own conceptual foundations. For would it not be a miracle if an intellectual apparatus which has evolved to cope with the primitive situations of daily life and which has been found to fail when confronted with the comparatively simple needs of modern physics should retain its validity in the incomparably more complex situations presented by human society and the humanities?

Let us now consider in more detail some of the implications of recent scientific experience for the broader question of what is involved in the proper use of our minds. One of the most obvious of the lessons of relativity theory is the importance of careful attention to the meanings of our words. This attention to meanings involves much more than heeding the admonition "define your terms" long accepted by every lawyer and debater. The objective of the lawyer or debater is primarily to secure conformity of verbal behavior and thus to permit communication. But conformity and consensus are not enough to ensure that a term can be used in the way we would like. In fact, the shocking quality of relativity theory consisted precisely in the discovery that such a term as "simultaneity," about which there had been universal agreement when regarded as merely a bit of verbal behavior, did not have the properties it was assumed to have outside the universe of verbal behavior. Words have implications in use which are as important as, or more important than, mere behavioral consensus, and the job of becoming aware of meanings includes discovering what these implications are. Thus, many of our terms are, by implication, capable of being put into statements. A statement, by its very form, implies that it may be true or false. We do not fully know the meaning of a term which is habitually used in statements unless we know whether it makes sense to say that a statement containing the term is either true or false, and still more, unless we can tell what to do to find whether the statement is true or false. This sort of analysis is not often made, and when it is made it often discloses things not suspected.

The physicist has by now found a way of dealing with his meanings which is fairly satisfactory for his purposes, and which does not commit him to preconceptions about fields not yet entered. This method of dealing with meanings I have called "operational." The essence of it is that to know adequately the meaning of a term we must be able to describe what we do when we use it. It is my personal opinion that this way of dealing with meanings has a wider application to all our language, in so far as that language is an activity of intelligence as distinguished from a purely emotional activity; but this is a matter of detail which is more or less beside the point I am trying to make here. This point is that we can always ask what the meaning of any term that we use is, and that in answering this question we have to satisfy *some* criterion of meaning. Whether the criterion is operational or not is not important in this context; there has to be some criterion, and if we can explicitly formulate it, we are in a position to judge from our other experience whether the meaning has the significance we had supposed. It will often be found that the term cannot have the supposed significance, just as the physicist's concept of simultaneity did not. I believe that very few of the terms of humanistic—as distinguished from scientific—import have been subjected to an analysis for meaning as articulate as this, and that when they are thus analyzed the entire situation may appear in a different light. In the case of such humanistic terms as justice, freedom, duty, responsibility or right, it will be found, I believe, that the verbal component is unexpectedly large, and that the meanings are applicable only in a universe which is predominantly verbal. Now it must not be hastily assumed that for this reason we must discard these terms—far from it—but a realization of the situation will, I believe, bring about a change of attitude. The resultant remaking of our concepts is still ahead of us.

Concern with meanings is only one aspect of a growing realization of the extent to which we are verbal animals. Philosophers and logicians are not unaware of this. Consider, for example, the active field of semantics. The realization is growing that the grammar of a language may almost compel certain attitudes. For example, reification is almost inevitable in a language with the structure of English and in other European languages. One cannot say "I do" without implying "I do *something*," and the something becomes reified. The situation is carried over into physics, where the almost universally accepted identity of mass and energy is the result of an unnecessary and illogical reification of energy.

The implications for logic are particularly interesting. It is popularly supposed that logic deals with something fundamental and universal—it was Boole who used the phrase "the laws of thought" in this connection. But one questions the validity of this point of view when one considers that there are languages, such as some of the North American Indian languages, in which it is difficult and uncongenial to formulate a universal statement, and therefore difficult to form a syllogism. Yet the people with such a language manage to meet the situations of daily life with a survival potential about as good as that of the rest of us. It begins to look as though formal logic, as we know it, is an attribute of the group of Indo-European languages with certain grammatical features.

The concern with words is rather near the surface. Physics has had deeper worries and insights, mainly as a result of the development of quantum theory. One of the most important of these insights has been concerned with the role of the observer. Now for the purposes of quantum theory the observer is highly specialized, and is essentially the measuring instrument. A detailed examination of the unavoidable reaction between instrument and object of measurement provides the justification for the Heisenberg Principle of Indetermination. But the point of view of quantum theory has implications for us much wider than the technical details. It forces us to realize that we cannot have information without acquiring that information by some method, and that the story is not complete until we have told both what we know and how we know it.

In other words, we have to remember that we always have an observer. Furthermore, this observer is ourselves, and therefore we cannot get away from him. But getting away from itself is what the human race has been trying to do ever since it started philosophizing or worshipping.

Let us face facts and not fear to say out loud that the one field of human activity in which we are most obviously trying to get away from ourselves is the field of religion. This, I take it, is historically true as a statement of what has been involved in the religious activity of the past. The beings and principles which are the concern of religion are beings and principles external to us and independent of us, eternal in the heavens and surrounded with an aura of absolute truth. This absolute truth is thought of as intrinsically knowable, by revelation if not by more mundane methods.

The fact that men have thought in this way has had a most important effect on their overt conduct; one need only consider the Inquisition or the spread of Mohammedanism. In this respect it must be conceded that Toynbee's conception of history is justified, although one may not be willing to assume with Toynbee that the religious attitude must necessarily be as decisive in the future as it has been in the past. Given the view that there exists an absolute truth, and given furthermore the conviction that one has found absolute truth, the intolerance of the Inquisition or the brain-washings of the Communists become logically inevitable. In such a setting, tolerance can be justified only as a Machiavellian measure, to be practiced only while one is too weak to control the social machinery. How secure are we today that the tolerance in which we take so much pride will continue to be accepted as a social virtue? Certainly a large number of our people hold views which if pushed to their logical conclusion would lead straight to intolerance. The reason these people do not act intolerantly is either that they have never thought things through to a logical conclusion or else that they know they do not have the power. I think we have to find other and better reasons for tolerance than any at present widely accepted.

Tolerance is only one of the issues that commonly present themselves in a religious setting. Not only must we find a new basis for tolerance, but we also must re-examine the broader issue of religion as a whole. To do less is to invite the catastrophe which Toynbee foresees for the Western world if our present religious drives are allowed uninhibited play. Since we cannot get away from ourselves, we must find our springs of action within ourselves, a task which the human race has been shirking since the beginning of recorded history. We have to find what admirable motivation is left when we repudiate the almost universal and irrepressible urge of men to get away from themselves, something that we are coming to realize simply cannot be done. It seems to me that we are not going to find how to get along without our absolutes by any "return" to points of view held in the past; rather, something vitally new is required which we can now only faintly glimpse. And there is no reason to fear that our aspirations and ideals will evoke emotions less poignant under the new dispensation than under the old.

In this connection the recent experience of mathematicians and logicians with Gödel's theorem is most illuminating. It is a consequence of this theorem that mathematics can never prove that mathematics is free from internal self-contradictions. The realization of this had a tremendous impact, for here was something that the greatest mathematicians had been vainly trying to do. Out of this experience mathematicians and logicians have acquired a new insight—the insight that there are some things that neither they nor anyone else can do with their minds. Perhaps the most devastating point is the realization that the human mind can never have certainty, by either logical, or metaphysical, or mystical methods. The realization that certainty is not logically attainable took Bertrand Russell all his life to acquire, and he acquired it by successively trying in detail one or another purported method of getting certainty—and finding it wanting. Gödel's theorem, as it were, cuts the Gordian knot with the insight that "certainty" is an illegitimate concept.

The list of illegitimate concepts will certainly grow. For it is beginning to dawn on us that in the world of mental activities there may be principles of impotency analogous to the impotency principles of physics. It took a long time to realize that it is impossible to create energy out of nothing or that it is impossible to get energy out of a system without paying the price in terms of entropy. It does not seem unreasonable that there should be corresponding principles in the mental world, or that it should take us longer to discover them, when we consider the incomparably greater simplicity of the physical as compared with the mental world. Some day, I have no doubt, we shall have formulated a set of laws of mental dynamics analogous to our present laws of thermodynamics. As it is, we can glimpse at least one such law in the light of Gödel's theorem. The reason mathematics cannot prove that mathematics is free from contradiction is that there are some things a system cannot do with itself. When we try to get away from ourselves by correcting what our senses or our perceptions or our reason presents us, it is *we* who are attempting to escape, and whatever the result of the attempt, it will be something of which *we* are aware. Here we have the system dealing with itself. But what we would like to do can neither be done nor even be talked about. Perhaps we have here a worthy candidate for the first law of mental dynamics, namely the law that we cannot get away from ourselves.

It seems to me that religion is the field of human concern in which we have most obviously pushed the common-sense assumption that we can get away from ourselves beyond the bound of validity, and in so doing are trying to do something with our minds that cannot be done. It would be rewarding to look in other directions for examples of intellectual impotency. I suspect that an observer from another planet, contemplating the inability of our philosophers to reach agreement on certain questions after three thousand years of effort, would conclude that in this field we have also been trying to do something with our minds that cannot be done.

Not only are we beginning to realize the general outlines of the way the brain can deal with the external world, but we are beginning to get some glimpse of how it works out in detail. Cybernetics, computer technology, and brain physiology, particularly the electrical study of the brain, are all providing valuable insights. Particularly valuable in this connection are the experiments on the nature of perception initiated by Ames and his colleagues at Hanover and now extended to well over a hundred research centers scattered through the world. These experiments are giving an insight into the nature of the perceptions in terms of which we see our world. These perceptions are so simple and immediate reaction to the stimuli acting on the sense organs, but are a most complicated product involving the past history of the brain, and have validity only in a context harmonious with that past experience. The mental machinery having been once conditioned, we have little or no control over the perceptions which ensue. By malicious manipulation it is possible so to arrange the operation of the sense organs that the resulting perceptions are palpably absurd and impossible, but nevertheless have a compulsive quality that can be appreciated only by experiencing it. One cannot see the experiments without asking oneself what is the significance of this compulsion, or, more generally, what is the significance of the compulsion that the entire human race feels in seeing the world as it does? At the very least, it is impossible to retain the conviction that one is seeing something absolute, independent of the seeing mechanism.

It will probably be objected that the insights we have been urging are all rather negative and destructive. Something more constructive will doubtless be demanded. But a change of outlook as revolutionary as is contemplated here almost inevitably has to begin by being destructive. Our first concern is whether what we have been saying is true, and destructive criticism may be as true as constructive criticism. If the criticism is true, any reconstruction will at the very least have to meet the objections of the criticism, and, of course, in addition find new constructive factors. I would not admit, however, that we are entirely destitute of constructive insights as to methods of meeting the situation revealed by our criticism. But if I had attempted to argue these constructive possibilities, I would have run the danger of obscuring the main point by introducing elements more controversial even than those I have admitted.

The main point is that the human race has not yet found how to use its mind. We are getting at this realization through the sciences, but the sciences have as yet by no means furnished all the answers. One reason is that for the particular purposes of science an incomplete view is adequate, particularly because the sciences are comparatively so simple. But for the wider purposes of the humanities—the complete human scene in all its scope—some more drastic reconstruction is necessary. It is, for example, obvious that the involvement of the humanities with the whole verbal machinery of thought is much more intimate than that of the sciences. I would place as the most important mark of an adequately educated man a realization that the tools of human thinking are not yet understood, and that they impose limitations of which we are not yet fully aware. As a corollary it follows that the most important intellectual task for the future is to acquire an understanding of the tools, and so to modify our outlook and ideals as to take account of their limitations.

This task is not to be accomplished by any "return" to the insights of the past. The insight that there is any problem here at all is devastatingly new in human history. The sciences and the humanities find themselves facing the problem together; it is too difficult and too pressing to permit the luxury of a division of forces. Appreciation of the existence and the nature of the problem is the first step toward the invention of the new methods and outlooks that will be necessary to solve it.

It seems to me that the human race stands on the brink of a major breakthrough. We have advanced to the point where we can put our hand on the hem of the curtain that separates us from an understanding of the nature of our minds. Is it conceivable that we will withdraw our hand and turn back through discouragement and lack of vision?